THE COMPLETE BOOK OF
ANIMALS

THE COMPLETE BOOK OF
ANIMALS

TOM JACKSON

CONSULTANT: MICHAEL CHINERY

HERMES
HOUSE

This edition is published by Hermes House

Hermes House is an imprint of Anness Publishing Ltd
Hermes House, 88–89 Blackfriars Road, London SE1 8HA
tel. 020 7401 2077; fax 020 7633 9499
www.hermeshouse.com; www.annesspublishing.com

If you like the images in this book and would like to investigate
using them for publishing, promotions or advertising, please
visit our website www.practical pictures.com for more
information.

A CIP catalogue record for this book
is available from the British Library.

Publisher: Joanna Lorenz
Editorial Director: Judith Simons
Project Editor: Felicity Forster
Copy Editors: Gerard Cheshire,
Richard Rosenfeld and Jen Green
Illustrators: Stuart Carter, Jim Channell,
John Francis, Stephen Lings, Alan Male,
Shane Marsh and Sarah Smith
Map Illustrator: Anthony Duke
Designer: Nigel Partridge
Editorial Reader: Jay Thundercliffe
Production Controller: Steve Lang

5 7 9 10 8 6

CONTENTS

Introduction   6

The Diversity of Life   **8**
What is an animal?   10
Evolution   12
Anatomy   14
Senses   16
Survival   18
Reproduction   20
Amphibians   22
Reptiles   24
Placental mammals   26
Monotremes and marsupials   28
Ecology   30
Migration and hibernation   32
Introduced species   34
Endangered species   36
Conserving wildlife   38
Biomes   40
Oceans   42
Fresh water   44

Tropical forests   46
Temperate forests   48
Boreal forests   50
Grasslands   52
Polar regions   54
Deserts   56
Islands   58
Mountains   60
Human settlements   62

Animals of the World   **64**
Animals of the Americas   66
Animals of Europe and Africa   126
Animals of Asia, Australia and
    New Zealand   186

Classification   246
Glossary   248
Index   250

INTRODUCTION

Animals populate every corner of the globe and can be found in an extraordinary array of shapes, sizes and colours; correspondingly, the subject of zoology is absolutely vast. This book concentrates on amphibians, reptiles and mammals, with a section about the diversity of life followed by an encyclopedia of animal species around the world.

The book opens with the question "what is an animal?" From very simple animals such as jellyfish and corals through to complex creatures such as birds and mammals, the first part of the book shows how animal bodies are organized, how they have evolved over time, and how their current forms survive and reproduce. Next, the section focuses on amphibians, reptiles, placental mammals, monotremes and marsupials, as well as providing information about migration and hibernation, introduced and endangered species, and how ecologists conserve wildlife. Finally, the section looks at the principal habitats, or biomes, in which animals live – oceans, fresh water, tropical forests, temperate forests, boreal forests, grasslands, polar regions, deserts, islands, mountains and human settlements – and how animals survive in such varied environments.

Below: Snakes are a large group of legless reptiles. Most, like this emerald boa, live in hotter parts of the world, such as rainforests. Many snakes have a venomous bite, while others squeeze the breath out of their prey with their muscular, coiled bodies.

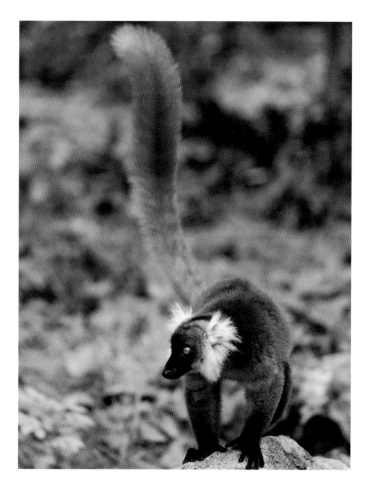

Above: Islands around the world are home to some of the most unusual animals in nature. For example, lemurs are found only in Madagascar. These animals live in the island's forests. Similar forests elsewhere in the world are populated by monkeys, not lemurs.

The encyclopedia section takes a journey across the globe, sampling the many animals that populate every region. It begins in the Americas and provides an introduction to the variety of wildlife there. Animals are displayed in related groups, focusing in turn on amphibians, reptiles and mammals. The encyclopedia continues along the same lines as it visits Europe and Africa, and then Asia, Australia and New Zealand.

In South America, the shallow waters of swamps and stream banks are home to the green anaconda. Away from the swamps in the dense jungle, one may encounter the world's largest otter basking by a stream, and the capybara, the biggest rodent, feeding close by. In North America, the book's focus includes the brown bear, the largest predator on land, and also highlights a variety of rattlesnakes, armadillos and some tiny snakes that live underground. On the opposite side of the Atlantic Ocean, Africa is home to great beasts such as the rhinoceros and lion, and Europe has a number of rare species such as the

Above: Not all mammals are furry and four-legged. Although dolphins have a few bristly hairs and are related to the land mammals, they never come on to land. Like whales and other sea mammals, a dolphin's limbs look more like a fish's fins than the legs of a land animal.

chamois and European bison. The Asian continent is renowned for its wild horses and the majestic tiger, while Australia is home to many unusual species, especially marsupials such as the koala, Tasmanian devil and red kangaroo.

Each geographical section of the book is prefaced by an introduction to the ecology and habitats of the region, and the characteristics of its animals.

Below: Cheetahs live in the open grasslands of Africa. They are the fastest-running animals on Earth and can accelerate as quickly as any sports car. These big cats use their speed to chase down nimble, dodging prey, such as the antelopes that graze on the plains.

Right: Amphibians were the first land animals, and have kept their close links to water, where their ancestors originated. Therefore amphibians such as this tree frog are most common in warm and damp places, such as rainforests, where they can easily keep their bodies damp.

THE DIVERSITY OF LIFE

This book examines amphibians, reptiles and mammals, but can only scratch the surface of the fantastic range of life forms packed on this planet. It concentrates on the vertebrates (the group of animals that have a backbone, which includes the above three groups as well as birds and fish); however, vertebrates form just one of the 31 major animal groups. The huge diversity of life contained in the other groups cannot rival the most familiar vertebrates for size, strength or general popularity. For most people, slugs are not in the same league as tigers, nor can crickets and crabs compete with dolphins and pandas. Yet these relatively unpopular animals are capable of amazing feats. For example, squid travel by jet propulsion, mussels change sex as they get older, and ants live in harmony in colonies of millions.

The diversity of life among the vertebrates is mind-boggling. A blue whale is 30m (100ft) long, while the smallest salamander is less than 3cm (1¼in) long. The rest appear in every shape and size in between. Yet vertebrates are not distinguished by their bodies alone but by the unusual ways in which they use them. For example, a lizard will shed its tail if a hungry predator clamps its jaws around it. And while the tailless reptile escapes, its attacker is kept occupied by the still-wriggling appendage. The paradoxical frog is another surprise. While every other vertebrate grows as it gets older, this amphibian actually shrinks so that the tadpoles are larger than the adults. And hunting bats, which can fly thanks to the skin stretched over their elongated hand bones, so creating wings, manage to locate their prey in the dark by using sonar. They bark out high-pitched calls that bounce off surrounding objects, and the time taken for the echo to return signifies the size and location of whatever is out there. These are just three examples of the extraordinary diversity found in the vertebrate kingdom.

Left: A young zebra and its mother take a drink at a watering hole in eastern Africa. Behind them a family of elephants plods past as they, too, head for the water. Some animals get all the moisture they need to survive from their food, but most need to drink water, so in dryish regions watering holes are often crowded with wildlife.

WHAT IS AN ANIMAL?

More than two million animal species have been described by scientists, and there are probably millions more waiting to be discovered. They live in all corners of the world, and come in a huge range of shapes and sizes. The largest weighs over a hundred tonnes, while the smallest is just a fraction of a millimetre long.

Active feeders

The living world is divided into five kingdoms: animals, plants, fungi, protists and monerans, which include bacteria. The protists and monerans are micro-organisms. Each individual is just a single cell, and although they often form large masses or colonies – for example, yoghurt is actually a colony of bacteria – the micro-organisms do not form bodies. The plants, fungi and animals do grow bodies, which are made from millions of cells, all of which work together. These three types of macro-organism, as they are called, tackle the problems of life in different ways.

Plants are the basis of life on Earth, and without them animals would not exist. This is because plants get the energy they need from sunlight (because they do not have to feed they are called autotrophes, meaning self-feeders). The green pigments in the plants' leaves trap the energy found in light and convert it into glucose, a simple sugar, in a process of food production called photosynthesis. Its by-product is oxygen, which gradually drifts into the atmosphere.

Below: Anemones are members of the group of cnidarians, like jellyfish. Starfish belong to the group of echinoderms.

Above: Jellyfish are very simple animals, related to corals and sea anemones. They catch food by spearing prey with tiny cells called nematocysts.

Above: Crabs, such as this hermit crab, are crustaceans. Other crustaceans include lobsters, prawns and krill. Their forelegs are armed with strong pincers.

Fungi are largely invisible organisms that live in large masses of tiny fibres which run through the soil. They only pop up above the surface in the form

Above: Snails belong to a large group of invertebrates called molluscs. Most live in water, but many snails, such as this giant land snail, survive on land.

Above: Spiders, scorpions and mites are arachnids. Many spiders build a sticky silk web to trap prey; others lie hidden and pounce on passing victims.

of mushrooms and toadstools when they are ready to reproduce. Fungi do not photosynthesize, but they are valuable as decomposers. They grow over the dead bodies of other organisms, such as trees which have fallen to the ground, secreting digestive enzymes that break down the dead body from the outside. They thereby release valuable carbon, nitrogen, phosphorus and other elements which each tree locks up in itself over its lifetime.

Animals, on the other hand, could not be more different. They are active feeders (called heterotrophes or "other-eaters") which collect food from their surroundings. Unlike plants and fungi, animals have bodies that can swim, walk, burrow or fly during at least the early part of their lives.

Body organization

With the exception of primitive forms, such as sponges, all animal bodies are organized along the same the lines. They process their food in a gut, a tube which passes through the body. In most cases the food enters the gut through an opening in the head, that is, the mouth. Once inside the body, the food is broken down into its constituent parts. The useful parts, such as proteins, fats and sugars – made by plants during photosynthesis – are absorbed into the body. The left-over waste material passes out of the gut through the anus, a hole at the other end of the body.

The useful substances absorbed from the food then need to be transported around the body to where they are needed. This job is done by the animal's circulatory system. The insides of many animals are simply bathed in a liquid containing everything required by the body. However, larger animals, including reptiles, amphibians and mammals, need to pump the useful substances around the body through the blood. The pump is the heart, a strong muscle that keeps the blood circulating through a system of vessels.

The blood carries food for the body and also oxygen, which reacts with the sugar and food, releasing the energy that is essential for all living things to survive. Animals get their oxygen in a number of ways. Some simply absorb it through their skin, many that live in water extract it using gills, and those that live in air breathe it into their lungs.

Compared with other organisms, animals are more aware of their surroundings and certainly more responsive to them. This is because they have a nervous system which uses sensors to detect what is happening in their environment, such as changes in temperature, the amount of light and various sounds. This information is then transmitted by means of nerves to what could be called the central control. This might just be a dense cluster of nerves, of which the animal might possess several, or it may be a single controlling brain. The brain or nerve cluster then passes the information from the senses to the muscles so that the body can respond appropriately, for example either by running away to avoid being eaten or by attacking its prey.

Mammals, reptiles and amphibians share a similar body plan, having four limbs. They are members of the larger group of tetrapods, to which birds also belong. Almost all possess a visible tail. The brain and most of the sensors are positioned at the front of the body in the head. The vital organs, such as the heart and lungs (or gills), are located in the central thorax (chest area), while the gut and sex organs are found mainly in the abdomen at the rear of the body.

Left: Apart from bats, birds, such as this bee-eater, are the only flying vertebrates. Their forelimbs have evolved into wings that allow them to perform amazing feats of flight. Feathers are better than hair for keeping the body streamlined for flight.

Above: Fish live in all corners of the world's oceans. They also live in fresh water, where they are found everywhere from submerged caves to mountain lakes.

Above: Frogs are the most familiar of the amphibians. Others include salamanders and newts. This frog spends its life in trees, using suckers on its feet to cling to the branches.

Above: While a few other lizards can alter the shade of their scales slightly, chameleons can change colour completely. This may help them hide from predators or it may reflect their mood.

Above: Mammals, such as this ground squirrel, are the most widespread of vertebrates. They can survive in just about any habitat on Earth.

EVOLUTION

Animals and other forms of life did not just suddenly appear on the Earth. They evolved over billions of years into countless different forms. The mechanism by which they evolved is called natural selection. The process of natural selection was first proposed by British naturalist Charles Darwin.

Many biologists estimate that there are approximately 30 million species on Earth, but to date only about two million have been discovered and recorded by scientists. So where are the rest? They live in a staggering array of habitats, from the waters of the deep oceans where sperm whales live to the deserts of Mexico, inhabited by the powerful, poisonous, gila monster lizard. The problems faced by animals in these and other habitats on Earth are very different, and so life has evolved in great variety. Each animal needs a body that can cope with its own environment.

Past evidence

At the turn of the 19th century, geologists began to realize that the world was extremely old. They used animal fossils – usually the hard remains, such as shells and bones, which are preserved in stone – to measure the age of the exposed layers of rock found in cliffs and canyons. Today we accept that the Earth is about 4.5 billion years old, but in the early 1800s the idea that the world was unimaginably old began to change people's ideas about the origins of life completely.

In addition, naturalists had always known that there was a fantastic variety of animals, but now they realized that many could be grouped into families, as if they were related. By the middle of 19th century, two British biologists had independently formulated an idea that would change the way that people saw themselves and the natural world forever. Charles Darwin and Alfred Wallace thought that the world's different animal species had gradually evolved from extinct relatives, like the ones preserved as fossils.

Darwin was the first to publish his ideas, in 1859. He had formulated them while touring South America where he studied the differences between varieties of finches and giant tortoises on the Galápagos Islands in the Pacific Ocean. Wallace came up with similar ideas about the same time, when studying different animals on the islands of South-east Asia and New Guinea.

Above: Scientists know about extinct animals from studying fossils such as these mammoth bones. Fossils are the remains of dead plants or animals that have been turned to stone by natural processes over millions of years.

Survival of the fittest

Both came up with the same idea – natural selection. As breeders had known for generations, animals pass on their characteristics to their young. Darwin and Wallace suggested that wild animal species also gradually evolved through natural selection, a similar system to the artificial selection that people were using to breed prize cattle, sheep and pedigree dogs.

The theory of natural selection is often described as the survival of the fittest. This is because animals must compete with each other for limited resources including food, water, shelter and mates. But they are not all equal or exactly similar, and some members of a population of animals will have characteristics which make them "fitter" – better suited to the environment at that time.

The fitter animals will therefore be more successful at finding food and avoiding predators. Consequently, they will probably produce more offspring, many of which will also have the same characteristics as their fit parents. Because of this, the next generation

---

Jumping animals

Most animals can leap into the air, but thanks to natural selection this simple ability has been harnessed by different animals in different ways. For example, click beetles jump in somersaults to frighten off attackers, while blood-sucking fleas can leap enormous heights to move from host to host.

Above: The flying frog uses flaps of skin between its toes to glide. This allows these tree-living frogs to leap huge distances between branches.

Above: This Thomson's gazelle is pronking, that is, leaping in high arcs to escape a chasing predator. Pronking makes it harder for predators to bring the antelope down.

will contain more individuals with the "fit" trait. And after many generations, it is possible that the whole population will carry the fit trait, since those without it die out.

Variation and time

The environment is not fixed, and does not stay the same for long. Volcanoes, diseases and gradual climate changes, for example, alter the conditions which animals have to confront. Natural selection relies on the way in which different individual animals cope with these changes. Those individuals that were once fit may later die out, as others that have a different set of characteristics become more successful in the changed environment.

Darwin did not know it, but parents pass their features on to their young through their genes. During sexual reproduction, the genes of both parents are jumbled up to produce a new individual with a unique set of characteristics. Every so often the genes mutate into a new form, and these mutations are the source of all new variations.

As the process of natural selection continues for millions of years, so groups of animals can change radically, giving rise to a new species. Life is thought to have been evolving for 3.5 billion years. In that time natural selection has produced a staggering number of species, with everything from oak trees to otters and coral to cobras.

A species is a group of organisms that can produce offspring with each other. A new species occurs once animals have changed so much that they are unable to breed with their ancestors. And if the latter no longer exist, then they have become extinct.

New species may gradually arise out of a single group of animals. In fact the original species may be replaced by one or more new species. This can happen when two separate groups of one species are kept apart by an impassable geographical feature, such as an ocean or mountain range. Kept isolated from each other, both groups then evolve in different ways and end up becoming new species.

Mammalian evolution

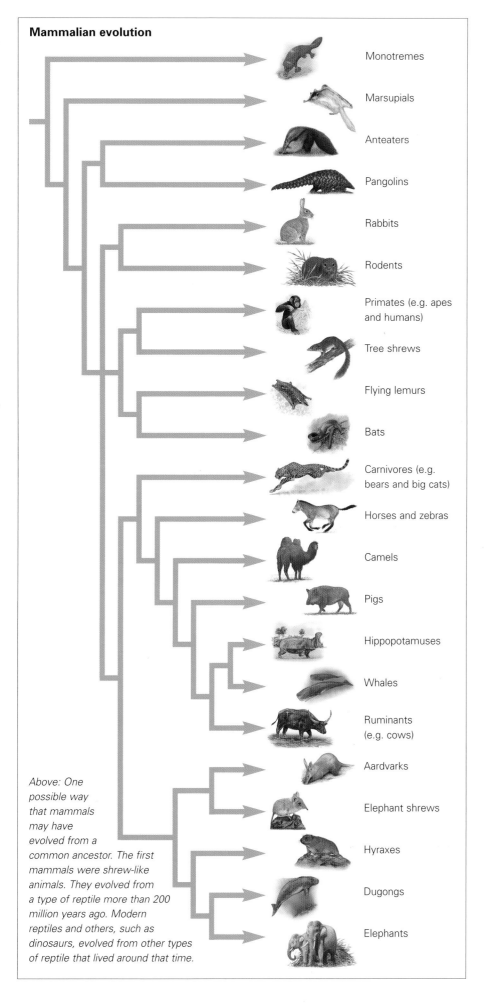

Above: One possible way that mammals may have evolved from a common ancestor. The first mammals were shrew-like animals. They evolved from a type of reptile more than 200 million years ago. Modern reptiles and others, such as dinosaurs, evolved from other types of reptile that lived around that time.

ANATOMY

Mammals, reptiles and amphibians (which are vertebrates, as are fish and birds), come in a mind-boggling array of shapes and sizes. However all of them, from whales to bats and frogs to snakes, share a basic body plan, both inside and out.

Vertebrates are animals with a spine, generally made of bone. Bone, the hard tissues of which contain chalky substances, is also the main component of the rest of the vertebrate skeleton. The bones of the skeleton link together to form a rigid frame to protect organs and give the body its shape, while also allowing it to move. Cartilage, a softer, more flexible but tough tissue is found, for example, at the ends of bones in mobile joints, in the ears and the nose (forming the sides and the partition between the two nostrils). Some fish, including sharks and rays, have skeletons that consist entirely of cartilage.

Nerves and muscles

Vertebrates also have a spinal cord, a thick bundle of nerves extending from the brain through the spine, and down into the tail. The nerves in the spinal cord are used to control walking and other reflex movements. They also coordinate blocks of muscle that work together for an animal to move properly. A vertebrate's skeleton is on the inside, in contrast to many invertebrates, which have an outer skeleton or exoskeleton.

The vertebrate skeleton provides a solid structure which the body's muscles pull against. Muscles are blocks of protein that can contract and relax when they get an electrical impulse from a nerve.

Invertebrates

The majority of animals are invertebrates. They are a much more varied group than the vertebrates and include creatures as varied as shrimps, slugs, butterflies and starfish. Although some squid are thought to reach the size of a small whale, and while octopuses are at least as intelligent as cats and dogs, most invertebrates are much smaller and simpler animals than the vertebrates.

Below: The most successful invertebrates are the insects, including ants. This soldier army ant is defending workers as they collect food.

Reptile bodies

Reptiles have internal skeletons made from bone and cartilage. Their skins are covered in scales, which are often toughened by a waxy protein called keratin. Turtles are quite different from other reptiles. They have simpler skulls and a shell that is joined to the animal's internal skeleton.

Below: Crocodiles have very strong bodies, designed for life in and around shallow water.

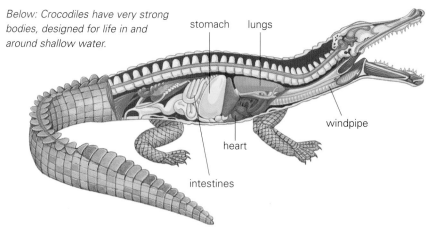

stomach　lungs

windpipe

heart

intestines

Below: Lizards have a similar body plan to crocodiles, although they are actually not very closely related.

Below: Snakes' internal organs are elongated so that they fit into their long, thin bodies. One of a pair of organs, such as the lungs, is often very small or missing.

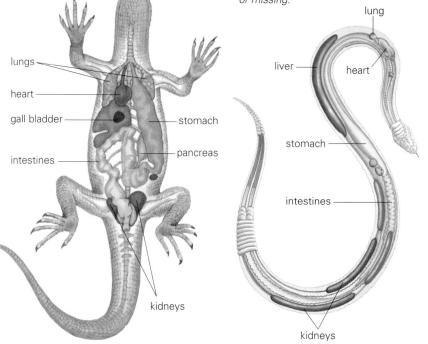

lungs

heart

gall bladder

intestines

stomach

pancreas

kidneys

lung

liver

heart

stomach

intestines

kidneys

When on the move, the vertebrate body works like a system of pulleys, pivots and levers. The muscles are the engines of the body, and are attached to bones – the levers – by strong cables called tendons. The joint between two bones forms a pivot, and the muscles work in pairs to move a bone. For example, when an arm is bent at the elbow to raise the forearm, the bicep muscle on the front of the upper arm has to contract. This pulls the forearm up, while the tricep muscle attached to the back of the upper arm remains relaxed. To straighten the arm again, the tricep contracts and the bicep relaxes. If both muscles contract at the same time, they pull against each other, and the arm remains locked in whatever position it is in.

Vital organs

Muscles are not only attached to the skeleton. The gut – including the stomach and intestines – is surrounded by muscles. These muscles contract in rhythmic waves to push food and waste products through the body. The heart is a muscular organ made of a very strong muscle which keeps on contracting and relaxing, pumping blood around the body. The heart and other vital organs are found in the thorax, that part of the body which lies between the forelimbs. In reptiles and mammals the thorax is kept well protected inside a rib cage, as are the lungs, liver and kidneys.

Vertebrates have a single liver consisting of a number of lobes. The liver has a varied role, making chemicals required by the body and storing food. Most vertebrates also have two kidneys. Their role is to clean the blood of any impurities and toxins, and to remove excess water. The main toxins that have to be removed are compounds containing nitrogen, the by-products of eating protein. Mammal and amphibian kidneys dissolve these toxins in water to make urine. However, since many reptiles live in very dry habitats, they cannot afford to use water to remove waste, and they instead get rid of it as a solid waste similar to bird excrement.

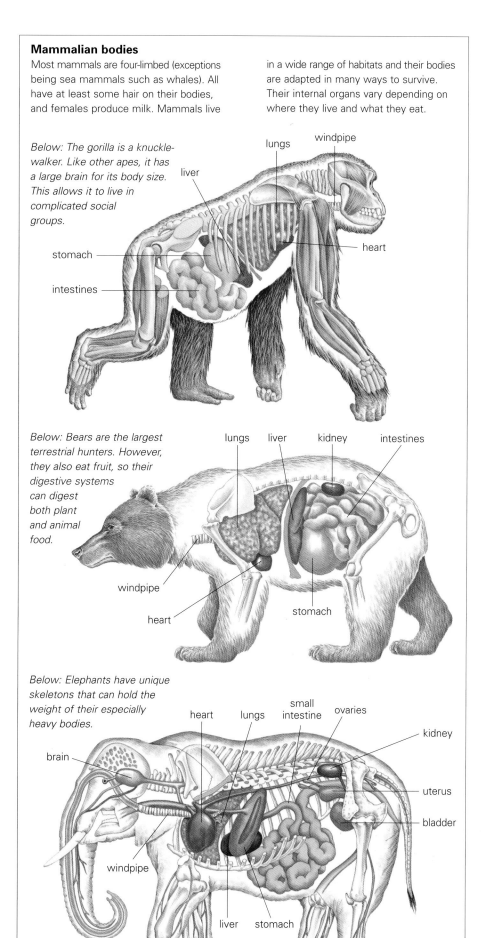

Mammalian bodies

Most mammals are four-limbed (exceptions being sea mammals such as whales). All have at least some hair on their bodies, and females produce milk. Mammals live in a wide range of habitats and their bodies are adapted in many ways to survive. Their internal organs vary depending on where they live and what they eat.

Below: The gorilla is a knuckle-walker. Like other apes, it has a large brain for its body size. This allows it to live in complicated social groups.

Below: Bears are the largest terrestrial hunters. However, they also eat fruit, so their digestive systems can digest both plant and animal food.

Below: Elephants have unique skeletons that can hold the weight of their especially heavy bodies.

SENSES

To stay alive, animals must find food and shelter, and defend themselves against predators. To achieve these things, they are equipped with an array of senses for monitoring their surroundings. Different species have senses adapted to nocturnal or diurnal (day-active) life.

An animal's senses are its early-warning system. They alert it to changes in its surroundings – changes which may signal an opportunity to feed or mate, or the need to escape imminent danger. The ability to act quickly and appropriately is made possible because the senses are linked to the brain by a network of nerves which send messages as electric pulses. When the brain receives the information from the senses it coordinates its response.

In many cases, generally in response to something touching the body, the signal from the sensor does not reach the brain before action is taken. Instead, it produces a reflex response which is hardwired into the nervous system. For example, when you touch a very hot object, your hand automatically recoils; you don't need to think about it.

All animals have to be sensitive to their environment to survive. Even the simplest animals, such as jellyfish and roundworms, react to changes in their surroundings. Simple animals, however, have only a limited ability to move or defend themselves, and therefore generally have limited senses. Larger animals, such as vertebrates,

Below: This slow loris is nocturnal, that is, night-active. It has very large eyes that collect as much light as possible so that it can see in the gloom of the night.

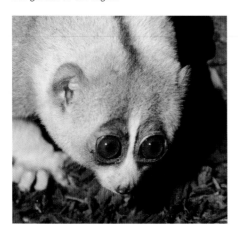

have a much more complex array of sense organs. Most vertebrates can hear, see, smell, taste and touch.

Vision

Invertebrates' eyes are generally designed to detect motion. Vertebrates' eyes, however, are better at forming clear images, often in colour. Vertebrates' eyes are balls of clear jelly which have an inner lining of light-sensitive cells. This lining, called the retina, is made up of one or two types of cell. The rod cells – named after their shape – are very sensitive to all types of light, but are only capable of forming black and white images. Animals which are active at night generally have (and need) only rods in their eyes.

Colour vision is important for just a few animals, such as monkeys, which need, for example, to see the brightest and therefore ripest fruits. Colour images are made by the cone cells – so-named because of their shape – in the retina. There are three types of cone, each of which is sensitive to a particular wavelength of light. Low wavelengths appear as reds, high wavelengths as blues, with green colours being detected in between.

Below: Like other hunters, a seal has eyes positioned on the front of its head. Forward-looking eyes are useful for judging distances, making it easier to chase down prey.

Above: Frogs have large eyes positioned on the upper side of the head so that the animals can lie mainly submerged in water with just their eyes poking out.

The light is focused on the retina by a lens to produce a clear image. Muscles change the shape of the lens so that it can focus the light arriving from different distances. While invertebrates may have several eyes, all vertebrates have just two, and they are always positioned on the head. Animals such as rabbits, which are constantly looking out for danger, have eyes on the side of the head to give a wide field of vision. But while they can see in almost all directions, rabbits have difficulty judging distances and speeds. Animals that have eyes pointing forward are better at doing this because each eye's field of vision overlaps with the other. This binocular vision helps hunting animals and others, such as tree-living primates, to judge distances more accurately.

Eyes can also detect radiation in a small band of wavelengths, and some animals detect radiation that is invisible to our eyes. Flying insects and birds can see ultraviolet light, which extends the range of their colour vision. At the other end of the spectrum many snakes can detect radiation with a lower wavelength. They sense infrared, or heat, through pits on the face which enables them to track their warm-blooded prey in pitch darkness.

Hearing

An animal's brain interprets waves of pressure travelling through the air, and detected by the ears, as sound. Many animals do not hear these waves with ears but detect them in other ways instead. For example, although snakes can hear, they are much more sensitive to vibrations through the lower jaw, travelling through the ground. Long facial whiskers sported by many mammals, from cats to dugongs, are very sensitive touch receptors. They can be so sensitive that they will even respond to currents in the air.

In many ways, hearing is a sensitive extension of the sense of touch. The ears of amphibians, reptiles and mammals have an eardrum which is sensitive to tiny changes in pressure. An eardrum is a thin membrane of skin which vibrates as the air waves hit it. A tiny bone (or in the case of mammals, three bones) attached to the drum transmit the vibrations to a shell-shaped structure called a cochlea. The cochlea is filled with a liquid which picks up the vibrations. As the liquid moves inside the cochlea, tiny hair-like structures lining it wave back and forth. Nerves stimulated by this wave motion send the information to the brain, which interprets it as sound.

A mammal's ear is divided into three sections. The cochlea forms the inner ear and the middle ear consists of the bones between the cochlea and eardrum. The outer ear is the tube joining the outside world and the

auricle – the fleshy structure on the side of the head that collects the sound waves – to the middle ear. Amphibians and reptiles do not possess auricles. Instead their eardrums are either on the side of the head – easily visible on many frogs and lizards – or under the skin, as in snakes.

Smell and taste

Smell and taste are so closely related as to form a single sense. Snakes and lizards, for example, taste the air with their forked tongues. However, it is perhaps the most complex sense. Noses, tongues and other smelling

Above: Snakes have forked tongues that they use to taste the air. The tips of the fork are slotted into an organ in the roof of the mouth. This organ is linked to the nose, and chemicals picked up by the tongue are identified with great sensitivity.

organs are lined with sensitive cells which can analyze a huge range of chemicals that float in the air or exist in food. Animals such as dogs, which rely on their sense of smell, have long noses packed with odour-sensitive cells. Monkeys, of the other hand, are less reliant on a sense of smell, and consequently have short noses capable only of detecting stronger odours.

Below: Hares have very large outer ears which they use like satellite dishes to pick up sound waves. They can rotate each ear separately to detect sound from all directions.

Below: Lizards do not have outer ears at all. Their hearing organs are contained inside the head and joined to the outside world through an eardrum membrane.

Below: Wolves have an excellent sense of smell and taste. They communicate with pack members and rival packs by smell, as part of a complex set of social behaviours.

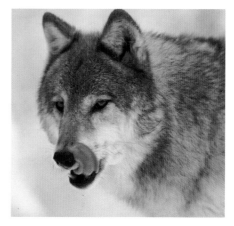

SURVIVAL

In order to stay alive, animals must not only find enough food, but also avoid becoming a predator's meal. To achieve this, animals have evolved many strategies to feed on a wide range of foods, and an array of weapons and defensive tactics to keep safe.

An animal must keep feeding in order to replace the energy used in staying alive. Substances in the food, such as sugars, are burned by the body, and the subsequent release of energy is used to heat the body and power its movements. Food is also essential for growth. Although most growth takes place during the early period of an animal's life, it never really stops because injuries need to heal and worn-out tissues need replacing. Some animals continue growing throughout life. Proteins in the food are the main building blocks of living bodies.

Plant food

Some animals will eat just about anything, while others are much more fussy. As a group, vertebrates get their energy from a wide range of sources – everything from shellfish and wood to honey and blood. Animals are often classified according to how they feed, forming several large groups filled with many otherwise unrelated animals.

Animals that eat plants are generally grouped together as herbivores. But this term is not very descriptive because there is such a wide range of plant foods. Animals that eat grass are known as grazers. However, this term can also apply to any animal which eats any plant that covers the ground

Below: Zebras are browsers, not grazers. They will eat some grass but also pick tastier leaves, buds and fruit off trees and shrubs. They often live in herds to stay safe from attack.

Above: Bison are grazers. They eat grass and plants that grow close to the ground. Because their food is all around them, grazers spend a long time out in the open. They feed together in large herds since there is safety in numbers.

in large amounts, such as seaweed or sedge. Typical grazers include bison and wildebeest but some, such as the marine iguana or gelada baboon, are not so typical. Animals such as giraffes or antelopes, which pick off the tastiest leaves, buds and fruit from bushes and trees, are called browsers. Other browsing animals include many monkeys, but some monkeys eat only leaves (the folivores) or fruit (the frugivores).

Below: Lions are unusual cats because they live together in prides. The members of the pride cooperate to catch food. They hunt as a team and share the food between them.

Many monkeys have a much broader diet, eating everything from insects to the sap which seeps out from the bark of tropical trees. Animals that eat both plant and animal foods are called omnivores. Bears are omnivorous, as are humans, but the most catholic of tastes belong to scavenging animals, such as rats and other rodents, which eat anything they can get their teeth into. Omnivores in general, and scavengers in particular, are very curious animals. They will investigate anything that looks or smells like food, and if it also tastes like food, then it probably is.

A taste for flesh

The term carnivore is often applied to any animal that eats flesh, but it is more correctly used to refer to an order of mammals which includes cats, dogs, bears and many smaller animals, such as weasels and mongooses. These animals are the kings of killing, armed with razor-sharp claws and powerful jaws crammed full of chisel-like teeth. They use their strength and speed to overpower their prey, either by running them down or taking them by surprise with an ambush.

Above: African elephants have few predators. Younger elephants are at risk of leopard attacks, and the adults defend them by trumpeting, stamping and flapping their large ears. If that fails, they will charge.

However, land-dwelling carnivores are not the only expert killers. The largest meat-eater is the orca, or killer whale, which is at least three times the size of the brown bear, the largest killer on land.

While snakes are much smaller in comparison, they are just as deadly, if not more so. They kill in one of two ways, either suffocating their prey by wrapping their coils tightly around them, or by injecting them with a poison through their fangs.

Arms race

Ironically, the same weapons used by predators are often used by their prey to defend themselves. For example, several species of frog, toad and salamander secrete poisons on to their skin. In some cases, such as the poison-dart frog, this poison is enough to kill any predator that tries to eat it, thus making sure that the killer won't repeat its performance. More often, though, a predator finds that its meal tastes horrible and remembers not to eat another one again. To remind the predators to keep away, many poisonous amphibians are brightly

coloured, which ensures that they are easily recognized.

Many predators rely on stealth to catch their prey, and staying hidden is part of the plan. A camouflaged coat, such as a tiger's stripes, helps animals blend into their surroundings. Many species also use this technique to ensure that they do not get eaten. Most freeze when danger approaches, and then scurry to safety as quickly as possible. Chameleons have taken camouflage to an even more sophisticated level as they can change the colour of their scaly skins, which helps them to blend in with their surrounding environment.

Plant-eating animals that live in the open cannot hide from predators that are armed with sharp teeth and claws. And the plant-eaters cannot rely on similar weapons to defend themselves. They are outgunned

Right: Chameleons have skin cells that can be opened and closed to make their skin colour change.

Filter-feeders

Some animals filter their food from water. The giant baleen whales do this, sieving tiny shrimp-like animals called krill out of great gulps of sea water. Some tadpoles and larval salamanders filter-feed as well, extracting tiny plant-like animals which float in fresh water. However, after becoming adults, all amphibians become hunters and eat other animals. All snakes and most lizards are meat-eaters, or carnivores, as well.

Below: The largest animals of all, baleen whales, are filter-feeders. They do not have teeth. Instead, their gums are lined with a thick curtain of baleen that filters out tiny shrimp-like krill from sea water.

because they do not possess sharp, pointed teeth but flattened ones to grind up their plant food. The best chance they have of avoiding danger is to run away. Animals such as antelopes or deer consequently have long, hoofed feet that lengthen their legs considerably; they are, in fact, standing on their toenails. These long legs allow them to run faster and leap high into the air to escape an attacker's jaws.

Animals that do not flee must stand and fight. Most large herbivores are armed with horns or antlers. Although used chiefly for display, the horns are the last line of defence when cornered.

REPRODUCTION

All animals share the urge to produce offspring which will survive after the parents die. The process of heredity is determined by genes, through which characteristics are passed from parents to offspring. Reproduction presents several problems, and animals have adopted different strategies for tackling them.

Animals have two main goals: to find food and a mate. To achieve these goals, they must survive everything that the environment throws at them, from extremes of the weather, such as floods and droughts, to hungry predators. They have to find sufficient supplies of food, and on top of that locate a mate before their competitors. If they find sufficient food but fail to produce any offspring, their struggle for survival will have been wasted.

One parent or two?

There are two ways in which an animal can reproduce, asexually or sexually. Animals that are produced by asexual reproduction, or parthenogenesis, have only one parent, a mother. The offspring are identical to their mother and to each other. Sexual reproduction involves two parents of the opposite sex. The offspring are hybrids of the two parents, with a mixture of their parents' characteristics.

The offspring inherit their parents' traits through their genes. Genes can be defined in various ways. One simple definition is that they are the unit of inheritance – a single inherited

Below: Crocodiles bury their eggs in a nest. The temperature of the nest determines the sex of the young reptiles. Hot nests produce more males than cool ones. Crocodile mothers are very gentle when it comes to raising young.

Above: Many male frogs croak by pumping air into an expandable throat sac. The croak is intended to attract females. The deeper the croak, the more attractive it is. However, some males lurk silently and mate with females as they approach the croaking males.

characteristic which cannot be subdivided any further. Genes are also segments of DNA (deoxyribonucleic acid), a complex chemical that forms long chains. It is found at the heart of every living cell. Each link in the DNA chain forms part of a code that controls how an animal's body develops and survives. And every cell in the body contains a full set of DNA which could be used to build a whole new body.

Animals produced through sexual reproduction receive half their DNA, or half their genes, from each parent. The male parent provides half the supply of genes, contained in a sperm. Each sperm's only role is to find its

Above: In deer and many other grazing animals, the males fight each other for the right to mate with the females in the herd. The deer with the largest antlers often wins without fighting, and real fights only break out if two males appear equally well-endowed.

way to, and fertilize, an egg, its female equivalent. Besides containing the other half of the DNA, the egg also holds a supply of food for the offspring as it develops into a new individual. Animals created through parthenogenesis get all their genes from their mother, and all of them are therefore the same sex – female.

Pros and cons

All mammals reproduce sexually, as do most reptiles and amphibians. However, there are a substantial number of reptiles and amphibians, especially lizards, which reproduce by parthenogenesis. There are benefits and disadvantages to both types of reproduction. Parthenogenesis is quick and convenient. The mother does not need to find a mate, and can devote all of her energy to producing huge numbers of young. This strategy is ideal for populating as yet unexploited territory. However, being identical, these animals are very vulnerable to attack. If, for example, one is killed by a disease or outwitted by a predator, it is very likely that they will all suffer the same fate. Consequently, whole communities of animals produced through parthenogenesis can be wiped out.

Sexual animals, on the other hand, are much more varied. Each one is unique, formed by a mixture of genes from both parents. This variation means that a group of animals produced by sexual reproduction is more likely to triumph over adversity than a group of asexual ones. However, sexual reproduction takes up a great deal of time and effort.

Attracting mates

Since females produce only a limited number of eggs, they are keen to make sure that they are fertilized by a male with good genes. If a male is fit and healthy, this is a sign that he has good genes. Good genes will ensure that the offspring will be able to compete with other animals for food and mates of their own. Because the females have the final say in agreeing to mate, the

Above: Lions live in prides, in which one or two males father all the children. When a new adult takes control of the pride, he kills the cubs of his deposed rival so that the pride's females will be ready to mate with him sooner.

Below: Rhinoceroses are generally solitary animals, but offspring stay with their mother for at least a year while they grow big enough to look after themselves.

Above: Gibbons are highly intelligent animals. Parents rear their offspring intensively while the young learn to survive the complexities and dangers of the rainforest. Many gibbons form strong male–female pair bonds that last throughout their lives.

males have to put a lot of effort into getting noticed. Many are brightly coloured, make loud noises, and they are often larger than the females. In many species the males even compete with each other for the right to display to the females. Winning that right is a good sign that they have the best genes.

Parental care

The amount of care that the offspring receive from their parents varies considerably. There is a necessary trade-off between the amount of useful care parents can give to each offspring, the number of offspring they can produce and how regularly they can breed. Mammals invest heavily in parental care, suckling their young after giving birth, while most young amphibians or reptiles never meet their parents at all.

By suckling, mammals ensure that their young grow to a size where they

can look after themselves. Generally, the young stay with the mother until it is time for her to give birth to the next litter – at least one or two months. However, in many species, including humans, the young stay with their parents for many years.

Other types of animals pursue the opposite strategy, producing large numbers of young that are left to fend for themselves. The vast majority in each batch of eggs – consisting of hundreds or even thousands – die before reaching adulthood, and many never even hatch. The survival rates, for example of frogs, are very low.

Animals that live in complicated societies, such as elephants, apes and humans, tend to produce a single offspring every few years. The parents direct their energies into protecting and rearing the young, giving them a good chance of survival. Animals which live for a only a short time, such as mice, rabbits, and reptiles and amphibians in general, need to reproduce quickly to make the most of their short lives. They produce high numbers of young, and do not waste time on anything more than the bare minimum of parental care. If successful, these animals can reproduce at an alarming pace.

AMPHIBIANS

Amphibians are the link between fish and land animals. One in eight of all vertebrate animals are amphibians. This group includes frogs, toads and newts as well as rarer types, such as giant sirens, hellbenders and worm-like caecilians. Amphibians are equally at home in water and on land.

Amphibians live on every continent except for Antarctica. None can survive in salt water, although a few species live close to the sea in the brackish water at river mouths. Being cold-blooded – their body temperature is always about the same as the temperature of their surroundings – most amphibians are found in the warmer regions of the world.

Unlike other land vertebrates, amphibians spend the early part of their lives in a different form from that of the adults. As they grow, the young gradually metamorphose into the adult body. Having a larval form means that the adults and their offspring live and feed in different places. In general the larvae are aquatic, while the adults spend most of their time on land.

The adults are hunters, feeding on other animals, while the young are generally plant eaters, filtering tiny plants from the water or grazing on aquatic plants which line the bottom of ponds and rivers.

Below: Amphibians must lay their eggs near a source of water. In most cases, such as this frog spawn, the eggs are laid straight into a pond or swamp. The tadpoles develop inside the jelly-like egg and then hatch out after the food supply in the egg's yolk runs out.

Above: Amphibians begin life looking very different from the adult form. Most of the time these larval forms, such as this frog tadpole, live in water as they slowly develop into the adult form, growing legs and lungs so that they can survive on land.

Life changing

Most amphibians hatch from eggs laid in water or, in a few cases, in moist soil or nests made of hardened mucus. Once hatched, the young amphibians, or larvae, live as completely aquatic animals. Those born on land wriggle to the nearest pool of water or drop from their nest into a river.

The larvae of frogs and toads are called tadpoles. Like the young of salamanders – a group that includes all other amphibians except caecilians – tadpoles do not have any legs at first. They swim using a long tail that has a fish-like fin extending along its length. As they grow, the larvae sprout legs. In general the back legs begin to grow first, followed by the front pair. Adult frogs do not have tails, and after the first few months a tadpole's tail begins to be reabsorbed into the body – it does not just fall away.

All adult salamanders keep their tails, and those species that spend their entire lives in water often retain the fin along the tail, along with other parts, such as external gills, a feature that is more commonly seen in the larval stage.

Body form

Amphibian larvae hatch with external gills but, as they grow, many (including all frogs and the many salamanders which live on land) develop internal gills. In most land-living species these internal gills are eventually replaced by lungs. Amphibians are also able to absorb oxygen directly through the skin, especially through the thin and moist tissues inside the mouth. A large number of land-living salamanders get all their oxygen in this way because they do not have lungs.

All adult frogs and toads return to the water to breed and lay their eggs, which are often deposited in a jelly-like mass called frog spawn. Several types of salamander do not lay eggs, and instead the females keep the fertilized eggs inside their bodies. The larvae develop inside the eggs, fed by a supply of rich yoke, and do not hatch until they have reached adult form.

Above: After the first few weeks, a tadpole acquires tiny back legs. As the legs grow, the long tail is gradually reabsorbed into the body. The front legs appear after the back ones have formed.

Adult form

Most adult amphibians have four limbs, with four digits on the front pair and five on the rear. Unlike other land-living animals, such as reptiles or mammals, their skin is naked and soft. Frogs' skin is smooth and moist, while toads generally have a warty appearance.

The skins of many salamanders are brightly coloured, with patterns that often change throughout the year. Colour change prior to the mating season signals the salamander's readiness to mate. Many frogs also have bright skin colours. Although their skin shades can change considerably in different light levels, these colours are generally not mating signals to fellow frogs. Instead they are warnings to predators that the frog's skin is laced with deadly poison. While toads tend to be drab in colour, many also secrete toxic chemicals to keep predators away. These substances are often stored in swollen warts which burst when the toad is attacked.

Below: Adult frogs may live in water or on land. Aquatic ones have webbed feet, while those on land have powerful legs for jumping and climbing. All frogs must return to a source of water to mate.

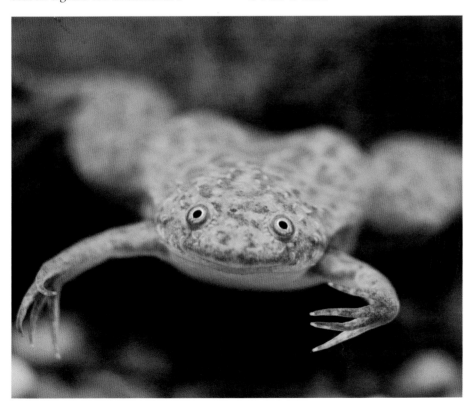

Forever young

Salamanders which have changed into adults, but which have not yet reached adult size, are called efts. The time it takes for an amphibian to grow from a newly hatched larva to an adult varies considerably, and the chief factor is the temperature of the water in which it is developing. Most frogs and toads develop in shallow waters, warmed by the summer sun, and they generally reach adulthood within three to four months. However, salamanders, especially the largest ones, can take much longer, and at the northern and southern limits of their geographical spread some salamanders stay as larvae for many years. It appears that the trigger for the change into adult form is linked to the temperature, and in cold climates this change happens only every few years. In fact it may not happen during a salamander's lifetime, and consequently several species have evolved the ability to develop sexual organs even when they still look like larvae.

Below: Marbled salamanders are unusual in that the females lay their eggs on dry land and coil themselves around them to keep them as moist as possible. They stay like this until the seasonal rains fall. The water stimulates the eggs to hatch.

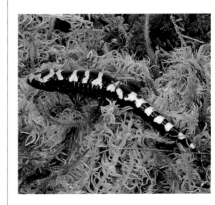

REPTILES

Reptiles include lizards, snakes, alligators, crocodiles, turtles and tortoises, as well as now-extinct creatures such as dinosaurs and the ancestors of birds. Crocodiles have roamed the Earth for 200 million years and are still highly successful hunters.

Reptiles are a large and diverse group of animals containing about 6,500 species. Many of these animals look very different from each other and live in a large number of habitats, from the deep ocean to the scorching desert. Despite their great diversity, all reptiles share certain characteristics.

Most reptiles lay eggs, but these are different from those of an amphibian because they have a hard, thin shell rather than a soft, jelly-like one. This protects the developing young inside and, more importantly, stops them from drying out. Shelled eggs were an evolutionary breakthrough because they meant that adult reptiles did not have to return to the water to breed. Their waterproof eggs could be laid anywhere, even in the driest places. Reptiles were also the first group of land-living animals to develop into an adult form inside the egg. They did not emerge as under-developed larvae like the young of most amphibians.

Below: Alligators and other crocodilians are an ancient group of reptiles that have no close living relatives. They are archosaurs, a group of reptiles that included the dinosaurs. Other living reptiles belong to a different group.

Released from their ties to water, the reptiles developed unique ways of retaining moisture. Their skins are covered by hardened plates or scales to stop water being lost. The scales are also coated with the protein keratin, the same substance used to make fingernails and hair.

All reptiles breathe using lungs; if they were to absorb air through the skin it would involve too much water loss. Like amphibians, reptiles are cold-blooded and cannot heat their bodies from within as mammals can. Consequently, reptiles are commonly found in warm climates.

Ancient killers

Being such a diverse group, reptiles share few defining characteristics besides their shelled eggs, scaly skin and lungs. They broadly divide into four orders. The first contains the crocodiles, and includes alligators and caimans; these are contemporaries of the dinosaurs, both groups being related to a common ancestor.

In fact today's crocodiles have changed little since the age when dinosaurs ruled the world over 200 million years

Above: Turtles and their relatives, such as these giant tortoises, are unusual reptiles. Not only do they have bony shells fused around their bodies, but they also have skulls that are quite different from other reptiles. Turtles are also unusual because many of them live in the ocean, while most reptiles live on land.

ago. Unlike the dinosaurs, which disappeared 65 million years ago, the crocodiles are still going strong. Technically speaking, the dinosaurs never actually died out; their direct descendents, the birds, are still thriving. Although birds are now grouped separately from reptiles, scientists know that they all evolved from ancestors which lived about 400 million years ago. Mammals, on the other hand, broke away from this group about 300 million years ago.

Above: Most reptiles, including this tree boa, lay eggs. The young hatch looking like small versions of the adults. However, several snakes and lizards give birth to live young, which emerge from their mother fully formed.

Distant relatives

The second reptile order includes turtles, terrapins and tortoises. These are only distantly related to other reptiles, and it shows. Turtles are also the oldest group of reptiles, evolving their bony shells and clumsy bodies before crocodiles, dinosaurs or any other living reptile group existed. Although turtles evolved on land, many have since returned to water. However, they still breathe air, and all must return to land to lay their eggs.

The third group of reptiles is the largest. Collectively called the squamates, this group includes snakes and lizards.

Snakes, with their legless bodies and formidable reputations, are perhaps the most familiar reptiles. They evolved from animals that did have legs, and many retain tiny vestiges of legs. The squamates include other legless members such as the amphisbaenians (or worm lizards) and slow worms. Both of these groups are more closely related to lizards than snakes, despite looking more like the latter. Lizards are not a simple group of reptiles, and many biologists refer to them as several different groups, including the skinks, monitors, geckos and iguanas.

Below: Lizards, such as this iguana, are the largest group of reptiles. Most are hunters that live in hot parts of the world, and they are especially successful in dry areas where other types of animal are not so common.

The squamates are so diverse in their lifestyles and body forms that it is hard to find factors which they have in common. One feature not found in other reptile orders is the Jacobson's organ. It is positioned in the roof of the mouth and is closely associated with the nose. All snakes and most lizards use this organ to "taste" the air and detect prey. The long forked tongue of most of these animals flicks out into the air, picking up tiny particles on its moist surface. Once back inside the mouth, each fork slots into the Jacobson's organ which then analyzes the substances.

The fourth and final order of reptiles is very small: the tuataras. These include just a few species, all of which are very rare indeed, clinging to life on islands off the mainland of New Zealand. To most people a tuatara looks like a large iguana. However, scientists believe that it is only a distant relative of lizards and other squamates because it has an odd-shaped skull and no eardrums.

Tuatara

Despite their differences from lizards and other squamates, tuataras do share one feature with lizards: the so-called third eye. This light-sensitive gland inside the head can detect light penetrating the thin skull. Both types of reptile use the third eye to regulate their exposure to the sun and so regulate their body temperature throughout the year.

Below: The tuatara is a living fossil, living on just a few islands around New Zealand. It looks like a lizard, but its skull and skeleton show that it is the last member of another ancient group of reptiles.

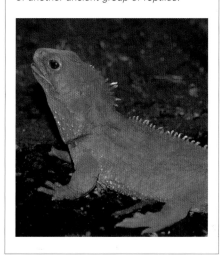

PLACENTAL MAMMALS

Mammals are the most familiar of all vertebrates. This is because not only are human beings mammals, but also most domestic animals and pets belong in this category. Placental mammals are also more widespread than other types of animal, being found in all parts of the world.

Mammals are grouped together because they share a number of characteristics. However, these common features do not come close to describing the huge diversity within the mammal class. For example, the largest animal that has ever existed on Earth – the blue whale – is a mammal, and so this monster of the deep shares several crucial traits with even the smallest mammals, such as the tiniest of shrews. Other mammals include elephants and moles, monkeys and hippopotamuses, and bats and camels. To add to this great diversity, mammals live in more places on Earth than any other group of animals, from the frozen ice fields of the Arctic to the humid treetops of the Amazon rainforest, and even under the sandy soil of African deserts.

Mammal bodies

The most obvious mammalian feature is hair. All mammals have hair made of keratin protein and, in most cases, it forms a thick coat of fur, though many

Below: Although they are often mistaken for fish, dolphins are mammals: they breathe air and suckle their young. However, life under water requires flippers and fins, not legs.

mammals are relatively naked, not least humans. Unlike reptiles and amphibians, all mammals are warm-blooded, which means that they can keep their body temperature at a constant level. While this requires quite a lot of energy, it means that mammals are not totally dependent on the temperature of their surroundings. In places where other vertebrates would be frozen solid, mammals can survive by seeking out food and keeping themselves warm. Many mammals,

Above: With their thick white fur and powerful clawed paws, polar bears are very well adapted to life on the pack ice. However, they are not so different from other types of bear. The adaptability of the basic body plan is what makes mammals so successful.

including humans, can also cool their bodies using sweat. The water secreted on the skin cools the body efficiently, but it does mean that these animals need to drink more replacement water than do other groups.

Incidentally, the name mammal comes from the mammary glands. These glands are the means by which all female mammals provide milk (or liquid food) to their developing young. The young suck the milk through teats or nipples for the first few weeks or months of life.

Reproduction

Mammals reproduce in a number of ways. Monotremes, such as the duck-billed platypus, lay eggs, but all other mammals give birth to their young. Marsupials, a relatively small group of animals which includes kangaroos, give birth to very undeveloped young which then continue to grow inside a fold or pouch on the mother's skin.

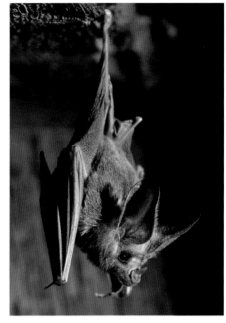

The majority of mammals, called the placental mammals or eutherians, do not give birth to their young until they are fully formed and resemble the adults. The developing young, or foetuses, grow inside a womb or uterus where they are fed by the mother through a placenta. This large organ allows the young to stay inside the mother for a lot longer than in most other animals. It forms the interface between the mother's blood supply and that of the developing foetus, where oxygen and food pass from the parent to her offspring. The placenta is attached to the foetus by means of an umbilical cord which withers and drops off soon after the birth.

Widespread range

Mammals are found in a wider variety of habitats than any other group of animals. While mammals all breathe air with their

Above: Elephants are the largest land mammals in the world. They are most closely related to rabbit-like hyraxes and walrus-like dugongs and manatees.

lungs, this has not prevented many from making their homes in water. In many ways the streamlined bodies of whales and dolphins, for example, resemble those of sharks and other large fish. However, they are very much mammals, breathing air through a large nostril or blowhole in the top of the head, but their body hair has been reduced to just a few thick bristles.

Above: Plenty of mammals can glide, but only bats join birds and insects in true flight. A bat wing is made from skin that is stretched between long finger bones.

At the other end of the spectrum, some mammals even fly. Bats darting through the gloom of a summer evening may appear to be small birds, but they too are mammals with furry bodies and wings made from stretched skin instead of feathers. Although most other mammals have a more conventional body plan, with four legs and tail, they too have evolved to survive in a startling range of habitats. They have achieved this not just by adapting their bodies but by changing their behaviour. In general, mammals have larger brains than reptiles and amphibians, and this allows them to understand their environment more fully. Many mammals, such as monkeys and dogs, survive by living in complex social groups in which individuals cooperate with each other when hunting food, protecting the group from danger and even finding mates.

Right: One factor that makes mammals unique is that the females have mammary glands. These glands produce milk for the young animals to drink, as this fallow deer fawn is doing. The milk is a mixture of fat, protein and sugars.

MONOTREMES AND MARSUPIALS

Not all mammals begin their lives as foetuses growing inside a uterus within their mother. Monotremes and marsupials develop in other ways. Monotremes are the only mammals to lay eggs like birds or lizards, while marsupials raise their young inside pouches on the outside of their bodies.

Egg-laying mammals

Monotremes are a group of just three mammal species which still lay their young inside eggs: two species of echidnas, short and long-nosed, (also called spiny anteaters), and the odd-looking duck-billed platypus. Although monotremes are hairy and feed their young with milk, they are distant relatives of other mammals.

Monotremes lay two or three very tiny spherical eggs which have a much softer shell than those of birds or many reptiles. And unlike other mammals, monotremes do not have a birth canal. Instead, their eggs travel through the same body opening as the urine and faeces. A single multi-purpose body opening like this is called a cloaca (Latin for drain), and is a feature that monotremes share with birds and reptiles. In fact, the name monotreme means one-holed animal.

The young of monotremes stay in the egg for only a matter of days before hatching out, and then they continue their development while being nursed by their mother. Nursing

Below: Kangaroos are the most familiar marsupial mammals. Like most marsupials, the young grow inside a pouch on the mother's belly, where they are fed on milk from a nipple. Some other marsupials do not have such a developed pouch.

Above: Monotremes, such as this echidna, are in the minority compared to other mammals. They lay eggs, more like a bird or a reptile, rather than give birth to their young. However, the monotremes are mammals because they feed their young on a supply of milk.

echidnas keep their young in a pouch on their underside, while platypus young spend their early days in an underground nest. While all other mammals have teats for delivering milk, the monotremes do not possess this adaptation. Instead, the mother secretes the fatty liquid on her fur and the young then lap it up.

Monotremes hatch out in a very undeveloped state. They are hairless, blind, barely 1cm (⅓in) long and have just blunt buds for limbs. The young are dependent on their mothers' milk for a long time – six months in the case of echidnas. Although they are a tiny group compared to other mammal orders, the monotremes are highly adapted to their habitats and are quite amazing mammals.

Life in a pouch

Although their 270 species make the marsupials a much larger group than the monotremes, they are still very much the minority compared to the

Monotreme features

Monotremes were living nearly 200 million years ago, long before any other types of mammal existed. However, this does not mean that animals similar to monotremes were the ancestors of all modern mammals. Further, today's monotremes (which live only in Australasia) are by no means primitive. In fact they have some highly developed features which are not found in any other mammal group. For example, male platypuses sport a venomous spur behind the knee which they use when defending themselves and fighting each other.

Below: Because of its strange appearance, the duck-billed platypus was thought to be a fake when specimens were first displayed. However, it is a very well-adapted underwater hunter, using its bill to detect the electric fields produced by its prey's muscles.

Above: Most marsupials live in Australia where there are few large predators. The koala is adapted to living in trees and eating leaves, and has evolved features that are seen in other animals who live in a similar way, for example grasping hands and a long, fermenting digestive system.

4,000 or so species of placental mammals that inhabit every corner of the world. Marsupials are found only in Australia and the islands of New Guinea, and a few species live in the Americas.

Marsupials are much more closely related to placental mammals than monotremes. Biologists believe that marsupials evolved first in the Americas and then spread to Australia via Antarctica, in the days when the three continents were joined together. Once Australia became an island, its marsupials remained the dominant mammals, while placental mammals began to take over from them elsewhere in the world.

The placental mammals have a single uterus connected to both ovaries by oviducts, while marsupials have two much smaller uteruses, each connected to a single ovary. The uterus of a placental mammal can swell up as the foetus grows. However, those of a marsupial cannot, which means that the young have to be born much earlier.

Like a newly hatched monotreme, the tiny marsupial baby is hairless and blind, and has stubby forelegs. After two or three weeks in the uterus, the baby makes its way out through a birth canal that grows especially for this journey. Once outside, the baby battles through its mother's fur to her nipples.

Many marsupials have their nipples inside a pouch or marsupium. Once inside, the baby latches on to the nipple which swells inside its mouth to create a very firm connection. The larger marsupials, such as red kangaroos, spend several months inside the pouch and may later be joined by younger siblings. The mother's milk supply is tailored for each of her young, with each baby getting the right amount of fats and proteins for its age. A baby marsupial that is old enough to leave the pouch is called a joey. Joeys often return to their mother's pouch to sleep or feed for several months more before becoming completely independent.

Right: Tasmanian devils used to be found right across Australia. Now they only survive on the southern island of Tasmania. Many other marsupial species have suffered due to the activities of humans and their domestic animals.

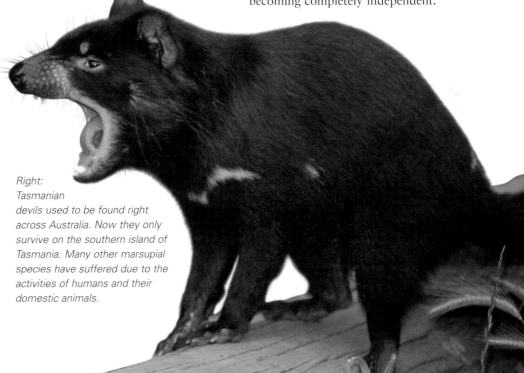

ECOLOGY

Ecology is the study of how groups of organisms interact with members of their own species, other organisms and the environment. All types of animals live in a community of interdependent organisms called an ecosystem, in which they have their own particular role.

The natural world is filled with a wealth of opportunities for animals to feed and breed. Every animal species has evolved to take advantage of a certain set of these opportunities, called a niche. A niche is not just a physical place but also a lifestyle exploited by that single species. For example, even though they live in the same rainforest habitat, sloths and tapirs occupy very different niches.

To understand how different organisms interrelate, ecologists combine all the niches in an area into a community, called an ecosystem. Ecosystems do not really exist because it is impossible to know where one ends and another begins, but the system is a useful tool when learning more about the natural world.

Food chains

One way of understanding how an ecosystem works is to follow the food chains within it. A food chain is made up of a series of organisms that prey on each other. Each habitat is filled with them, and since they often merge into and converge from each other, they are often combined into food webs.

Below: Nature creates some incredible alliances. The American badger, for example, goes on hunting trips with a coyote. The coyote sniffs out the prey, and the badger digs it out of its burrow for both of them to eat.

Ecologists use food chains to see how energy and nutrients flow through natural communities. Food chains always begin with plants. Plants are the only organisms on Earth that do not need to feed, deriving their energy from sunlight, whereas all other organisms, including animals, get theirs from food. At the next level up the food chain come the plant-eaters. They eat the plants, and extract the sugar and other useful substances made by them. And, like the plants, they use these substances to power their bodies and stay alive. The predators occupy the next level up, and they eat the bodies of the plant-eating animals.

At each stage of the food chain, energy is lost, mainly as heat given out by the animals' bodies. Because of this, less energy is available at each level up the food chain. This means that in a healthy ecosystem there are always fewer predators than prey, and always more plants than plant-eaters.

Nutrient cycles

A very simple food chain would be as follows: grass, wildebeest and lion. However, the reality of most ecosystems is much more complex, with many more layers, including certain animals that eat both plants and animals. Every food chain ends with a top predator, in our example, the lion. Nothing preys on the lion, at least when it is alive, but once it dies the food chain continues as insects, fungi and other decomposers feed on the carcass. Eventually nothing is left of the lion's body. All the energy stored in it is removed by the decomposers, and the chemicals which made up its body have returned to the environment as carbon dioxide gas, water and minerals in the soil. And these are the very same substances needed by a growing plant. The cycle is complete.

Above: Nothing is wasted in nature. The dung beetle uses the droppings of larger grazing animals as a supply of food for its developing young. Since the beetles clear away all the dung, the soil is not damaged by it, the grass continues to grow, and the grazers have plenty of food.

Living together

As food chains show, the lives of different animals in an ecosystem are closely related. If all the plants died for some reason, it would not just be the plant-eaters that would go hungry. As all of them begin to die, the predators would starve too. Only the decomposers might appear to benefit. Put another way, the other species living alongside an animal are just as integral to that animal's environment as the weather and landscape. This is yet another way of saying that animal species have not evolved isolated from each another.

The result is that as predators have evolved new ways of catching their prey, the prey has had to evolve new ways of escaping. On many occasions this process of co-evolution has created symbiotic relationships between two different species. For example, honeyguide birds lead badgers to bees' nests.

Some niches are very simple, and the animals that occupy them live simple, solitary lives. Others, especially those occupied by mammals, are much more complex and require members of a species to live closely together. These aggregations of animals may be simple herds or more structured social groups.

Food chain

Food chains show how the energy needed for life passes through an ecosystem. The energy originates in the Sun. This makes plants grow, which are then eaten by animals. The plant-eating animals then become meals themselves.

Below: This food chain shows what animals eat in a temperate country, such as Britain. Herbivores eat only plants, while carnivores eat mainly other animals. Animals that eat both plants and animals are omnivores – for example, humans.

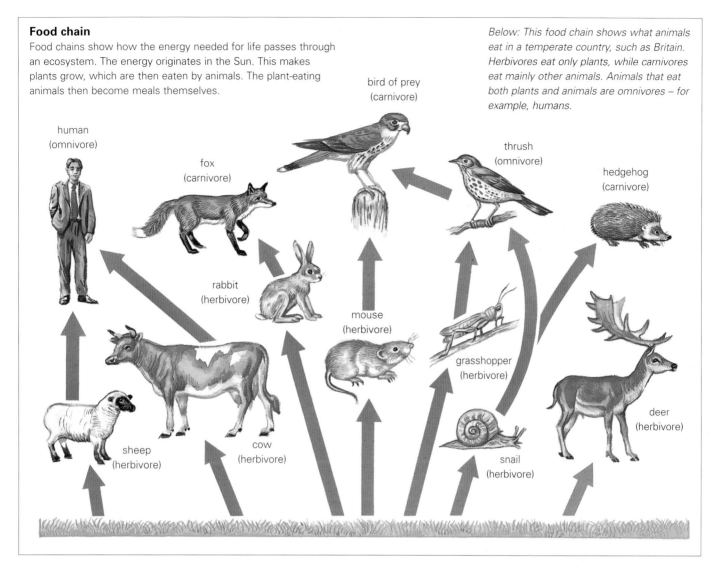

human (omnivore)

fox (carnivore)

bird of prey (carnivore)

thrush (omnivore)

hedgehog (carnivore)

rabbit (herbivore)

mouse (herbivore)

grasshopper (herbivore)

deer (herbivore)

sheep (herbivore)

cow (herbivore)

snail (herbivore)

Group living

A herd, flock or shoal is a group of animals which gathers together for safety. Each member operates as an individual, but is physically safest in the centre of the group, the danger of attack being greatest on the edge. Herd members do not actively communicate dangers to each other. When one is startled by something and bolts, the rest will probably follow.

Members of a social group, on the other hand, work together to find food, raise their young and defend themselves. Many mammals, for example apes, monkeys, dogs, dolphins and elephants, form social groups, and these groups exist in many forms. At one end of the spectrum are highly ordered societies, such as lion prides and baboon troops, which are often controlled by one dominant male, the other members often having their own ranking in a strict hierarchical structure. At the other end of the spectrum are leaderless gangs of animals, such as squirrel monkeys, which merge and split with no real guiding purpose.

There are many advantages of living in social groups, with members finding more food and being warned of danger, for example. However, in many societies only a handful of high-ranking members are allowed to breed. In these cases, the groups are held together by a complex fusion of family ties in which brothers and sisters help to raise nephews and nieces. Politics also plays its cohesive part, with members forming and breaking alliances in order to rise to the top.

Below: Meerkats live in family groups called bands. They need to live together because they live in a dry habitat where they must cooperate to find food, raise young and avoid being eaten by predators.

MIGRATION AND HIBERNATION

Migration and hibernation are two ways in which animals cope with the changing seasons and fluctuations in the supply of food. By hibernating, they sleep through periods of bad weather when food is hard to find, and by migrating, they reach places where food is more readily available.

Everywhere on Earth, the climate changes throughout the year with the cycle of seasons. In some places these changes are hardly noticeable from month to month, while in others each new season brings extremes of weather from blistering hot summers to freezing winters, or torrential rains followed by drought.

Change of lifestyle

In temperate regions, such as Europe, the year is generally divided into four seasons. Other regions experience a different annual cycle of changes. For example, tropical regions do not really have fluctuating temperatures, but many areas do experience periods of relative dry and at least one period of heavier rains each year. By contrast, in the far north, the change between the short summer and long winter is so quick that, in effect, there are only two seasons.

Hibernating heart rate

The hibernating animal's heart rate slows to just a few beats per minute. It breathes more slowly and its body temperature drops to just a few degrees above the surrounding air temperature.

Below: The bodies of true hibernators, such as the dormouse, shut down almost completely during hibernation. Other hibernators, such as bears, may be out of sight for most of the winter, but they do not become completely dormant and their temperature does not fall drastically.

Above: Reptiles that live in cooler parts of the world – rattlesnakes, for example – spend a long time lying dormant. They do not hibernate like mammals, but because they are cold-blooded and do not need lots of energy to function, they can go for long periods without food.

Animals must, of course, react to these changes if they are to survive the harshest weather and make the most of clement conditions. Monkeys, for example, build up a mental map of their patch of forest so that they know where the fresh leaves will be after the rains, and where to find the hardier forest fruits during a drought. Wolves living in chilly northern forests hunt together in packs during the cold winter, working together to kill animals which are much larger than they are. However, when the summer arrives they tend to forage alone, picking off the many smaller animals, such as rodents and rabbits, which appear when the snow melts.

Hibernation

The reason the wolves find these smaller animals in the summer is that they suddenly emerge having passed the winter in cosy burrows or nests. This behaviour is commonly called hibernating, but there is a distinction between true hibernation and simply being inactive over winter.

Animals such as bears and tree squirrels are not true hibernators. Although they generally sleep for long periods during the coldest parts of winter, hunkered down in a den or drey, they do not enter the deep, unconscious state of hibernation. Unable to feed while asleep, these animals rely on their bodily reserves of fat to stay alive. However, they often wake up during breaks in the harshest weather and venture outside to urinate or snatch a meal. Because tree squirrels have less fat reserves than bears, they frequently visit caches (stores) of food which they filled in the autumn.

On the other hand, the true hibernators, such as dormice or woodchucks, do not stir at all over winter. They rely completely on their reserves of fat to stay alive, and to save energy their metabolism slows to a fraction of its normal pace.

Only warm-blooded animals hibernate because they are the main types of animals which can survive in places where hibernation is necessary. However, rattlesnakes often pass the winter in rocky crevices and burrows. Reptiles and amphibians which live in very hot and dry places have their own form of hibernation, called aestivation.

They become dormant when their habitat becomes too dry. Most bury themselves in moist sand or under rocks, only becoming active again when rain brings the habitat back to life. Some aestivating frogs even grow a skin cocoon which traps moisture and keeps their bodies moist while they wait for the rains to return.

Migration

Another way of coping with bad conditions is to migrate. Migrations are not just random wanderings, but involve following a set route each year. In general they are two-way trips, with animals returning to where they started once conditions back home become favourable again.

All sorts of animals migrate, from insects to whales, and there are many reasons for doing so. Most migrators are looking for supplies of food, or for a safe place to rear their young. For example, once their home territory becomes too crowded, young lemmings stampede over wide areas looking for new places to live, sometimes dying in the process. Herds of reindeer leave the barren tundra as winter approaches, and head for the relative warmth of the forest. Mountain goats act in a similar way: having spent the summer grazing in high alpine meadows, they descend below the treeline when winter snow begins to cover their pastures.

Other migrations are on a much grander scale, and in some cases an animal's whole life can be a continual migration. Wildebeest travel in huge

Above: Whales have the longest migrations of all mammals. They move from their warm breeding grounds near the Equator to feeding areas in cooler waters near the poles.

herds across southern Africa in search of fresh pastures. They follow age-old routes but may take a detour if grass is growing in unusual places. Among the greatest migrants are the giant whales, which travel thousands of miles from their breeding grounds in the tropics to their feeding grounds near the poles. The cool waters around the poles teem with plankton food, while the warmer tropical waters are a better place for giving birth.

Day length

How do animals know that it is time to hibernate or migrate? The answer lies in the changing number of hours of daylight as the seasons change.

All animals are sensitive to daylight, and use it to set their body clocks or circadian rhythms. These rhythms

Above: Bats spend long periods hibernating. They mate before winter, and the females store the sperm inside their body, only releasing it on the eggs as spring approaches.

affect all bodily processes, including the build-up to the breeding season. The hibernators begin to put on weight or store food as the days shorten, and many migrants start to get restless before setting off on their journey. However, not all migrations are controlled by the number of hours of daylight. Some migrators, such as wildebeest and lemmings, move because of other environmental factors, such as the lack of food caused by drought or overcrowding.

Below: The migrations of enormous herds of wildebeest across the huge grasslands of Africa is one of the natural wonders of the world. These large antelopes travel in search of watering holes and new areas of fresh grass. The migrations do not follow the same route each year, but the herds generally do stay on tried and tested trails.

INTRODUCED SPECIES

*Centuries ago, as people started exploring and conquering new lands, many animals travelled with them.
In fact, that's the only way many animals could travel such long distances, often crossing seas. Many
introduced species then thrived in their new habitats, often at the expense of the native wildlife.*

Perhaps one of the first introduced animals was the dingo. This Australian dog is now regarded as a species in its own right, but it was introduced to the region by the Aboriginals. These migrants had domesticated the ancestors of the dingo, probably from grey wolves, many years before.

Dingoes were one of the first placental mammals to come to Australia, which had previously been populated by marsupial mammals. In a chain of events that has been repeated many times since, the introduced dingoes became feral (living as wild animals), and were soon competing with native hunters for food. Not only did the introduced mammals begin to take over from the marsupial predators, such as Tasmanian devils and marsupial wolves, but they also wiped out many smaller marsupials which were unable to defend themselves against these ferocious foreign hunters. In fact, many more of the native Australian marsupials have now become extinct, or are in danger of doing so, though not just dingoes are responsible. As European settlers have arrived over the last couple of centuries, they have also introduced many new animals, including cats.

Domestic animals

Looking around the European countryside, you would be forgiven for thinking that cows, sheep and other farm animals are naturally occurring species. In fact, all come from distant parts of the world. Over the centuries, livestock animals have been selectively bred to develop desirable characteristics, such as lean meat or high milk production. Despite this, they can be traced back to ancestral species. For example, goats – a domestic breed of an Asian ibex – were introduced to North Africa about 3,000 years ago. These goats, with their voracious appetites, did well feeding on dry scrubland. In fact they did too well, and had soon stripped the plants, turning even more of North Africa into desert. Similarly, horses introduced to the Americas by European settlers had

Left: Dingoes are wild dogs that live in Australia. However, they did not evolve there; no large placental mammals did. They are actually the relatives of pet dogs that travelled with the first people to reach Australia.

Cows and sheep

European cows are believed to be descendents of a now-extinct species of oxen called the auroch, while modern sheep are descended from the mouflon. From their beginnings in the Middle East, new breeds were introduced to all corners of the world, where they had a huge effect on the native animals and wildlife.

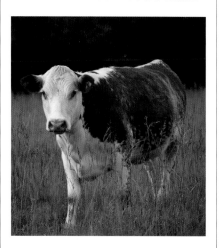

Above: Cattle have been bred to look and behave very differently from their wild ancestors. Few breeds have horns, and they are generally docile animals. Some breeds produce a good supply of milk, while others are bred for their meat.

Below: Sheep were one of the first domestic animals. They are kept for their meat and sometimes milk, which is used for cheese. The thick coat or fleece that kept their ancestors warm on mountain slopes is now used to make woollen garments.

Above: While the ancestors of domestic horses have become extinct, horses have become wild in several parts of the world. Perhaps the most celebrated of these feral horses are the mustangs, which run free in the wild American West, after escaping from early European settlers.

a marked effect on that continent. Native people, as well as the settlers, began to use them to hunt bison on the plains, which eventually gave way to cattle. Groups of the introduced horses escaped from captivity and began to live wild. The feral American horses were called mustangs.

Rodent invaders

While many animals were introduced to new areas on purpose as livestock or pets, other animals hitched a lift. For example, some animals were more or less stowaways on ships, but only those that could fend for themselves at their new destination were successfully introduced. These species tended to be generalist feeders, and none was more successful than rodents, such as mice and rats. In fact the house mouse is the second most widespread mammal of all,

after humans. It lives almost everywhere that people do, except in the icy polar regions, although it is very likely that rodents did reach these places but then failed to thrive in the cold.

The black rat – also known as the ship rat – has spread right around the world from Asia over the last 2,000 years. On several occasions it has brought diseases with it, including bubonic plague, or the Black Death, which has killed millions of people. Another prolific travelling rodent is the brown rat which is thought to have

spread from Europe, and now exists everywhere except the poles.

Rodents are so successful because they will eat almost anything and can reproduce at a prolific rate. These two characteristics have meant that mice and rats have become pests wherever they breed.

Below: With their sharp and ever-growing teeth, rodents are very adaptable animals. Mice and rats have spread alongside humans, and wherever people go, these little gnawing beasts soon become established, breeding very quickly and spreading into new areas.

ENDANGERED SPECIES

Many animals are threatened with extinction because they cannot survive in a world which is constantly being changed by human intervention. Many species have already become extinct, and if people do nothing to save them, a great many more will follow.

Surprising though it may sound, there is nothing unusual in extinctions, for they are an important part of the natural world. As the climate and landscape have changed in a given area over millions of years, the animals that live there have also changed. And as a new species evolves, so another is forced out of its habitat and becomes extinct. All that remains, if we are lucky, are a few fosslized bones – a record in stone.

Mass extinction?

Biologists estimate that there are at least several million species alive today, and possibly as many as 30 million. Whatever the figure, there are probably more species on Earth right now than at any other time. Therefore, because of the habitat destruction caused by people, more species are becoming extinct or are being threatened with extinction than ever before.

Geologists and biologists know that every now and then there are mass extinctions, in which great

Below: Okapis are rare mammals whose closest living relatives are giraffes, despite the zebra-stripes on their hindquarters and forelegs. They live in the forest of the Congo in central Africa. This forest has been ravaged by war and deforestation, and okapis and other forest-dwellers are now very rare.

Above: Leatherback turtles are the largest turtles in the world – even larger than the better-known giant tortoises. They are becoming rare because of the decline in untouched beaches on which to lay their eggs. Fewer leatherbacks are being born, and even fewer reach adulthood.

numbers of the world's animals die out forever. For example, it is widely believed that the dinosaurs and many other reptiles were wiped out after a meteorite smashed into Mexico 65 million years ago. But the questions are now: are we witnessing the natural world's latest mass extinction? And are humans the cause?

Most of the world's animal species are insects – especially beetles – and other invertebrates. It is likely that many of these species, especially those living in tropical forests, are becoming extinct. However, since scientists may never have had a chance to describe many of them, nobody knows the true number.

Life list

With vertebrate animals, it is a different story. Because there are only a few thousand species of animals with backbones, most of which have been recognized for hundreds of years, we know a great deal more about the plight of each species. Many species, for example mice, dogs and horses, thrive in a world dominated by people. However, a great many more species have suffered as people have destroyed their habitats, either deliberately or by upsetting the balance of nature by introducing species from other parts of the world.

The International Union for the Conservation of Nature and Natural Resources (IUCN) produces a Red List of animals which are in danger of extinction. There are currently about 5,500 animals listed in a number of categories, including extinct in the wild, endangered and vulnerable. Nearly one quarter of all mammals are included on the list, and about four per cent of reptiles and three of amphibians. However, while the status of all mammals has been assessed by the IUCN, only a fraction of reptiles and amphibians has been as thoroughly checked, and it is very likely that many more species are much closer to extinction than was previously thought.

Below: Golden lion tamarins are small monkeys that have been saved from extinction by extensive captive breeding programmes in zoos around the world. An area of the monkey's forest habitat in Brazil is now being protected, and captive-bred monkeys are being reintroduced to the wild.

Above: Gorillas are endangered because their forest habitats are being destroyed. They are not able to thrive anywhere else. Also, these great apes are hunted for meat. Although illegal, the bush-meat trade is highly profitable, but soon there may be no gorillas left.

Wiped out

As the forests of Europe and China were cleared over the past thousand years, forest animals had increasingly fewer places to live. And as they inevitably came into increasingly close contact with people, wild animals, such as boars, bears and wolves, became persecuted and were eventually wiped out in many areas.

Above: Pandas live in bamboo forests and do not breed very often or eagerly. They were once on the verge of extinction, however the latest technology – from artificial insemination to test-tube baby pandas – is increasing the numbers of these popular mammals.

As the world's human population soared in the 20th century, a similar process took place elsewhere. Another major habitat being destroyed was, and still is, the tropical rainforest. The number of species living in these areas is much higher than elsewhere, and a proportionately huge number of species are finding it harder to survive.

Although few animals on the Red List have actually become extinct, the situation is becoming graver for most species. The monkeys and apes of the tropical rainforests are among the worst affected, with nearly one in four species being very close to extinction. This is because rainforests are complicated places, and many primate species there have evolved a specialized lifestyle, for example feeding on fruit in the tallest trees. These species are very badly affected by sudden changes in their environment, for example when a logging team cuts down all the tall trees leaving, just the shorter ones behind.

CONSERVING WILDLIFE

With so many species facing extinction, conservationists have their work cut out. Conservationists try to protect habitats and provide safe places for threatened animals to thrive, but the activities of ordinary people can often also have an adverse effect on the future of natural habitats.

People give many reasons why wildlife should be conserved. Some argue that if all the forests were cleared and the oceans polluted, the delicate balance of nature would be so ruined that Earth would not be able to support any life, including humans. Others suggest that if vulnerable species were allowed to die, the natural world would not be sufficiently diverse to cope with future changes in the environment. Another reason to save diversity is that we have not yet fully recorded it. Also, there are undoubtedly many as yet unknown species – especially of plants – which could be useful to humankind, for example in the field of medicine. But perhaps the strongest argument for the conservation of wildlife is that it would be totally irresponsible to let it disappear.

Habitat protection

Whatever the reasons, the best way to protect species in danger of being wiped out is to protect their habitats so that the complex communities of plants and animals can continue to live. However, with the human population growing so rapidly, people are often forced to choose between promoting their own interests and protecting wildlife. Of course, people invariably put themselves first, which means that the conservationists have to employ a range of techniques in order to save wildlife.

In many countries it has now become illegal to hunt certain endangered animals, or to trade in any products made from their bodies. Whales, gorillas and elephants are protected in this way. Many governments and charitable organizations have also set up wildlife reserves, where the animals stand a good chance of thriving. The oldest

Below: One of the main causes of deforestation is people clearing the trees and burning them to make way for farmland. The ash makes good soil for a few years, but eventually the nutrients needed by the crops run out and so the farmers often begin to clear more forest.

Above: If logging is done properly, it can make enough money to pay to protect the rest of the rainforest. Only selected trees are cut down and they are removed without damaging younger growth. Forests can be used to grow crops, such as coffee and nuts, without cutting down all the trees.

protected areas are in North America and Europe, where it is illegal to ruin areas of forest wilderness and wetland. Consequently, these places have become wildlife havens. Other protected areas include semi-natural landscapes which double as beauty spots and tourist attractions. Although these areas often have to be extensively altered and managed to meet the needs of the visitors, most still support wildlife communities.

In the developing world, wildlife refuges are a newer phenomenon. Huge areas of Africa's savannahs are protected and populated with many amazing animals. However, the enormous size of these parks makes it very hard to protect the animals, especially elephants and rhinoceroses, from poachers.

Reintroduction

Large areas of tropical forests are now protected in countries such as Brazil and Costa Rica, but often conservation efforts come too late because many animals have either become rare or are completely absent after years of human

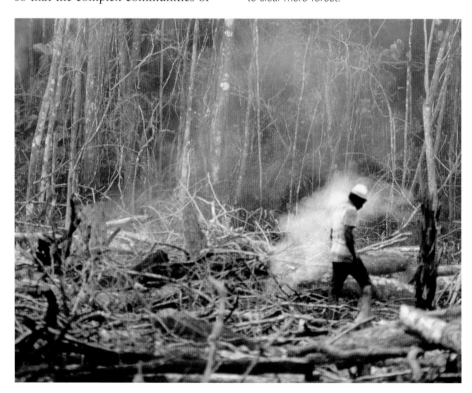

Zoo animals

Once zoos were places where exotic animals were merely put on display. Such establishments were increasingly regarded as cruel. Today, the world's best zoos are an integral part of conservation. Several animals, which are classified as extinct in the wild, can only be found in zoos where they are being bred. These breeding programmes are heavily controlled to make sure that closely related animals do not breed with each other. Later, individual animals may be sent around the world to mate in different zoos to avoid in-breeding.

Below: Many of the world's rarest species, such as the red panda, are kept in zoos, partly so that people can see them, since they are too rare to be spotted in the wild. Some people are opposed to animals being put on display for this reason.

damage. However, several conservation programmes have reintroduced animals bred in zoos into the wild.

To reintroduce a group of zoo-bred animals successfully into the wild, conservationists need to know how the animal fits into the habitat and interacts with the other animals living there. In addition, for example when trying to reintroduce orang-utans to the forests of Borneo, people have to teach the young animals how to find food and fend for themselves.

Below: Breeding centres are an important way of increasing the number of rare animals. Most, such as this giant panda centre in China, are in the natural habitat. If the animals kept there are treated properly, they should be able to fend for themselves when released back into the wild.

Above: Tourism, such as safaris, is one of the best ways of ensuring that rare animals have somewhere to live. Tourists coming to see the animals in their natural habitat are paying for the upkeep of the nature reserve. However, too many tourists can cause more damage than they prevent.

Understanding habitats

A full understanding of how animals live in the wild is also vitally important when conservationists are working in a habitat that has been damaged by human activity. For example, in areas of rainforest which are being heavily logged, the trees are often divided into isolated islands of growth surrounded by cleared ground. This altered habitat is no good for monkeys, which need large areas of forest to swing through throughout the year. The solution is to plant strips of forest to connect the islands of untouched habitat, creating a continuous mass again.

Another example of beneficial human intervention involves protecting rare frogs in the process of migrating to a breeding pond. If their migration necessitates crossing a busy road, it is likely that many of them will be run over. Conservationists now dig little tunnels under the roads so that the frogs can travel in safety. Similar protection schemes have been set up for hedgehogs and ducks, to allow them safe passageways.

BIOMES

The Earth is not a uniform place but has a complex patchwork of habitats covering its surface from the equator to the poles. Biologists have simplified this patchwork by dividing it into zones called biomes, each of which has a particular climate and a distinct community of animals.

The places where animal communities live can be radically different. So, for example, vipers slither along the tops of sand dunes in the middle of the Sahara Desert while sperm whales live hundreds of metres down in the gloomy, ice-cold depths of the ocean. The environmental conditions determine what kind of animals and plants are able to survive there.

Climate control

The world's habitats are generally divided into 11 biomes: oceans, freshwater rivers and wetlands, tropical forests, temperate forests, boreal forests, tropical grasslands or savannahs, temperate grasslands or prairies, tundra, polar ice caps, deserts and mountains.

The overriding factor that determines whether a piece of land belongs to one biome or another is its climate – chiefly the rainfall and temperature. Understanding the climate of a place is a complicated business because the factors involved – including rainfall, temperature and light levels – vary from day to night and throughout the year. The latitude is probably the best place to start. In general terms, regions close to the equator, at a latitude of 0°, are hot. The coldest places are the poles, with a latitude of 90°. The territory in between generally cools as you travel to higher latitudes.

However, other factors also affect climate. For example, during the hot days of summer, the land at certain latitudes warms up more quickly than the ocean. Six months later, in the depths of winter, the land cools down more quickly than the ocean. This means that the oceans and the areas of land bordering them tend to enjoy a mild climate with smaller fluctuations of temperature each year, while the interiors of large continental landmasses experience very hot summers and extremely chilly winters.

Animal communities

Other geographical factors – ocean currents, mountains and depressions in the Earth's surface – also have a major influence on climate and biomes. The climate defines which plants can grow in any particular spot and how quickly. And since the plants form the basis of all food webs and ecosystems, each biome has a particular community of animals which have evolved to exploit the plant life.

Below: This map shows how the world can be divided into biomes. The climate of a region has the greatest effect on the sorts of plants and animals that can survive there. Some animals may live across an entire biome, while others are found only in particular habitats.

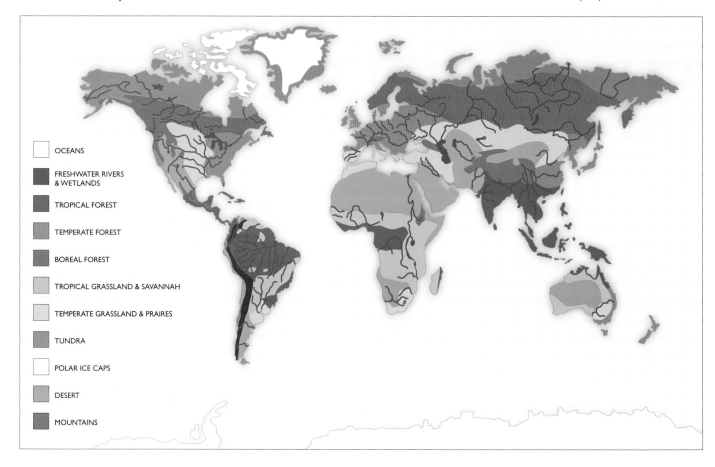

- OCEANS
- FRESHWATER RIVERS & WETLANDS
- TROPICAL FOREST
- TEMPERATE FOREST
- BOREAL FOREST
- TROPICAL GRASSLAND & SAVANNAH
- TEMPERATE GRASSLAND & PRAIRES
- TUNDRA
- POLAR ICE CAPS
- DESERT
- MOUNTAINS

Biomes and ear size

Closely related animals that live in different biomes have different features that help them function under different conditions. For example, foxes live in similar ways across the world. However, the Arctic fox, which lives in cold polar areas, has very small outer ears. The red fox that lives in the mild temperate biome of Europe has medium-sized ears, while the bat-eared fox and other species that live in hot areas have very large ears. Ear size is linked to the control of body heat. The small size of the Arctic fox's ears prevents heat wastage, while the large ears of the bat-eared fox are useful for radiating away unwanted heat, helping the animal keep cool. The red fox's ears are a compromise: large enough to hear very clearly, but small enough to conserve heat in the winter.

Arctic fox

Red fox

Bat-eared fox

Rainfall has a major influence on biomes. It is generally heaviest in tropical regions, resulting in lush rainforests. In colder regions, rainfall may be almost as high but it results in a different type of forest. In areas with less rain, deserts or grasslands appear.

The animals in different biomes face the same challenges: finding enough food and water, and finding a mate to raise offspring. However, the different conditions in each biome mean that the animals have to meet these challenges in very different ways.

In all biomes, the animal communities have a similar structure. Grazers and other plant-eating animals survive by eating any plants which have evolved to make the most of the climatic conditions. These grazers are, in turn, preyed upon by a series of hunters. In the most productive biomes, such as forests, many of these hunting animals might be hunted in turn by larger, fiercer predators.

However, the plant-eaters of grasslands, such as bison and antelopes, live a very different life from their counterparts in tropical forests, such as monkeys and tapirs. Similarly, ocean hunters, such as mighty orcas (killer whales), have a body adapted to swimming at great speed through the water; the predators in a boreal forest, such as wolves, have very different bodies for covering long distances quickly and bringing down animals more than twice their size. One of the main purposes of biology is to understand how communities of plants and animals have evolved to survive in the world's different biomes.

Grassland animals

Grasslands are unusual habitats because food is everywhere. While animals that live in other biomes must seek out and defend a source of food, grazing animals are surrounded by it, and no single animal can control it. Instead of competing for food, they compete for mates, and many grazers are big and tough fighters. Grass and other plant foods are not very nutritious, so animals have to eat a lot of them. Therefore many of them, such as bison and elephants, are big. Being large also helps defence against predators. Grassland predators such as lions tend to hunt in groups so that they can work together to bring down powerful animals.

Bison

Elephant

Lion

OCEANS

The oceans cover nearly three-quarters of the Earth's surface and create by far the largest and most complex biome. They contain the world's largest and smallest animals, from tiny zooplankton to the mighty blue whale. Between these two extremes, the oceans contain an incredible wealth of life.

The oceans are not a simple biome because they consist of countless habitats, including everything from colourful coral reefs to mysterious, deep-sea hydrothermal vents. The depth of the ocean obviously has a marked effect on the conditions. Depth can range from just few a centimetres along the coast to 11km (6.8 miles), the deepest ocean point in the Mariana Trench, near the Pacific island of Guam.

Light matters

The first few 100m (330ft) or so below the surface is called the photic zone, where the water is bathed in sunlight during the day. This upper layer is the limit of plant growth in the ocean because below this depth the light fades, unable to penetrate any deeper, and plants rely on light to make their food.

As on land, many ocean animals graze on plants, which means that they have to live in the photic zone. Ocean

*Below: **1** marine iguana, **2** loggerhead turtle, **3** sea otter, **4** orca (killer whale), **5** minke whale, **6** harbour porpoise, **7** common seal, **8** white-beaked dolphin, **9** saltwater crocodile, **10** dugong, **11** horned sea snake.*

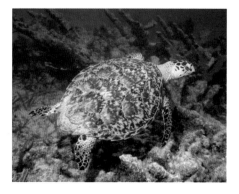

Above: Turtles are the most common ocean reptiles. They breath air, but spend long periods underwater. Like many other sea animals, they have flippers rather than legs.

Above: Dolphins are sea mammals that are found throughout the oceans. These hunting animals live in family groups, and are known to be highly intelligent.

plants tend to be simple algae, known as phytoplankton, which float in the current. These plants do not have complicated body structures, and many are just single cells. Consequently, many of the ocean plant-eaters are also tiny floating organisms, known collectively as zooplankton. Zooplankton – largely shrimp-like crustaceans – is a very important part

of the ocean food chain, being the main food for toothless baleen whales. These ocean giants filter out the zooplankton from gulps of seawater.

Deeper down, in the dark depths, life continues without plants. Despite conditions being too dark for plants, most deep-sea animals still get their energy from them indirectly by feeding on marine "snow". This consists of the waste products of the organisms higher up.

Coastal waters

These food chains provide the basis of animal life in the ocean, feeding many types of larger vertebrate animals including fish, turtles and sea mammals. While fish evolved in the sea, the sea-living reptiles, such as turtles and sea snakes, and the sea mammals, such as seals and whales, actually evolved from animals which once lived on land. A great deal of this evolution must have taken place in shallow coastal waters, and while whales and dolphins have become completely independent of land, other sea mammals and most reptiles must return to land at some point during the year to breed.

Seals and sea lions make their homes in coastal waters where the ocean meets the land. These shallow waters are very different from the dark abyss of the deep ocean. Coral reefs, sometimes described as the rainforests of the ocean because they support so much life, are a feature of coastal waters in the tropics. In shallow seas, tall kelps and other kinds of seaweed can grow into thick underwater forests, providing habitats for a whole range of animals, such as sea otters.

Salt water

Relatively few animals live in both salty and fresh water. For example, there are no true marine amphibians. A few species, such as the marine toad,

can survive the brackish water in river mouths or salt marshes, but none actually lives in the sea. This is because the salt in sea water is a problem for any animal. Sea water has more substances dissolved in it than do the body fluids of living things, and therefore water tends to flow out of the body when it is immersed in salty water. This process is called osmosis, and it is the same principle which makes a wilted flower stem perk up when placed in clean water; if placed in salt water the reverse happens, causing the body to wilt and dry out.

Ocean animals have different ways of coping

Above: Unlike dolphins and whales, seals, such as these Cape fur seals, divide their time between the water and land. Their limbs are flattened into flippers but are still capable of pulling the animals along the ground.

with this problem. Sea mammals and turtles have thick skin to keep the moisture in and, like many other ocean residents, the skin also has a slimy consistency that makes it more waterproof. Other species of sea life must keep drinking sea water to replace lost fluids.

FRESH WATER

Only three per cent of the world's water is fresh, but experts estimate that this covers a total of over 100,000sq km (38,610sq miles), including the polar icecaps. The rivers, lakes and wetlands supplied by fresh water are some of the best places to see wildlife. But where does fresh water come from?

The Earth's atmosphere is a huge water pump that transfers water from the oceans to the land. The heat from the sun makes water evaporate from the surface of the ocean, and the water vapour produced becomes part of the atmosphere. The warm water vapour in the air may then cool down for various reasons. As it cools, the vapour begins to turn back into a liquid, forming tiny droplets on the surface of particles of

Below: 1 beaver, 2 capybara, 3 North American river otter, 4 water moccasin, 5 muskrat, 6 green anaconda, 7 Amazon river dolphin, 8 hippopotamuses, 9 desman, 10 Nile crocodile, 11 gharial, 12 giant salamander.

dust carried in the wind. These moist dust particles gather together to form the clouds that often obscure clear skies. If the air cools even more, the amount of water condensing in cloud becomes too much for it to hold, and the water falls to the surface as rain.

River systems

Since most of the Earth's surface is covered by oceans, most of the rain falls back into the sea. However, some falls on to land where it forms rivers, lakes and waterlogged ground, such as swamps and marshes, known collectively as wetlands. Mountain ranges receive high rainfall because they force the moist air to rise up over them and cool. The rain then flows down the mountainsides in torrents and waterfalls. Down on the lowlands, these fast-flowing streams

join together to make larger, deeper rivers which move more slowly across the landscape. Nearly all the fresh water falling on land eventually makes its way back to the oceans via rivers. Some fresh water does seep into rocks under the ground, but it reappears as springs which feed yet more rivers.

All the rivers in the world combined contain just a fraction of the Earth's water, though some of them form huge freshwater systems. The largest river system is in the Amazon Basin. This South American network of rivers contains more water than the Nile, Mississippi and Yangtze rivers together, and hosts many thousands of animal and plant species.

Salinity

Rain water and other forms of precipitation provide fresh water. When water evaporates from the oceans, the salt is left behind and only the water molecules rise into the

Above: Otters are small carnivores that hunt in rivers and along their banks. They are good swimmers, but they also stray from the water if there is no food to be had there.

Above: The word hippopotamus means river horse in Greek. These animals are more closely related to whales than horses, but they are not strong swimmers.

Above: Beavers are very active freshwater animals. They dam rivers with logs to create large pools. To achieve this, they cut down the logs with their teeth and float them into position.

atmosphere. Although fresh water acquires small amounts of dissolved salts as it flows over rocks on its journey to the sea, it is much less salty than sea water, and this has a marked effect on the animals that live in it. While sea water is saltier than the body fluids of animals, fresh water is less salty, which means that water tends to flow into the animal from outside. If the animal does not frequently get rid of some moisture, it will become swollen, and its body fluids will be too diluted to work efficiently.

Freshwater fish and amphibians tackle this problem by urinating all their excess water. Semi-aquatic animals, such as otters and anacondas, rely on their skin to act as a barrier to the influx of water.

Other factors

The salinity of fresh water varies considerably, and this has an effect on the types of animals that can flourish there. For example, the water of a mountain stream is fed by rain water or melting snow and contains very little salt. But a watering hole where water is being slowly evaporated by the tropical sun will become more salty as the water level goes down and the salt concentration becomes stronger.

There are several other factors that can change the conditions of freshwater habitats. Fast-flowing water, for example in a mountain stream, does not stay still for long enough to be heated by the sun and is therefore often cold. But as

it gurgles over the rocks, the water mixes with the air and oxygen gets dissolved in it. Therefore, mountain streams tend to contain a good supply of oxygen.

At the other extreme, the slow-flowing waters of a pond or marsh mix little with air and are therefore lower in oxygen. Animals that live in stagnant water generally come up to the surface to gulp in air instead of relying on gills to extract oxygen from the water. Animals living in oxygen-rich waters, on the other hand, may not have gills either, because they can absorb oxygen through their skin.

TROPICAL FORESTS

Tropical forests are the oldest and most complex forests on Earth. They contain a greater variety of animal species than anywhere else, from the great apes, such as gorillas and orang-utans, and big cats, such as tigers and leopards, to tiny frogs and pencil-thin snakes.

The lush, steamy jungles of tropical forest grow in a band around the Earth's equator. These forests are packed with wildlife, more so than any other biome. The total number of animal species living in tropical forests is unknown because most have never been identified, but it probably adds up to several million. The majority of these species are insects, such as beetles and bugs, but tropical forests also contain the greatest diversity of vertebrate animals. Unfortunately, large tracts of these forests are now under threat from human activities such as logging.

Below: 1 emerald tree boa, 2 tapir, 3 capuchin monkey, 4 ocelot, 5 okapi, 6 mandrill, 7 Bengal tiger, 8 Asian elephants, 9 orang-utan.

Hard rain

Tropical forests are among the wettest places on Earth. Most receive about 2.5m (8ft) of rain every year, while forests that grow on ocean islands often receive over 6m (19½ft). The tropics receive so much rain because near the equator the sun is always high in the sky, keeping temperatures elevated. Consequently, a great deal of water evaporates from the oceans and rises into the sky here. The water vapour cools as it rises and condenses into vast rain clouds. Generally towards the end of the day, these clouds release their load of water on to the lush forests beneath.

Rainfall defines the two main types of tropical forest – rainforest and monsoon forest.

Rainforests grow in places where rainfall is heavy all year round, although there

Above: Tree frogs never come to the ground throughout their adult life. The suckers on their fingers and toes cling to the branches, and eggs are laid in foam nests above a source of water. When the eggs hatch, the tadpoles fall into the water.

are often drier spells throughout the year. The main areas of rainforest are South America's Amazon Basin, the African Congo and South-east Asia. Monsoon forests grow in tropical areas where most rain falls during an annual wet season. The largest monsoon forests are found in India, Australia and along the coast of Brazil.

Complex habitats

With so much water and warmth, plants grow larger and more quickly than just about anywhere else on land. Most trees reach at least 50m (165ft) tall and form a dense network of branches, or canopy, high above the ground. The canopy is so thick in places that underneath it is very gloomy and humid. Taller trees poke their crowns out above the canopy. The tallest of these emergent trees grow over 100m (330ft) high.

Tropical forest plants grow more thickly than elsewhere, too. Some plants, known as air plants or epiphytes, do not grow in the ground but attach themselves on to the trunks or branches of larger plants. Within this complex framework of plant life, there are countless places for all types of animal to thrive. For example, amphibians need to live in water during the early stages of their life. And with so much rain falling, tropical forests are rarely short of water. Some epiphytes have bowl-shaped leaves to catch the rain, and several amphibian species use these aerial ponds as breeding sites. Down on the ground some frogs and salamanders just lay their eggs in damp soil, which is wet enough for their young to develop in.

Forest life

Most forest animals have adapted to life in the canopy, high above the forest floor. Compared to life down below, life in a tree is a complicated business. Tree-dwellers can move in all directions if needed, including up and down. They must move through flimsy branches and across open spaces, judging distances accurately and looking out for danger as they go. One wrong move could spell a long fall to certain death.

The undoubted masters of tree life are the primates, especially monkeys. Nearly all primates live in tropical forests where their gripping hands and large brains help them to move with incredible agility. Other animals have adapted to living in trees in other ways. Vine snakes, for example, have thin, wiry bodies and can spread their weight evenly as they slide between even the thinnest twigs. Tree frogs and lizards have suction cups or sticky pads on their hands and feet to enable them to cling on to branches.

Above: A green iguana makes its way along a branch in search of insect food. Its body is coloured green so it does not stand out to predators, such as snakes and eagles.

Down on the ground, life is very different. The dense undergrowth of many forests makes it hard for large animals to get around, and they consequently live alone or in small groups.

TEMPERATE FORESTS

Before the rise of agriculture, temperate forests covered most of Europe, the eastern part of North America and China. Today, however, nearly all of these wild woodlands have been replaced by meadows and farmland. After tropical forests, temperate forests contain the greatest diversity of animal life.

Temperate forests grow in mild regions that receive a lot of rain but do not get too hot or cold. The largest temperate forests are in the northern hemisphere, in a belt north of subtropical regions.

Shedding leaves

The main difference between the temperate forests and other forest biomes is that most temperate trees are deciduous, dropping their leaves in the autumn, and growing new ones in spring. Although there are a few deciduous trees, such as paper birch, growing in the southern zones of northern boreal forests, there are many more evergreen conifers.

The lush plants of tropical forests also keep their leaves all

Above: American black bears are good climbers. They use their long hooked claws to pull themselves up trees, where they feed on fruit and nuts. On the forest floor they attack small deer and will catch fish from rivers.

year, or rather do not drop them all at once. Instead, as an old leaf falls to the ground a new one starts growing on another part of the tree.

The reason why temperate forests lose their leaves is to save energy during the winter. Because it is rarely very bright over winter, the leaves would not be able to photosynthesize food from sunlight. And because the cold and frosts would damage the redundant leaves during winter, it is best that they are dropped. As autumn progresses, the leaves' valuable green pigments, which trap the sun's energy, withdraw back into the tree. Then, as the green disappears, so the less important red and brown pigments are revealed, giving the forest its beautiful autumn colours.

Forest types

As with a few other land biomes, temperate forests are poorly represented in the southern hemisphere, with only a few patches in South Africa and Australia, because there is very little southern land with an appropriate climate. One exception is New Zealand, which once had many areas of temperate forest. However, the forests of this isolated region are very different from the huge forests which grow in the north. Instead of the

Above: Squirrels are superbly adapted to forest life. They use their claws to run up and down tree trunks, and can rotate their hind feet to hang upside down to get at food.

broad-leaved flowering trees, such as oak, ash and maple that are common in most temperate forests, many New Zealand forests are dominated by tree-sized ferns and other plants which were common many millions of years ago.

The temperate forests that grow in slightly warmer and drier regions, such as California, the Mediterranean and South Africa, are not deciduous. They are populated with evergreen trees with toughened leaves that keep the

Below: 1 eastern grey squirrel, 2 skunk, 3 wood bison, 4 pine marten, 5 North American porcupine, 6 sika deer, 7 common toad, 8 grass snake, 9 wild boar, 10 fallow deer, 11 wombat, 12 koala.

moisture in with a coating of oily resin. Perhaps the most spectacular forests in this biome are the temperate rainforests found on the coast of British Columbia, Canada. Due to the unusual climate, the forests receive more rain than most tropical rainforests, which is one reason why the redwood, the world's largest tree, flourishes here.

Animal life

Although temperate forests do not grow as densely as tropical forests, they still contain many places for animals to thrive. While a few primate species live in the temperate forests of east Asia, squirrels and other tree-dwelling rodents are actually the most commonly found arboreal members of most forests. They scamper from tree to tree collecting seeds and fruit, and snatching insects to eat. Down on the ground, the forests are populated by larger animals such as wild boar and deer and, in a few places, wood bison – the even rarer woodland relative of the plains bison.

During winter, with the leaves fallen and growth almost stopped completely, temperate forests become desolate places with little food available.

Above: Pine martens spend most of their time in trees, often taking shelter in tree holes or nests made by other forest animals. These hunters eat birds, insects and small rodents.

Larger animals may migrate to warmer, more productive areas to spend the winter, or scratch out a living while depending on their body fat reserves. Smaller animals, such as dormice and ground squirrels, hibernate to save energy until the spring, while others, such as most tree-living squirrels, rely on food caches that they built up in the autumn.

BOREAL FORESTS

Boreal forest, or taiga as it is also known, grows in the icy conditions of the far north. This biome is dominated by conifers, which are the only trees that can survive the harsh conditions. Boreal forests form the largest swathes of continuous forest and cover about ten percent of the Earth's land.

Boreal forest gets its name from the Greek god of the north wind, Boreas. The name is apt because this type of forest only grows in the northern hemisphere – not because the climatic conditions for boreal forest do not exist in the southern hemisphere, but because there is little land down there where such forests can grow. The alternative name, taiga, is a Russian word meaning marshy pine forest. This name is also apt because boreal forests often grow around moss-filled bogs, the actual bogs being too wet for tree growth.

Boreal forests grow in huge unbroken swathes in Siberia and Canada, and are also found in

Above: Wolverines may resemble dogs or bears, but they are actually a giant relative of the weasel or mink. Wolverines come into their own in winter, when they use their wide feet to pad across the snow.

Scandinavia, Alaska and northern Japan. A few small patches have survived in Scotland, but most natural conifer forests were cut down many

years ago. These parts of the far north enjoy a short summer with very long days and a long, cold winter when the sun only rises for a few hours. Winter temperatures regularly plunge to –25°C (–13°F).

Cones and needles

Compared to other forests, boreal ones are very simple because they contain far fewer species; in fact, almost all the trees in these forests are conifers.

Conifer trees, such as pine, spruce and fir, are different in a number of ways from other forest trees. Instead of broad flattened leaves, they have small waxy needles, and instead of flowers, they produce seeds inside cones. The conifer needles obviously

*Below: **1** brown bear, **2** grey wolf, **3** moose, **4** marmot, **5** American red squirrel, **6** lynx, **7** wolverine, **8** Siberian tiger.*

have a smaller surface area than broad leaves, and are therefore less efficient at photosynthesis. However, their small size and thick, waxy covering protect them from the ice and wind which would severely damage broader leaves.

The evergreen conifers do not drop their needles in the autumn. Although it is too gloomy for these trees to photosynthesize for most of the winter, dropping needles and growing them again in time for the short summer would waste too much energy.

Tough life

Because of the cold and dark, boreal forests appear frozen in time for much of the year as the wildlife endures the cold, waiting for the intense activity of the short summer growing season. Even the summer is too cold for nearly all cold-blooded animals, such as amphibians and reptiles. Rattlesnakes do survive in the southern fringes of the Canadian forest, but amphibians are uncommon on land and only a few survive in the often-frozen water. Mammals such as marmots and bears, and also the rattlesnakes, hibernate or become inactive during the coldest months of the year. Incredibly, wood frogs endure the winter frozen inside river ice, becoming active again after the thaw.

Mammals that do not hibernate often adopt a very different lifestyle to survive the winter months. For example, herds of reindeer migrate into the forests, only heading back to the barren tundra in summer. Small rodents, such as mice or shrews, construct tunnels in the snow during winter, and moose survive by eating strips of bark.

Because their growth is so slow and intermittent, boreal forests are relatively free of animals compared to other forests. However, many of the animals that do live there are much larger than their relatives living farther south. For example, the moose is the world's largest deer and the Siberian tiger is the largest cat. Wolverines are much larger than most mustelids, and the grizzly bears of Canada are much larger than bears found farther south.

The reason for this is that to stay alive, larger animals need to eat less food per unit weight than smaller ones. This is because a larger animal has a higher body mass compared to its surface area than a smaller animal. Therefore larger animals lose heat more slowly than smaller ones – just as a large pot

Above: Moose, or elk, are the largest deer in the world. They spend the short summer close to water, grazing in the shallows and dipping themselves to ward off biting insects.

of tea stays warm for longer than a small cup – and do not have to burn food at a such a high rate. Scientists have noticed that even animals of the same species, such as weasels or rabbits, tend to be bigger if they are living farther north.

GRASSLANDS

Although a lot of wild countryside is covered in different grasses – not to mention the many acres of garden lawns – little of it is true grassland. If left alone, these habitats would eventually become thick woodland. True grasslands, from prairies to the savannah, have very few trees but contain many creatures.

Grasslands appear in areas where there is some rain, but not enough to support the growth of large numbers of trees. These conditions exist on all continents, and consequently grasslands come in many forms, growing in both tropical and more temperate regions. The world's grasslands also have many different names. The temperate grasslands of North America are called prairies, in South America they are known as the pampas, and in Europe and Asia they are the steppes. The tropical grasslands of east Africa and Australia are called savannah, and in southern Africa they are the veldt.

Temperate grasslands tend to be located in so-called rain shadows. For example, the North American prairies are in the rain shadow of the Rocky Mountains. A rain shadow is an area which rarely gets rain because the wind bringing it must first travel over a range of mountains. As the wind rises up it cools and releases the rainwater on the windward side. The wind then whistles down the leeward side carrying much less water. If the wind is very dry, then that area becomes a desert. However, the wind often carries enough moisture to let grasses grow.

Grassland ecology

The main plant food in grasslands is, of course, grass. Grass is an unusual type of plant because its growing points are near to the ground rather than at the tip of the stem, as with most other plants. This means that it can keep growing despite having its juicy blades eaten by grazing animals.

Grazing animals are commonly found in grasslands, as are the browsers which pick the leaves and fruit of small shrubs which often grow in the area. With few places to hide in the wide-open spaces, grazing animals group together into herds for safety.

Above: Prairie dogs are very social animals that live in large burrows called towns. They live on temperate grasslands in North America. However, they have become rare in the wild because farmers fill in their holes to stop them damaging the feet of grazing cattle.

Below: **1** black-tailed prairie dogs, **2** bison, **3** pronghorn, **4** giant anteater, **5** cheetah, **6** black mamba, **7** impala, **8** zebra, **9** rhinoceros, **10** Przewalski's horse, **11** saiga antelope, **12** kangaroo.

Fortunately, grass and other plant foods are virtually omnipresent, which means that members of these herds only need to compete when it comes to choosing a mate. This has led them, especially the males, to evolve elaborate weapons and display structures, such as horns or tusks. Grazing animals are large anyway because they have to survive on huge meals of tough grass which is low in nutrition, while the pressure to compete with each other has made them even larger.

Without trees to hide in, smaller animals, such as ground squirrels and marmots, take refuge under the ground in burrow complexes. Many, such as moles and mole rats, have adapted to a totally subterranean lifestyle.

Grassland animals

Much of the world's temperate grasslands have been turned into farmland for growing cereal crops and raising livestock. Cereals, such as wheat and rye, are actually domestic breeds of grass which would naturally grow in these regions anyway.

Most of the animals once found on grasslands have suffered badly because of the rise of agriculture. The prairies of North America used to contain huge

Above: Giraffes are familiar animals from the tropical grasslands of Africa. Their long necks allow them to reach the softest leaves and freshest shoots that are high up on the few trees that grow in these regions.

herds of bison, but now these are very rare, having been slaughtered in their millions by hunters. Wild horses once galloped over the rolling plains of Mongolia, and massive herds of saiga antelope once dominated the wilds of central Asia, but the horses are extinct in the wild and the saiga may soon be too. Similarly, in South America pampas deer were once common but have now been pushed out

by cattle and other livestock. Meanwhile, burrowing animals, such as prairie dogs, have been persecuted by cattle ranchers because the holes they make injure grazing cattle.

In Africa, safari tours have helped to maintain the grassland animals. These areas contain elephants, rhinoceroses, lions and cheetahs, as well as antelopes and other hoofed animals. The Australian savannah is not populated by hoofed animals but by native grazing animals, such as kangaroos.

POLAR REGIONS

Despite being freezing cold and largely covered with ice, polar regions can be characterized as deserts. Although there is solid water almost everywhere, the few plants and animals which do live there often have great difficulty in obtaining liquid water, just like the wildlife in scorching deserts.

The polar regions – the Arctic in the north and Antarctic in the south – begin at 66° North and 66° South. These positions on the globe are marked as the Arctic and Antarctic Circles. Within these imaginary circles, something very strange happens on at least one day every summer: the sun does not set. Similarly for at least a single 24 hours in winter, it does not rise. Travelling closer to the poles, these periods of total day and total night become longer as several days merge into one another. At the poles the sun stays above the horizon for a whole six months each year before setting and plunging the region into a bitterly cold period of darkness that lasts for another six months. With just one sunrise and sunset six months apart, the poles themselves experience just one day and night every year.

Below: 1 polar bear, 2 snowshoe hare, 3 walruses, 4 musk oxen, 5 Arctic fox, 6 Steller's sea lions, 7 lemmings, 8 caribou.

Above: Walruses are relatives of seals and sea lions that live on ice floes in the Arctic. Their long tusks are useful for pulling their heavily blubbered bodies on to the ice.

The reason for this is the angle of the Earth's axis. As the Earth moves around the Sun each year, one hemisphere points toward the Sun for the first six months, followed by the other for the remainder of the year. This creates the seasons and causes the length of days across the world to change from month to month. When the northern hemisphere is angled toward the Sun, it is enjoying summer, while the southern hemisphere is shrouded in winter. Six months later, when the Earth has swung around to the other side of the Sun, the situation is reversed.

In summer the days are longer and hotter than in winter. This is because that hemisphere is bathed in more sunlight. At the equator, the days are more or less the same length all year around. But as one travels toward the poles, summer days become longer, and the winter days shorten. This principle reaches its extremes within the polar regions, where in summer you can see the midnight sun.

Complete opposites

The wildlife of the Arctic is not similar to that of the Antarctic. This is not just because they are at opposite ends of the world, but also because the geography of the two areas is very different. The Antarctic is dominated by Antarctica, a mountainous landmass which is a significantly sized continent, larger than Australia.

Above: Polar bears are the largest predators in this region. They spend most of the year out on the ice, preying on sea birds and sea mammals. They will even swim large distances across open water to reach feeding grounds.

Meanwhile the Arctic has the Arctic Ocean – the world's smallest ocean – at its centre.

The wildernesses of ice and rock in the Antarctic are the coldest places on Earth, and are too inhospitable for any completely terrestrial animals. Antarctic animals, such as seals, penguins and whales, rely on the sea for their survival.

No reptiles or amphibians survive there, and even warm-blooded animals leave in winter, with the exception of the hardy emperor penguin.

In the Arctic, seals, whales and other sea life also thrive, while the lands and islands of the Arctic Ocean provide a home for many animals dependent on land, such as musk ox and reindeer. Animals such as polar bears spend their time on the thick shelves of sea ice which extend from the frozen coastlines for much of the year.

Tundra

While Antarctica is almost entirely covered in snow and ice, the ground in lands around the Arctic circle is mainly ice-free during the summer and so has periods of frenzied growth and breeding. North of the boreal forests it is too cold and dark for trees to grow, and treeless tundra takes over. Plants – mainly tough grass and sedges, mosses and lichens (not actually a plant but a symbiotic relationship between fungi and tiny algae) must be able to survive the long and desolate winters. When the summer – which generally lasts little more than six weeks – arrives, they must be ready to reproduce.

While the summer sun thaws the snow and ice, it never heats the soil for more than a few centimetres below the surface. The deep layer of soil remains frozen and is called permafrost. It forms a solid barrier which prevents the melt waters from seeping away. The trapped water forms shallow pools and bogs, which are a haven for insects.

Billions of insects, which spent the winter underground as inactive pupae, emerge from hiding in the spring. They swarm across the tundra, mating and laying eggs in the water as they race against time to produce the next generation before winter arrives again.

DESERTS

*Deserts make up the largest terrestrial biome, covering about one-fifth of the world's dry land.
The popular image of a desert is a parched wilderness with towering sand dunes and no sign of life.
However, deserts can also be very cold places and most contain a surprising amount of wildlife.*

A desert forms wherever less than 25cm (10in) of rain falls in a year. Areas that get less than about 40cm (16in) of rain per year are semi-deserts. The largest desert is the Sahara in North Africa, which covers about the same area as the United States. Other desert regions are found in the south-western USA, southern Africa, Australia, central Asia, South America and China.

Aridity

There are two main reasons why desert regions receive very little rain. Some deserts are positioned on the edge of the tropical zone. They receive little moisture because the winds that flow over them from the humid and stormy equator have already dumped all their water on to the forest regions, and consequently are now hot and dry.

Below: 1 desert tortoise, 2 gila monster, 3 kangaroo rat, 4 Arabian oryx, 5 desert horned viper, 6 camel, 7 fennec fox, 8 sand gecko, 9 thorny devil, 10 dingo.

The deserts of Australia and southern Africa are formed in this way. Other deserts form because they are a very long way from the ocean. The Gobi Desert in China and Mongolia is a good example. The wind that reaches this land seldom brings rain because any moisture has already been released in coastal regions. Huge mountain ranges, such as the Himalayas, also act as a barrier blocking moist winds. The mighty Sahara Desert is so large because it was created by both of these causes. Not only is it on the edge of the tropics, but its centre is also thousands of miles from the ocean.

Desert conditions

Desert life is tough. The wildlife has to contend with lack of water and also survive extremes of temperature. With little or no cloud cover for most of the year, land temperatures rocket during the day to over 40°C (104°F) but can plunge to near freezing at night.

Above: Fennec foxes live in the blistering heat of the Sahara. Their large ears are filled with blood vessels and are used to radiate away body heat when the fox gets too hot.

Desert plants are the basis for all life in this biome, being the food for grazing animals. Some plants have to extend enormously long underground roots to collect enough water to live. For example, the roots of mesquite trees in the Sonoran Desert of Mexico grow down over 80m (262ft) to reach

Above: The thorny devil is an aptly named lizard because of the spines on its body. Thorny devils need these defences because they station themselves out in the open to catch ants, in full view of many predators.

water. Other plants, such as cacti and other succulents, store water inside their fleshy stems and leaves, and have a thick, waxy covering to stop the water from evaporating.

Deserts are not completely dry, of course, because rain does eventually arrive. True to the extremes of a desert, rainstorms are so violent that they often cause devastating flash floods which gush down temporary rivers, known as wadis or arroyos. Then the desert plants bloom and breed for a few short weeks before withering and waiting for the next supply of water.

Many desert animals, such as blind snakes and several types of frog, follow a similar pattern. They only come to the surface during and after the rains, preferring to stay moist underground during the hot and dry parts of the year. Desert frogs prevent themselves from drying out by growing a thin, fluid-filled skin bag around their bodies.

Out and about

Even the more active desert animals remain hidden during the day, sheltering from the scorching sun among rocks or in burrows. When night falls, plant-eaters, such as the addax and ass, begin to pick at the dried leaves, fruit and twigs of scrawny desert plants, while smaller jerboas and ground squirrels collect seeds and insects. Other insect-eaters include geckoes and other lizards. Many have wide, webbed feet to help them walk across the loose sand and burrow into it when danger approaches. Larger meat-eaters include vipers, which patrol in search of small rodents, and jackals, which scavenge for the carcasses of dead animals.

Most of these animals never drink liquid water, getting all the moisture they need from their food. They have to hold on to every last drop, though. The kidneys – the organs responsible for cleaning the blood – of desert

Above: The desert tortoise lives in the Mojave Desert in the USA and Mexico, where it eats cacti. These tortoises escape the intense heat of the day by digging burrows with their shovel-shaped forefeet.

animals are very good at retaining water. They release as little moisture as possible as urine.

Food supplies

The camel is one of the few desert animals to be active during the day. Dromedaries (with one hump) are found in Africa and southern Asia, and have been released into Australia, while bactrian camels (with two humps) are found in central Asia. The humps store fat, which keeps the animals alive when there is no food. Gila monsters and other lizards store fat in their tails, while many desert rodents build up food stores in their burrows to survive long periods of drought.

ISLANDS

Because they have been isolated from the rest of the world for so long, islands tend to contain species which have evolved independently of their relatives on the mainland. Consequently, islands are good place to observe the process of natural selection at work.

Islands do not really constitute a biome because they exist in all parts of the world and come in all sorts of shapes and sizes. For example, Greenland, the world's largest island, is a place of vast ice fields edged with tundra. Most islands lie in warmer climes and are little more than rocks or reefs poking a few centimetres above the surrouding surf.

Coastal lands

Small islands and coasts generally are unusual places to live because they are regularly transformed by tides washing in and out. While life in a desert or on an icy mountain may have its

Above: Komodo dragons are the world's largest lizards. They live on just a few islands in Indonesia. They are fierce hunters, ambushing their prey, and they will target animals as large as buffaloes and deer.

challenges, coastal plants and animals must cope with being immersed in salt water twice a day and then being dried by the sun and wind. Where the land meets the sea, marine life has adapted to stay alive when it is left exposed, while land-living plants and animals have ways of coping with the sea water that sprays over them every day.

However, coastal life is more complicated because the tides do not follow a daily pattern but undergo monthly and annual changes in height. So higher parts of the coast might

only be submerged by the tide twice a year, while lower areas may only be exposed above the water during the very lowest tides. All of these factors influence the kinds of wildlife found on specific coasts. As one travels inland, the plants and animals change from being completely reliant on the ocean to those which can only live on land. In between, coastal life is positioned according to how well it can cope with being wet and then dry.

Unique animals

While island edges are a haven for coastal wildlife, many of the animals found inland are rather unusual. This is because islands are populated by animals which were there before the land became an island, or by those which have flown or swum from the mainland. On continents, an animal that is successful in a

Below: 1 ruffed lemur, 2 Galápagos giant tortoise, 3 giant chameleon, 4 round island boa, 5 tarsier, 6 Komodo dragon, 7 spotted cuscus, 8 short-nosed echidna, 9 tree kangaroo.

Above: There are several species of Galápagos giant tortoises living on individual islands. Some species have saddle-shaped shells that allow them to reach up to eat leaves from tall plants.

Above: Madagascar is home to a unique group of primates called lemurs. Since Madagascar became an island before monkeys had evolved, the primates on the island resemble more primitive species.

Above: Australia has been isolated from the rest of the world for so long that it has a unique set of mammals, such as this wallaby. As marsupials, wallabies keep their young in pouches as they develop.

particular habitat will eventually spread across the land until it lives in all areas where that habitat is found. For example, brown bears live in conifer forests across the world. They did not evolve in all these places at the same time but spread out from a single location. But because brown bears and many other continental animals cannot get to islands, their place is filled by the animals that were originally there.

An excellent example of this is in New Zealand, an isolated group of islands in the south Pacific. Before people arrived on these islands about 1,000 years ago, and then in greater numbers in the early 20th century, there were only two species of mammal in the region. Both were bats descended

from individuals which must have flown the 2,400km (1,500 miles) from Australia. Interestingly, these New Zealand bats have evolved to become ground-feeders, living a life more similar to that of a mouse than their winged relatives.

Without many mammals, New Zealand's birds took over. The famous kiwi, which uses its long bill to dig out insects, lives like an anteater or hedgehog. The kakapo, a large flightless parrot, digs out roots and eats plants like a pig or woodchuck. And the kea, another parrot, lives like a rat or raccoon, eating anything within reach of its beak.

New Zealand is also home to the tuataras, a tiny group of reptiles which are distantly related to lizards and snakes.

Other island dwellers

The Galápagos Islands, 1,610km (1,000 miles) off the coast of Ecuador in the Pacific Ocean, contain a couple of extremely unusual reptiles: the marine iguana, which is one of the few lizards to feed in salt water (it grazes on seaweed) and the extraordinary Galápagos giant tortoises. These huge reptiles, which are thought to live for at least 100 years, are now highly endangered. The different shell shapes of the tortoises on each of the Galápagos Islands helped Charles Darwin to formulate his theory of evolution.

MOUNTAINS

Mountains form an unusual biome because they encapsulate a number of climate zones within a small geographical area. This variation defines the lives of the inhabitants. Some animals are highly evolved for mountain life; others have extended their lowland ranges into high altitudes.

A mountainside is like several biomes stacked on top of one another. As the mountain rises out of the surrounding lowlands, the air temperature, wind speed, light levels, water supply and, on the highest peaks, even the amount of oxygen begin to change.

One way to picture how these changes occur is to compare them to the changes in climate that occur on a journey from the warm tropics to the distinctly chillier polar regions. On the journey north the climate gradually changes along with the wildlife. The same changes occur on a journey vertically up a mountain.

Zones of growth

Most of the largest mountain ranges, such as the Himalayas of Asia, the Alps of Europe and the Rockies of North America, rise out of temperate or boreal biomes. Therefore the foothills of these ranges are generally

Above: Cougars, also known as pumas, panthers or mountain lions, live in the Americas. As well as high mountain habitats, cougars also live in steamy jungles and dry deserts.

covered in temperate forest or woodland. As the altitude increases, the weather conditions become colder and harsher and the trees of the temperate forest find it increasingly hard to grow. They eventually become smaller and more gnarled, and then

conifer trees take over. Like their relatives in boreal forests, mountain conifers are better at surviving in colder conditions than broad-leaved trees.

As the journey up the mountain continues, the conditions get worse. Rain that falls on the mountain runs through or over the surface before joining a torrential mountain stream and being carried swiftly down. With all the water sluicing rapidly down the mountain, territory nearer the top has less water for the plants to draw on, and eventually there is not enough moisture in the soil for trees to grow. The point where conditions become just too tough for even conifer trees to grow is called the timberline.

Above the timberline, small, hardy alpine plants grow in regions which resemble a cold desert. Alpine plants share features with desert species because they, too, must hang on to

Below: 1 mountain goat, 2 pika, 3 cougar, 4 llamas, 5 ibex, 6 chamois, 7 gorillas, 8 giant panda, 9 Tibetan gazelle, 10 yak, 11 snub-nosed monkeys, 12 snow leopard.

Above: Mountain goats are very sure-footed. They have soft pads at the centre of their otherwise hard hooves, which help them grip the icy rocks of their high-mountain habitat.

thinner canopy. In the humid tropics, these mountain forests are often shrouded in cloud, and this extra moisture makes them ideal places for epiphytes (plants which grow on other plants rather than in the ground). Cloud forests sometimes look as if they are dripping with plant life.

Few tropical mountains are as high as the towering peaks elsewhere on Earth, but a few are too high for cloud forest to grow on. However, they do not give way to conifer trees, which are rare in the tropics. Instead, alpine meadows and shrublands appear, which are often unique to each high-altitude tropical mountain.

Life in the clouds

The forests on mountain slopes are generally not so different from those found in the lowlands that lowland animals cannot survive there. Many forests do have mountain populations or subspecies which are distinct from lowland populations, but they are still fundamentally the same species. Above the forests, however, many of the animals found have adapted specially to the conditions.

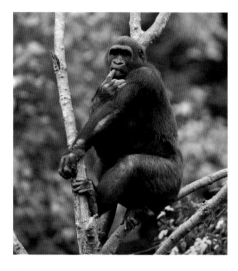

Above: Mountain gorillas live in the mountains of central Africa, where they eat fruit and leaves. The mountain variety of gorilla is slightly smaller than the lowland types.

any water they can get before it is evaporated by the strong mountain wind. At even higher altitudes, as in the polar regions, plant life eventually gives way to snow and ice at the snowline. From here upwards very little plant life survives and animals are infrequent visitors, except for the birds of prey soaring on the thermals of warmer air high above the peaks.

The story is different in tropical regions. Here the mountain slopes are clothed in so-called cloud forests which are similar to other tropical forests, but with shorter trees and a

Despite the rain and snow, water is often scarce at the top of mountains, which is why many desert animals have relatives living there. For example, Asian camels are related to the South American vicuña – the wild relative of the llama. Like the camel, the vicuña is able to operate for long periods without water.

HUMAN SETTLEMENTS

The fastest growing habitats are those made by humans, which are generally expanding at the expense of natural ones. Fortunately, many animals (as well as pets) do thrive with people. Animals that feed on a wide range of foods are the most successful species in human settlements.

Human beings have a huge effect on their environment. Since the dawn of agriculture, people have been clearing natural landscapes to make way for their livestock and crops. Agriculture began in the Middle East 14,000 years ago, and is now so extensive that nearly all the world's grasslands and temperate forests have been replaced by fields. More recently, tropical and boreal forests have also been cut back to make room for agriculture. In evolutionary terms, this change has been very fast, and the natural world is reeling in shock, unable to respond to the changes quickly enough.

Building cities

Several thousand years ago, people began to learn how to farm more efficiently, and farmers began to produce more than they could consume themselves. With a surplus of food, farmers began to trade it for other items. In the fertile river valleys of the Middle East, India and China, agricultural communities were so successful that the first cities grew up. Uniquely among mammals, some members of these large human communities did not find any of their own food. Instead, they bought what they needed with other products.

But while agriculture creates a habitat that mirrors the grassland in some ways, cities were a brand new type of habitat. In 1500, the world population was about 500 million. Only 500 years later, this figure had increased 12-fold, topping six billion in 2000. By this time there were over 200 cities containing over one million

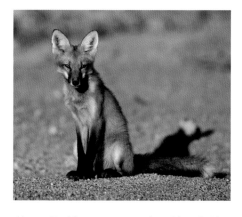

Above: Red foxes are very adaptable animals. They have become very common in suburban and more built-up areas, where they make their homes in gardens and wasteland, and feed on rubbish.

Below: Barbary macaques on Gibraltar are the only monkeys living in Europe. They were introduced to the rock by the Romans, and those that survive there rely on being fed by tourists or stealing food from people's homes.

Above: Raccoons are generalist feeders that have found rich pickings in human settlements. They use their climbing and digging abilities to get at food wherever it may be.

people each. Huge sprawling urban centres, such as Mexico City and Tokyo, now contain more than 25 million people each – and, of course, also millions of animals.

Opportunists

Although changes to the environment caused by humans are happening at a lightning pace, many animals have made the most of the opportunity presented. The destruction of natural habitats has had a terrible effect on those animals which live in particular places. For example, leaf-eating monkeys cannot survive without trees bearing plentiful leaves. However, animals which make the most of any feeding opportunity can survive anywhere, including cities. These so-called generalist feeders have thrived alongside humans for many thousands of years. The most familiar generalists are rodents such as mice and rats. They are typical generalist feeders because they will investigate anything for its food potential and are not fussy about what they eat. Other generalists are monkeys, such as macaques, vervets and capuchins, which are a common sight in many tropical cities. Here and elsewhere, suburban areas packed with gardens are the perfect environment for many other adaptable animals, such as squirrels, racoons and foxes.

Although some people enjoy sharing their cities with wildlife, others regard wild creatures in cities as dirty and dangerous. Several diseases, such as typhus and plague, are associated with rats and other city animals. These animals are so successful that their populations have to be controlled. On the whole, however, as cities mature, their wildlife communities stabilize into a sustainable ecosystem, just as they do in the wild.

Prized pets

Another group of animals live in our cities – pets. People have kept pets for thousands of years. Typical pets, such as cats and dogs, are not generalist feeders and rely on their owners to provide food and shelter. Unlike scavenging city animals, pets live in partnership with people and have done well out of this relationship in which almost every facet of their lives, including their reproduction, is often controlled. Without their human masters, many of these species would now be close to extinction.

Below: The domestic cat is a very popular pet. Like most wild cats, domestic ones are solitary animals and spend their time patrolling their territory looking for mates and rivals.

Below: Domestic guinea pigs, or cavies, are related to wild forms that live in South America. Selective breeding has resulted in individuals that have long, colourful fur.

Below: Perhaps the most popular pet reptiles are tortoises, which can live for many years if properly looked after. Trade in tortoises is heavily controlled to protect wild populations.

ANIMALS OF THE WORLD

Animals are an incredibly dominant form of life. The oceans teem with life, and have done so for nearly 3.5 billion years, while the land is home to the most complex and intelligent animals of all – the six billion people that inhabit the planet. In a few short millennia, humans have spread across the globe and brought many other animal species with them. For other types of animals, similar journeys took a lot longer.

Today, the world has five main landmasses – North and South America, Antarctica, Australia, Africa and Eurasia, this last one being the largest of them all. But this was not always the case. About 200 million years ago, scientists believe, all the land was joined into one huge continent called Pangaea. Animals could walk from Australia to South America via Antarctica, which in those days was a green and pleasant region rather than a desert of ice and snow. South America was joined to North America by more than a thin bridge or isthmus of jungle-clad land as it is today, and animals could pass through to the Old World continents without even wetting their feet.

By about this time, amphibians were well established, having been in existence for over 100 million years. While turtles swam in the oceans, the snakes and lizards of today were a rare sight. Dinosaurs, now long extinct, were masters of the land. However, scurrying out of sight and lurking in the shadows were some curious, small, hairy animals – the first mammals. As the dinosaurs spread across the globe, the mammals followed, and by the time Pangaea began to split up, isolating animals on new landmasses, the world had a relatively uniform covering of animals.

Since then, of course, natural selection has created the incredible amount of diversity which can now be found on every continent, from the platypuses of Australia and Komodo dragons of Indonesia to the giant tortoises of the Galápagos Islands and the tigers of Siberia. Marine life includes the mightiest animals of all, the whales, which along with dolphins and seals have left the land where their ancestors evolved and returned to an aquatic life.

Left: A herd of springboks rest on an African grassland. These wild grasslands host the largest populations of grazing beasts on Earth. The springboks are known for "pronking" – leaping high into the air – when predators attack.

ANIMALS OF THE AMERICAS

North and South America stretch from the barren ice fields of the Arctic to the stormy coast of Cape Horn, which twists into the Southern Ocean. A huge number of different animals make their home in the Americas because the continents support a wide range of habitats. These include the humid forests of the Amazon – the world's largest jungle; the searing Atacama Desert – the world's driest place; and the rolling plains of the American wild west. The Americas are home to many of the world's record-breaking animals. The world's largest deer, the moose, is a common resident of the conifer forests of Canada and the northern United States. The largest land carnivore, the Kodiak bear, is found on Alaska's Kodiak Island. The world's largest rodent, the capybara, lives in the Amazon rainforest, and the largest snake in the world, the green anaconda, is found in the wetlands across tropical South America.

Above from left: Caribou, grizzly bear, double-crested basilisk.

ALASKA

GREENLAND

ARCTIC CIRCLE

CANADA

UNITED STATES OF AMERICA

MEXICO

THE BAHAMAS

TURKS AND
CAICOS ISLANDS

CUBA
VIRGIN ISLANDS

CAYMAN
ISLANDS
DOMINICAN
REPUBLIC
SAINT KITTS AND NEVIS

BELIZE
HAITI
ANTIGUA AND BARBUDA

GUATEMALA
JAMAICA
PUERTO
RICO
GUADELOUPE

HONDURAS
DOMINICA

EL SALVADOR
SAINT LUCIA

NICARAGUA
SAINT VINCENT AND THE GRENADINES
BARBADOS

NETHERLANDS
ANTILLES
ARUBA
GRENADA

COSTA RICA

PANAMA
TRINIDAD AND TOBAGO

ATLANTIC OCEAN

VENEZUELA

GUYANA

FRENCH
GUIANA

GALAPAGOS
ISLANDS
COLOMBIA
SURINAM

ECUADOR

BRAZIL

PERU

BOLIVIA

PARAGUAY

SAN FÉLIX AND SAN AMBROSIO
CHILE

JUAN FERNANDEZ ISLANDS
URUGUAY

ARGENTINA

PACIFIC OCEAN

FALKLAND ISLANDS

SOUTH GEORGIA

SOUTH
SANDWICH
ISLANDS

SALAMANDERS

Salamanders and newts are amphibians with tails. All of them have legs, although a few species have lost a pair or have vestigial limbs. Like all amphibians, salamanders need a certain amount of water to reproduce. Some species are completely aquatic, while others live entirely on land. Many species are truly amphibious, spending the early part of their lives in water and living both on land and in water as adults.

Hellbender

Cryptobranchus alleganiensis

Hellbenders are among the largest salamanders in the Americas and one of three giant salamanders in the world. These monstrous and heavyset amphibians spend their entire lives on the beds of rivers and streams.

Hellbenders are nocturnal and spend the day sheltering under rocks. At night the animals become more active, but generally lurk in crevices while waiting for prey. Giant salamanders lose their gills as they change from larvae into adults. They absorb most of their oxygen through their wrinkly skin but will sometimes rise to the surface to take gulps of air into their small lungs.

Hellbenders breed in late summer. A male digs a hole under a rock and will only allow females that are still carrying eggs into his hole. Several females may lay their eggs in a single male's hole before he fertilizes them with a cloud of sperm. The male guards them for three months until the young hatch out.

Hellbenders have a dark, wrinkled skin that secretes toxic slime. These salamanders do not have gills, and the wrinkles in their skin increase the surface area of their bodies so that they can absorb more oxygen directly from the water.

Distribution: Eastern North America.
Habitat: Rivers and streams.
Food: Crayfishes, worms, insects, fish and snails.
Size: 30–74cm (12–30in).
Maturity: 2–3 years.
Breeding: 450 eggs laid in late summer.
Life span: 50 years.
Status: Not known.

Greater siren

Siren lacertina

Distribution: Eastern United States.
Habitat: Swamps, streams and lakes.
Food: Crayfishes, worms and snails.
Size: 50–90cm (20–36in).
Maturity: Not known.
Breeding: Eggs laid in spring.
Life span: 25 years.
Status: Not known.

The greater siren lives in the mud on the bottom of slow-flowing creeks and in swamps. Most salamanders change considerably as they mature into adults, but the adult body of a siren, with its external gills, long tail and single pair of legs, is very similar to the larval form. Greater sirens spend the day resting on the bottom. At night they drag themselves through the mud with their small legs or swim, with an S-shaped motion, through the murky water. These salamanders do not have teeth, but suck their prey through tough, horny lips. Greater sirens sometimes live in seasonal pools, which dry up in the summer. The salamanders survive these droughts by burying themselves in the moist sediment and coating their bodies with slimy mucus. Breeding takes place at night, under mud. It is thought that females lay single eggs on water plants and males follow the females around, fertilizing each egg soon after it is laid.

Greater sirens have very long bodies with feathery gills behind their heads and a single pair of legs. Their bodies are mottled to help them hide on the river bed. The salamander propels itself through the water, twisting its body into S-shaped curves.

Mudpuppy

Necturus maculosus

Mudpuppies and their close relatives, waterdogs, derive their names from the myth that they bark like dogs when handled. This confuses them with greater sirens – sirens being winged creatures from Greek mythology reputed to have lured sailors on to rocks with their song.

Mudpuppies spend their whole lives underwater. They do not change a great deal when they metamorphose from larvae into adults, retaining gills for breathing and long tails for swimming. The gills vary in size depending on how much oxygen there is dissolved in the water. They are very large in stagnant pools, where there is not very much oxygen available, and smaller in faster-running streams. Mudpuppies mate in the late autumn or early winter. The females' eggs are fertilized inside their bodies and they do not lay them until the spring. Before laying, the females make nests in hollows under rocks or logs on the beds of shallow streams. The eggs have sticky gelatinous coatings and stick together in layers.

Distribution: Eastern United States.
Habitat: Muddy ponds, lakes and streams.
Food: Aquatic insects, crayfishes and fish.
Size: 29–49cm (12–20in).
Maturity: 4–6 years.
Breeding: Mate in autumn, eggs laid in spring.
Life span: Not known.
Status: Common.

Mudpuppies have long, mottled bodies with two pairs of legs and a laterally flattened tail. There is a pair of feathery gills behind the head, but mudpuppies also have small lungs.

Cave salamander (*Eurycea lucifuga*): 8–16cm (3–6in)
Cave salamanders are pale orange amphibians with black spots on their backs. They live in the mouths of caves in the Midwest region of the United States. Cave salamanders have long, grasping tails used for clinging to the rocky cave wall. They lack lungs, but still absorb all of their oxygen from the air through their skin and through the linings of their mouths. Because of this, they can only live in damp areas while on land and have long periods of inactivity.

Olympic torrent salamander (*Rhyacotriton olympicus*): 9–12cm (3.5–5in)
The Olympic torrent salamander is one of four salamanders that live in the rocky streams of the Pacific Northwest in North America. They live in crystal-clear streams that tumble down mountainsides. The water is so rich in oxygen that the adult salamanders have only tiny lungs because they can easily get enough oxygen through their skins.

Coastal giant salamander (*Dicamptodon tenebrosus*): 17–34cm (6.5–13.5in)
Coastal giant salamanders are the largest land-living salamanders in the world. They have brown skins, mottled with black, which help them blend in with the floor of their woodland homes. They secrete foul-tasting chemicals through their skins as a defence when attacked by predators.

Three-toed amphiuma

Amphiuma tridactylum

With their slimy, cylindrical bodies, three-toed amphiumas and other species are also known as Congo eels. This is a misleading name because they are amphibians, not eels, which are fish. Also, they live only in North America, not in the African Congo.

Three-toed amphiumas are the longest salamanders in the Americas, although large hellbenders are probably heavier. Adult amphiumas have neither lungs nor gills. They have to take in oxygen directly through their skin. Three-toed amphiumas spend most of their lives in water, foraging at night and sheltering in streambed burrows during the day. However, during periods of heavy rainfall, the salamanders may make brief trips across areas of damp ground.

Three-toed amphiumas begin to mate in late winter. The females rub their snouts on males they want to attract. During mating males and females wrap around each other, while sperm is transferred into the female's body. The females guard their strings of eggs by coiling their bodies around them until they hatch, about 20 weeks later. By the time the eggs hatch, the water level may have dropped so the larvae have to wriggle over land to reach the water.

Three-toed amphiumas have very long, cylindrical bodies with laterally flattened tails. They have two pairs of tiny legs, each with three toes. The legs are too small to be of use for locomotion.

Distribution: Southern United States.
Habitat: Swamps and ponds.
Food: Worms and crayfishes.
Size: 0.5–1.1m (1.5–3.5ft).
Maturity: Not known.
Breeding: 200 eggs laid in spring.
Life span: Not known.
Status: Common.

Tiger salamander

Ambystoma tigrinum

Tiger salamanders start life in pools of water. While larvae, they have external gills and a fin down the middle of their tails. They feed on aquatic insects and even on other tiger salamander larvae. The larvae may stay in the water for several years before metamorphosing into the adult body form. The gills are then absorbed into the body, the tail fin is lost, and the skin becomes tougher and more resistant to desiccation. This change is thought to be catalyzed by warming of the water. Warm water can absorb more oxygen than cold water, which may trigger the change. However, the warming of the water may also suggest to the animal that the pool is in danger of drying up, indicating that it ought to leave.

   The metamorphosed salamander now looks like an adult, but it is still smaller than the mature animal. This subadult form is called an eft. The eft crawls out of the water and begins to forage on the leaf-strewn floor. It catches insects and other animals with flicks of its sticky tongue and then shakes them to death before chewing them up. After hibernating in burrows, mature adults make mass migrations in springtime to pools and mate over a period of two or three days.

Tiger salamanders may be dark green or grey with black markings, or yellow with black markings. Some specimens have yellow and black stripes, which make them even more reminiscent of their namesake.

Distribution: Central and south-eastern North America.
Habitat: Woodland.
Food: Worms and insects.
Size: 18–30cm (7–12in).
Maturity: Not known.
Breeding: Migrate to breeding pools in spring.
Life span: 20 years.
Status: Common.

Axolotl

Ambystoma mexicanum

Distribution: Lake Xochimilco, Mexico.
Habitat: Water.
Food: Aquatic insects.
Size: 10–20cm (4–8in).
Maturity: Not known.
Breeding: Not known.
Life span: 25 years.
Status: Vulnerable.

In the wild, most axolotls are black, but several colour variants have been bred in captivity. In fact there are more axolotls in captivity around the world than in the wild.

Axolotls are related to tiger salamanders and other species that spend their adult lives on land. However, axolotls never go through the change from the aquatic larval stage to the more robust, terrestrial adult form. Consequently, they spend their whole lives in water.

   Adult axolotls look almost identical to the larval stage. They have four legs – which are too small for walking on land – feathery gills behind their heads and long, finned tails used for swimming. Like the larvae, the adults feed on aquatic insects and other invertebrates, such as worms. The only major difference between the two forms is that the adults have sexual organs, so they can transfer sperm from the male to the female during mating.

   Axolotls do not metamorphose because their thyroid glands cannot produce the hormone necessary to bring about the change. Biologists have injected captive axolotls with the right hormone, and the salamanders then change into a land-living form similar to other species.

   Because they cannot naturally get out of the water, axolotls are confined to their aquatic habitat. They live in a single lake system in Mexico and are therefore vulnerable to pollution and exploitation, and are becoming increasingly rare.

Red-spotted newt

Notophthalmus viridescens

Red-spotted newts, also known as eastern newts, have a very complex lifecycle. Their lives begin in water, where they hatch out from eggs as aquatic larvae. The larvae then develop into land-living juveniles called efts. The eft stage has the body form of a normal adult salamander, with four legs and a long, grasping tail. However, it is unable to breed.

The eft spends up to four years living out of water in damp woodland and grassland. Red-spotted newts must return to ponds and streams to become mature. When they return to water, the maturing red-spotted newts actually redevelop many larval features, such as a deep tail – ideal for swimming – and a thinner skin, used for absorbing oxygen directly from the water.

The adults spend the spring and early summer breeding in bodies of fresh water. After the breeding season the adults leave the water and return to a life on land. Many newts return to the same ponds to breed each year. They may navigate by storing complex maps of their surroundings in their memories, or by using either the Earth's magnetic field or polarized light.

Red-spotted newts are so-named due to the red and black markings along their backs. During the juvenile or eft stage, the newts are bright orange, but when they eventually reach maturity, they turn green with yellow undersides.

Distribution: Eastern United States.
Habitat: Damp land and fresh water.
Food: Tadpoles, insects, slugs, worms and other small invertebrates.
Size: 6.5–11.5cm (2.5–4.5in).
Maturity: 1–4 years.
Breeding: In water in spring.
Life span: Not known.
Status: Common.

Long-toed salamander (*Ambystoma macrodactylum croceum*): 10–17cm (4–6.5in) The long-toed salamander is found in the Pacific Northwest from northern Canada to British Columbia. It is a member of the mole salamander group, which includes tiger salamanders and axolotls. These amphibians are called mole salamanders because many, such as the long-toed salamander, live in burrows below damp ground. In spring, they breed in ponds.

Cayenne caecilian (*Typhlonectes compressicauda*): 30–60cm (12–24 in) The Cayenne caecilian lives in the tributaries and lakes of the Amazon River basin system. Its long, dark body resembles that of an eel at first glance, but, like other caecilians, it has well-defined rings around its body. This species is completely aquatic: its tail is flattened into a paddle shape, and a small fin runs along the top of the body. Female Cayenne caecilians carry their developing eggs inside their bodies. Then they give birth to live young, which look like miniature adults.

Ringed caecilian

Siphonops annulatus

Caecilians are amphibians, but they belong to a separate group entirely from salamanders, newts, frogs and toads. All caecilians lack legs altogether and they resemble large worms. The ringed caecilian burrows through the soil of steamy tropical forests, wriggling its body in waves to push its way forward. They breathe with only one properly developed lung.

Ringed caecilians eat anything they come across while on the move, providing it is small enough. They use their heads like trowels to probe areas of soil and use their tentacles to pick up the scent of prey. The tentacles are closely linked to the nose, and detect chemicals in the soil. They can also detect the movements and faint electric currents produced by the muscles of prey animals.

Ringed caecilians mate when the soil is at its most damp, during the rainy seasons. The female's eggs are fertilized by the male when they are still inside her body. She lays the eggs in the soil. Unlike many species of caecilian, which have an aquatic larval stage, young ringed caecilians hatch looking like miniature adults.

Distribution: North-eastern South America.
Habitat: Tropical forest.
Food: Worms and insects.
Size: 20–40cm (8–16in).
Maturity: Not known.
Breeding: Rainy season.
Life span: 10 years.
Status: Common.

Ringed caecilians have blue, scaly bands around their bodies. Like all caecilians, ringed caecilians have a retractable tentacle on each side of the head, near to their nostrils.

FROGS AND TOADS

Frogs and toads form the largest group of amphibians, called Anura. *Toads are better adapted to terrestrial habitats with thicker, warty skin to avoid desiccation, while frogs have thin, smooth skin that needs to be kept moist. Most species follow similar lifecycles. Tailed larvae called tadpoles hatch from eggs called spawn and develop in water before sprouting legs, losing their tails and emerging on to land.*

Surinam toad

Pipa pipa

Distribution: Amazon Basin and northern South America.
Habitat: Muddy water.
Food: Small fish and aquatic invertebrates.
Size: 5–20cm (2–8in).
Maturity: Not known.
Breeding: Rainy season.
Life span: Not known.
Status: Common.

Surinam toads spend their whole lives in water. Their bodies are well adapted to a life foraging on the muddy bottoms of turbid streams and ponds. The fingers have a star of tentacles at their tips that makes them extremely sensitive feelers. The toads also have sense organs along their sides that can detect the motion in the water caused by other animals. Their eyes are positioned on the top of their heads so they can look up through the water to the see if danger is approaching from above the surface.

The toads mate during the wettest time of the year. A male grabs a female around the waist and the couple spin around in the water several times. The female releases her eggs and the male uses his hind feet to sweep them into the space between her back and his belly. His sperm fertilizes the eggs, which then embed themselves on the mother's back. The eggs develop into tiny toadlets after three or four months.

Surinam toads have flattened bodies with triangular heads and large webbed hind feet. Their forefeet have sensitive fingers for feeling around in murky waters. A female may bear up to 100 fertilized eggs on her back.

Darwin's frog

Rhinoderma darwinii

Darwin's frogs have small, slender bodies with pointed snouts and long fingers. The upper parts of their bodies are green or brown. The undersides are a dark brown or black. The long digits on the hind feet are webbed.

Darwin's frogs live in the steamy mountain forests of the Chilean Andes. Despite their natural habitat being damp and lush, Darwin's frogs do not have a typical aquatic life stage. Most frogs, toads and other amphibians spend at least part of their lives – generally the larval stage – living in water, but the water is in an unusual location in this case.

Darwin's frogs do not need this truly aquatic stage because of their unusual breeding system. The frogs breed at all times of the year. The male first attracts the female with a bell-like call. The female lays around 20 eggs in a suitably moist spot, and the male fertilizes the eggs and guards them for about 25 days until they hatch into tadpoles. He then scoops the tadpoles into his mouth. Males of a species related to Darwin's frogs carry the tadpoles to the nearest body of water, but Darwin's frogs keep the tadpoles in their mouths until they develop into froglets. The tadpoles develop in their father's vocal pouch for another 50 days before climbing out and becoming independent.

Distribution: Southern Andes, in southern Chile and Argentina.
Habitat: Shallow cold streams in mountain forests.
Food: Insects.
Size: 2.5–3cm (1–1.25in).
Maturity: Not known.
Breeding: All year.
Life span: Not known.
Status: Common.

South American bullfrog

Leptodactylus pentadactylus

Distribution: Central and northern South America, from Costa Rica to Brazil.
Habitat: Tropical forest near water.
Food: Insects and other invertebrates.
Size: 8–22cm (3–9in).
Maturity: Not known.
Breeding: Rainy season.
Life span: Not known.
Status: Common, although these frogs are hunted by humans in some areas and their hind legs eaten.

South American bullfrogs are not closely related to the bullfrogs of North America. They all have powerful bodies and large external eardrums, but the similarity ends there. The South American bullfrog is, in fact, more closely related to the horned frogs, which have pointed protuberances of skin above their eyes.

South American bullfrogs are mainly nocturnal. They shelter under logs or in burrows during the day and during periods when it is too dry to move around. These bullfrogs reportedly give a piercing scream when picked up. This probably serves to startle predators that might then drop them in fright.

South American bullfrogs breed in the wet season when the forest streams and ponds are swelled by the rains. The males whip up mucus into a blob of foam, using their hind legs, and attach it to a branch over a body of water. The females then choose a male's foam nest in which to lay their eggs. The tadpoles hatch out and fall into the water below.

The South American bullfrog is a large, robust animal with long limbs and widely spaced toes without webbing. The males have sharp spines on their forethumbs. During the mating season they use these weapons in fights with other males over the females.

Four-eyed frog

Physalaemus nattereri

Distribution: Southern Brazil and northern Argentina.
Habitat: Coastal forest.
Food: Insects.
Size: 3–4cm (1.25–1.5in).
Maturity: Not known.
Breeding: Rainy season.
Status: Not known.

Four-eyed – or false-eyed – frogs live in the tropical forest near the Atlantic coast of South America. The adults spend their lives foraging on land. They breed after heavy rains have created ponds and puddles for the tadpoles to develop in. The male whips up a nest of mucus and foam, placing it near to a body of water. The female's eggs hatch into tadpoles, which wriggle or drop the short distance into the water.

While most frogs rely on poisons in the skin or alarm calls to ward off predators, four-eyed frogs have a different strategy. When threatened, they inflate their bodies so that they appear to be much larger. They then turn around and point their rump at the attacker. The eyespots on the frog's rump fool the predator into thinking that it is looking at the face of a much larger, and potentially dangerous, animal. To make matters worse, the frogs secrete a foul-smelling fluid. This fluid is released from a gland in the frog's groin.

Four-eyed frogs are so-named because of the two black eyespots on their rumps.

Tailed frog (*Ascaphus truei*): 4cm (1.5in)
Tailed frogs lives in the clear mountain streams of the Cascade Range in the north-western United States and southern Canada. They have flattened heads with rounded snouts. The males have a short tail-like extension that contains their anus and sexual opening. The females lay short strings of eggs on rocks after mating with the males. The larvae develop into adults slowly, taking up to four years in colder parts of their range.

North American bullfrog (*Rana catesbeiana*): 9–20cm (3.5–8in)
The North American bullfrog is the largest frog in North America. It has a reputation for having a large appetite. It lives in lakes, ponds and slow-flowing streams, where it preys on small snakes, mammals and other frogs. During the summer breeding season, males defend territories and attract females by voicing deep croaks.

Greenhouse frog (*Eleutherodactylus planirostris*): 2–4cm (0.75–1.5in)
One of the world's smallest frogs, this species lives in Florida, Cuba and several other Caribbean islands. The greenhouse frog lives in woodland, where it uses suction discs on its fingers and toes to cling to flat surfaces, such as smooth bark, large leaves or, on occasion, greenhouse glass.

Marine toad

Bufo marinus

Distribution: Southern North America, Central and South America from Texas to Chile, and now introduced to other areas, including eastern Australia.
Habitat: Most land habitats, often near pools and swamps.
Food: Insects, particulary beetles, snakes, lizards and small mammals.
Size: 5–23cm (2–9in).
Maturity: 1 year.
Breeding: 2 clutches of between 8,000 and 35,000 eggs produced each year. Eggs hatch into tadpoles that become adult in 45–55 days.
Life span: 40 years.
Status: Common.

Marine toads are the largest toads in the world. They have several other common names, including giant toads and cane toads, their Australian name. Marine toads occur naturally from the southern USA southwards through Mexico to Chile. They were introduced to Queensland, Australia, in the 1930s to help control the pest beetles that were infesting sugar cane crops. However, the toads did not like living amongst the cane plants because there were few places to shelter during the day. So the toads spread out over the countryside, where they ate not beetle pests but small reptiles and mammals, some of which are now rare because of their predation. Today the toads are a serious pest.

Marine toads are extremely adaptable. They live in all sorts of habitats, eating just about anything they can get into their mouths. They protect themselves against attack using the toxin glands on their backs, which ooze a fluid that can kill many animals that ingest it. In small quantities, the toxin causes humans to hallucinate. Female cane toads produce several thousand eggs each year. They lay them in long strings, wrapped around water plants. The eggs are fertilized by the males after they have been laid.

Female marine toads are larger than the males. Both sexes have warty glands on their backs that squirt a milky toxin when squeezed.

Red-eyed tree frog

Agalychnis callidryas

Red-eyed tree frogs live high up in the trees in the rainforests of Central America. Their long legs allow them to reach for branches and then spread their body weight over a wide area when climbing through flimsy foliage. The discs on the tips of each toe act as suction cups, so the frogs can cling to flat surfaces, such as leaves.

Red-eyed tree frogs are nocturnal. Their large eyes gather as much light as possible so the frogs can see even on the darkest nights. During the day, the frogs rest on leaves. They tuck their brightly coloured legs under their bodies so only their camouflaged, leaf-green upper sides are showing.

When it is time to breed, males gather on a branch above a pond. They call to the females by exciting clicking sounds. When a female arrives, a male climbs on to her back and she carries him down to the water. She takes in water and climbs back to the branch again, where she lays eggs on a leaf. The male fertilizes the eggs and they are left to develop into tadpoles. After hatching, the tadpoles fall into the water below.

Red-eyed tree frogs have long toes with rounded suction discs at their tips. Their bodies have a bright green upper side. These colourful frogs have blue and white stripes on their flanks and yellow and red legs. The family of tree frogs, about 600 species strong, is found on all the continents except Antarctica.

Distribution: Caribbean coast of Central America.
Habitat: Tropical forests in the vicinity of streams.
Food: Insects.
Size: 4–7cm (1.5–2.75in).
Maturity: Not known.
Breeding: Summer.
Life span: Not known.
Status: Common.

Strawberry poison-dart frog

Dendrobates pumilio

Strawberry poison-dart frogs have bright red bodies with blue on their hind legs. These bright colours serve as a warning to predators that their skins are covered in a poison so deadly that just one lick is generally fatal. The poison-dart family has around 120 species.

Many frogs and toads secrete toxic chemicals on to their skins. Most are harmless to humans, but many make predators sick after they eat the frogs. However, the strawberry poison-dart frog and other closely related species have much more potent toxins. A single lick is enough to kill most predators.

The frogs earn their name from the fact that their skins are used by forest people to make poison for hunting darts. The toxins of some frogs are so strong that a single skin can produce enough poison to tip 50 darts. Hunters use them to kill monkeys and other forest animals.

The strawberry poison-dart frog is not always red. During the breeding season, males often change colour to brown, blue or green. Although they rarely climb trees when foraging, the females climb trees to lay their eggs in tree holes filled with water. The males then fertilize the eggs.

Distribution: Southern Central America.
Habitat: Tropical forest.
Food: Insects.
Size: 2–2.5cm (0.75–1in).
Maturity: Not known.
Breeding: Rainy season.
Life span: Not known.
Status: Common.

Mexican burrowing frog (*Rhinophrynus dorsalis*): 6–8cm (2.5–3.25in)
Mexican burrowing frogs have bloated, almost disc-shaped, black bodies and pointed snouts. They live in areas of Mexico and Central America with soft, sandy soils that are easy to burrow into. The frogs spend most of their time underground, only coming to the surface after heavy rain. They breed in temporary pools. The tadpoles are filter-feeders, straining tiny, floating plants and animals from the water.

Reticulated glass frog (*Centrolenella valerioi*): 2–5cm (0.75–2in)
This species of glass frog lives in the trees of mountain rainforests in South America. It is an expert climber, having slender legs with suction discs on its toes for clinging to the flat surfaces of leaves. The name "glass frog" refers to the species' translucent skin. The major bones and blood vessels are visible through it.

American toad (*Bufo americanus*): 5–9cm (2–3.5in)
The American toad is similar to its European cousin, the common toad, in that it has a brown, wart-covered body. It has large glands on its shoulder, which release a foul-tasting liquid on to the skin. American toads are found in most parts of eastern North America, from Hudson Bay to the Carolinas.

Paradoxical frog

Pseudis paradoxa

The paradoxical frog is aptly named. Most other frogs are considerably larger than their tadpoles. However, adult paradoxical frogs are smaller than their fully grown tadpoles, hence the paradox. Young paradoxical frogs stay in their larval tadpole stage for much longer than other species. They grow to 25cm (10in) long – four or five times the size of an adult. As they metamorphose into adults, the frogs therefore shrink in size, mainly by absorbing their tails back into their bodies.

Adult paradoxical frogs have bodies that are well adapted to a life in water. Their powerful hind limbs are webbed and are used as the main means of propulsion. Like many other aquatic frogs, this species has long fingers that are good for delving into the muddy beds of lakes and ponds. They stir up the mud to disturb prey animals and catch them in their mouths. The female lays her eggs in a floating foam nest, before the male fertilizes them.

Paradoxical frogs have slimy, dark green and brown bodies. They have very long hind legs with webbed feet. Their forefeet have two long toes.

Distribution: Central and eastern South America.
Habitat: Fresh water.
Food: Aquatic invertebrates.
Size: 5–7cm (2–2.75in).
Maturity: Not known.
Breeding: Rainy season.
Life span: Not known.
Status: Common.

TURTLES AND TORTOISES

Turtles and tortoises have lived on Earth for over 200 million years. They belong to a group of reptiles that have existed since the dinosaurs roamed the Earth. Their soft bodies are protected by shells called carapaces. There is no major difference between turtles and tortoises, however turtles (and terrapins) live in water, while tortoises tend to live on land.

Matamata

Chelys fimbriatus

Distribution: Amazon basin and northern South America.
Habitat: Beds of rivers and streams.
Food: Fish.
Size: 30–45cm (12–18in).
Maturity: Not known.
Breeding: 20–30 eggs laid.
Life span: 40 years.
Status: Common.

Matamatas live on the bottom of tropical lakes and rivers. They take breaths by poking their long snouts out of the water, so they can remain hidden below the water at all times. Their knobbly shells are often turned green and red by algae growing on them, helping them blend with rocky river beds. Matamatas wait in ambush for prey to swim near. They have small eyes, set on the sides of their flattened heads, which are useless for hunting in the murky waters, but they are sensitive to the water currents created by prey close by. The flaps of skin on their long necks aid their camouflage, and may also act as lures to attract fish. When the fish come within range matamatas strike with great speed. They suck the unsuspecting fish into their wide mouths. The suction is caused by rapid opening of the mouth, creating an area of low pressure inside. Matamatas have also been observed walking along river beds, herding fish into shallow water where they can be sucked up more easily.

Matamatas are unusual-looking turtles. They have triangular heads with long flexible snouts, which are used as snorkels to breathe air from above the surface.

Alligator snapping turtle

Macroclemys temminckii

Alligator snapping turtles are the largest freshwater turtles. During the day they are mainly ambush hunters, lying half-buried in mud on the river bed. While waiting for prey to approach, these turtles hold their large mouths open.

The turtle's tongue has a small projection on it, which becomes pink when engorged with blood. The turtle wiggles it as a lure to attract prey. Fish and other animals approach the lure, thinking they see a worm in the mud. However, they are heading for an almost certain death. As the prey swims into a turtle's mouth, it snaps shut. Small prey are swallowed whole, while the sharp, horny beak makes light work of larger prey, which may even be another species of turtle. The largest prey are held in the jaws, while the snapping turtle uses its forefeet to tear it apart. Male snapping turtles spend their whole lives in muddy rivers and lakes. Females, however, climb on to land in spring to lay eggs in holes dug into mud or sand.

Distribution: South-eastern United States, in the lower Mississippi River Valley.
Habitat: Beds of lakes and slow-flowing rivers.
Food: Fish and turtles.
Size: 40–80cm (16–32in).
Maturity: Not known.
Breeding: 10–50 eggs buried in mud.
Life span: 70 years.
Status: Vulnerable.

Alligator snapping turtles have a tough carapace, covered in pointed, triangular knobbles. They have a large head with a sharp, horny beak.

Galápagos tortoise

Geochelone elephantopus

Distribution: Galápagos Islands in the eastern Pacific.
Habitat: Varied on the islands, from moist forest to arid land.
Food: Plants.
Size: 1–1.4m (3.25–4.5ft).
Maturity: Not known.
Breeding: Several large eggs.
Life span: Over 100 years.
Status: Vulnerable in general; some sub-species are endangered.

Galápagos tortoises are the largest of all the testudines (tortoises and turtles). They are found only on the islands of the Galápagos Archipelago in the equatorial Pacific, off the coast of Ecuador. In general, the shell folds around the body like a saddle. However, the different subspecies located on various islands in the group have varying shell shapes. The general saddle shape allows the forefeet and neck to move more freely than for most tortoises.

Galápagos tortoises are plant-eaters. They use their long necks to reach up to bushes and shrubs, foraging for leaves with their toothless jaws. They also eat grass and even cacti. Their giant size is probably due to this diet. The Galápagos Islands are arid places and plants are not widely available. Plant food contains only small amounts of energy, and larger animals use energy more efficiently than small ones.

For most of the year, the tortoises live in small herds. During the breeding season, however, males defend territories. The dominant males are the ones that can lift their heads higher than other males. They hector passing females into mating with them. The females dig nest chambers and lay large spherical eggs.

These giant tortoises have different shell shapes depending on which island they live among the Galápagos Archipelago. Charles Darwin cited these shell differences to support his theory of natural selection.

Painted turtle (*Chrysemys picta*): 15–25cm (6–10in)
Painted turtles lives in fresh water across central North America, from British Columbia to Georgia. They have smooth shells with a red stripe down their backs, small limbs and yellow stripes along their necks. The turtles eat both plants and animals during the day and sleep on river beds at night.

Green turtle (*Chelonia mydas*): 1–1.2m (3.25–4ft)
Green turtles spend their whole lives at sea. They have flipper-like legs and smooth carapaces. They only visit land to lay eggs. The turtles gather in shallow water near deserted, sandy beaches across the world, including the Americas, where they mate. Then the females come out of the sea and lay their eggs in holes dug with their flippers in the sand. While at sea, the turtles eat jellyfish, sponges and molluscs.

Wood turtle (*Clemmys insculpta*): 14–19cm (5.5–7.5in)
Wood turtles wander between bodies of water in woodland and meadowland of eastern Canada and New England. They are omnivores, eating worms, slugs, tadpoles, insects and plants.

Stinkpot

Sternotherus odoratus

Stinkpots are so-named because they release a nasty smelling musk from glands beneath their shells. This smell is meant to ward off predators, but the stinkpot will also give a painful bite if the musk does not do its job.

Stinkpots spend their lives in slow-flowing, shallow streams and muddy ponds and lakes. Their shells often have mats of microscopic algae growing on them. Stinkpots feed during both the day and night. They use the barbels on their chins to sense the movements of prey buried in the muddy streambeds. Like many other musk turtles, stinkpots have a toughened shelf attached to their upper jaws. The turtle uses this shelf to crush the shells of water snails and other prey.

Female stinkpots leave the water to lay their elongated eggs. They make nests under mats of decaying plant matter or under the stumps of trees. Stinkpots lay the smallest eggs of all turtles – only 1.5 × 2.5cm (0.5 × 1in).

Stinkpots have smooth, streamlined shells suitable for living in running water. They have sensitive fleshy projections, called barbels, on their chins.

Distribution: South-eastern United States.
Habitat: Shallow, muddy water.
Food: Insects, molluscs, plants and carrion.
Size: 8–13cm (3–5in).
Maturity: Not known.
Breeding: Eggs laid under tree stumps.
Life span: 54 years.
Status: Common.

LIZARDS

Lizards are reptiles, belonging to the same group as snakes. They are found all over the world except for Antarctica, especially in places that are too hot or dry for mammals to thrive. The main group of American lizards are the iguanas, which include the basilisks and anoles. More widespread lizards, such as geckos and skinks, are also found in the Americas, especially South America.

Rhinoceros iguana

Cyclura cornuta

Distribution: Island of Hispaniola and other Caribbean islands.
Habitat: Forest.
Food: Leaves and fruit.
Size: 1–1.2m (3.25–4ft).
Maturity: Not known.
Breeding: 2–20 eggs laid in burrow.
Life span: Not known.
Status: Vulnerable.

These large grey iguanas live on the island of Hispaniola – divided into the countries of Haiti and the Dominican Republic – as well as a few smaller islands in the Caribbean Sea. They are most active during the day and often bask in the sun to warm up their bodies. They walk slowly through the forest, browsing on leaves and fruit. Their teeth are very sharp and are ideal for cutting through tough leaves and other plant materials.

The rhinoceros iguana gets its name from the toughened scales on its snout that resemble small horns. Males have larger "horns" than females.

When threatened, rhinoceros iguanas will run away at high speed. They can only achieve these speeds over short distances. If cornered they will give a painful bite and thrash their tails, which are armoured with spiky scales.

Male rhinoceros iguanas maintain a hierarchy based on the size of their chin flaps, or dewlaps. The males frequently contest this social structure during the short summer breeding season. The top-ranked males control access to females. They attract females with elaborate displays involving bobs of their heads, press-ups and showing off their dewlaps. Females lay up to 20 eggs in burrows and guard them until they hatch three months later.

Gila monster

Heloderma suspectum

Gila monsters are one of only two poisonous lizards in the world. They produce venom in salivary glands in their lower jaws. The venom flows by capillary action along grooves in their teeth, giving the lizard a poisonous bite. The venom acts on the prey animal's nervous system, preventing the heart and lungs from working. For a healthy human, a bite from a gila monster will be very painful but not life-threatening.

Gila monsters are most active at night. They shelter from the heat of the day in rocky crevices or burrows abandoned by mammals. However, in northern parts of their range, the lizards are completely inactive for several months during the winter. Inactive individuals rely on fat stored in their tails to keep them alive when they cannot feed.

Distribution: South-west United States and northern Mexico.
Habitat: Desert.
Food: Small mammals and eggs.
Size: 35–50cm (14–20in).
Maturity: Not known.
Breeding: Eggs laid in summer.
Life span: 20 years.
Status: Vulnerable.

Gila monsters mate in springtime, and their copulation can last for over an hour. The eggs develop inside the females for about ten weeks. They then bury the eggs in areas that are often bathed in sunlight. The eggs incubate for up to ten months.

Gila monsters have long, robust bodies with short legs. Their bodies are covered in rounded, bead-like scales. Most of them are dark but some have blotches of pink, yellow or orange.

Green basilisk

Basiliscus plumifrons

Distribution: Central America.
Habitat: Forest.
Food: Insects, small vertebrates and fruit, often feeding in trees.
Size: 60–75cm (24–29in).
Maturity: Not known.
Breeding: 20 eggs per year.
Life span: 10 years.
Status: Common.

Green basilisks spend most of their time in trees. They have long fingers and toes that help them grasp branches as they scuttle about looking for food. However, they prefer to stay in trees that are close to water. When threatened by predators, such as birds of prey, the lizards dive into the water below. The crests on their backs and tails are used to propel the reptiles through the water to safety. Basilisks will also shimmy into soft sand to avoid a predator. They can close their nostrils to keep sand out. On land, they run at high speed on their hind legs. They do not have to stop running when they reach water because their hind feet have scaly fringes that spread the lizard's body weight, so they can run on the surface of water. This adaptive ability has earned them (along with other related species) the nickname of "Jesus Christ lizards".

Male basilisks control their territories very aggressively, chasing any other males away. A successful male will control an area that contains a number of females. He has sole mating rights to this harem.

Green basilisks are also known as plumed basilisks because they have crests on the backs of their heads, down their back and along their long tails.

Marine iguana (*Amblyrhynchus cristatus*): 50–100cm (20–40in)
Marine iguanas live on the coastline of the Galápagos Islands in the Pacific Ocean. They dive into seawater to feed on seaweed growing on rocks. Large adults can stay underwater for over an hour at a time. They spend the rest of the time basking in the sun on the rocky shoreline. They need to keep warm when on land because the islands are surrounded by cold ocean currents. Marine iguanas may gather in crowds containing thousands of individuals. They expel salt through glands in their noses. Their dark bodies become covered in pale salt crystals from the cold sea water.

Western banded gecko (*Coleonyx variegatus*): 12–15cm (5–6in)
The western banded gecko is found in southern California, Arizona and northern Mexico. It is active at night, when it forages for insects and spiders. Its days are spent sheltering in rocky crevices. When trapped, this lizard gives high-pitched squeaks and, like many other gecko species, it may shed its tail to confuse a predator.

Green anole

Anolis carolinensis

Green anoles live in trees. Their long, thin legs are well adapted for leaping from branch to branch and perching on all but the flimsiest of branches. Thanks to the pads on the tips of their fingers and toes, anoles can grip on to just about any surface, including the fronds of palm trees.

Green anoles rest in dense cover at night. When not foraging in daylight, the lizards bask in the sun, generally on vertical surfaces, such as tree trunks or walls. Anoles can change their body colour, although not to the same extent as chameleons. For example, they may darken their normally bright skin when resting in the shade so as not to attract attention.

Although both sexes have dewlaps, only the males use them for communication. They extend them to signal to rival males and mates. A male begins courtship by bobbing his head and displaying his dewlap to a female. He then walks towards her with his legs straightened. If she is receptive to his advances, she allows him to position his body next to hers. He then grasps the back of her neck with his mouth and holds her tail with his hind legs as they copulate. The female lays one egg at a time under moist leaf litter.

Both male and female green anoles have pink dewlaps – fans of skin beneath their throats. The lizards have very long tails – nearly twice the length of the rest of their bodies – and their elongated fingers and toes are tipped with pads.

Distribution: South-eastern United States.
Habitat: Woodland and shrubbery.
Food: Insects.
Size: 12–20cm (5–8in).
Maturity: Not known.
Breeding: Single eggs laid throughout breeding season.
Life span: Not known.
Status: Common.

Desert horned lizard

Phrynosoma platyrhinos

These small reptiles are sometimes referred to as horned toads, because of their rounded bodies. Despite living in dry areas, much of the desert horned lizard's range can get cold, especially at night. Its round body helps it warm up quickly in the morning sunshine. The lizard can eat huge quantities of ants, which it licks up with its long tongue.

The many spikes on their bodies serve two functions. They help to break up the profiles of the lizards so they can blend into the rocky terrain. If they are spotted by a sharp-eyed predator, the tough spikes make horned lizards a difficult and potentially painful meal.

Armed with these weapons, a horned lizard will not run when danger approaches. Instead, it will freeze to avoid giving its position away and rely on its camouflage to hide it. If this defensive strategy fails and it is scooped into the mouth of a predator, such as a coyote, the reptile has one final weapon. The horned lizard can ooze blood from membranes that haemorrhage around its eyeballs. The blood mixes with a foul-tasting chemical, causing the predator to release its grip on the lizard.

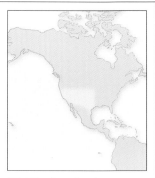

Distribution: South-western United States.
Habitat: Rocky desert.
Food: Ants.
Size: 7.5–13.5cm (3–5.5in).
Maturity: Not known.
Breeding: Eggs laid in spring.
Life span: Not known.
Status: Common.

The desert horned lizard has three pointed scales that form horns pointing backwards from the back of its head. There are smaller spikes on its back and along the tail.

Chuckwalla

Sauromalus obesus

Chuckwallas live in the Mojave Desert, one of the driest and hottest places in North America. Like all other living reptiles, chuckwallas are cold-blooded or exothermic. Their bodies do not make any heat of their own apart from that generated by muscle movement. The lizards rely on sunlight and the temperature of the air around them to warm up enough for daily activity. Chuckwallas only become fully active when their body temperature exceeds 38°C (100°F). The temperature of the Mojave Desert regularly exceeds this, but in other areas of their range, chuckwallas remain inside their rocky dens until the weather gets warm enough.

Chuckwallas are herbivores. They search through the rock-strewn desert for hardy plants that can survive the scorching conditions. With only a limited food supply, female chuckwallas may not be able to reproduce every year. Some females save energy by skipping a breeding season.

Chuckwallas have an unusual defence strategy. When they are under attack by a bird of prey or coyote, they scuttle into a tight crevice between rocks and inflate their lungs. These reptiles have loose folds of skin around their throats and flanks which allow their bodies to swell up to a considerable size. This makes it difficult for a predator to extract the lizard from its hiding place.

Distribution: California, Arizona and northern Mexico.
Habitat: Desert.
Food: Fruit, leaves and flowers.
Size: 28–42cm (11–16in).
Maturity: Not known.
Breeding: Females breed every 1–2 years.
Life span: Not known.
Status: Common.

Chuckwallas have powerful limbs and thick tails. The males have completely black heads, while the females have yellow and orange patches on black.

Black tegu

Tupinambis teguixin

Black tegus are among the largest lizards in South America. They live in forest clearings, often close to river banks. They are good swimmers and can also walk on their hind legs.

Black tegus find their prey by tasting the air with their forked tongues. The lizards flick their tongues in the air and then place each prong into a double olfactory organ at the top of their mouths. The organ is used to analyze the air for any chemicals contained within it.

When they are attacked, these large lizards scratch and bite predators and often use their muscular tails as clubs. Black tegus communicate with each other with loud snorting noises, which carry through the forest. The males have paired sexual organs called hemipenes. During mating, the male grabs the female's neck and twists his body under hers. He then inserts his hemipenes into her sexual opening, which is called a cloaca.

Females may lay eggs in burrows, but typically they dig into the bases of termite mounds because termites keep these nests at a constant temperature.

The black tegu has a thick tail and powerful limbs. Its scales are small and give the body a glossy appearance. Although it is not related, the black tegu resembles the monitor lizards.

Distribution: South America from Panama to Argentina.
Habitat: Tropical forest.
Food: Insects, lizards, small birds and mammals.
Size: 80–110cm (31–43in).
Maturity: Not known.
Breeding: Eggs laid in termite mounds.
Life span: Not known.
Status: Common.

Pink tailed skink (*Eumeces lagunensis*): 16–20cm (6–8in)
This skink lives in Baja California. When young, the lizard's long tail is bright pink, but it fades with age. The bright tail probably serves as a diversion to predators, which are more likely to strike at the brightly coloured tail than the camouflaged head. Many lizards can live without their tails, and skinks have special bones in their tails that are designed to break when the tail is attacked. In most cases a lost tail will grow back again in a matter of weeks.

Middle American night lizard (*Lepidophyma flavimaculatum*): 7–12cm (3–5in)
Female Middle American night lizards produce young without having to mate – parthenogenetically. Some populations of these lizards contain no males at all. The lizards do not lay eggs, but keep them inside their bodies until they hatch. The young are then born live from the mother.

Crocodile skink (*Tribolonotus gracilis*): 15–20cm (6–8in)
This armoured lizard lives on the island of Hispaniola in the Caribbean. Its triangular head is protected by a bony shield and it has four rows of scaly spines running along its back and tail, making it look somewhat like a crocodile. Crocodile skinks live in pairs or threesomes, consisting of a male and one or two females. The females lay single eggs in leaf litter.

Ajolote

Bipes biporus

Ajolotes are not snakes or lizards, but amphisbaenians, belonging to a small group of reptiles, which are sometimes called worm lizards. These reptiles spend their whole lives burrowing through soft soil, feeding on subterranean prey.

The ajolote is also called the mole lizard or "little lizard with ears". Early observers must have mistaken the ajolote's tiny but powerful forelimbs for ears. This is an easy mistake to make, since the forelegs are so near to the head. Ajolotes use their clawed forefeet to dig tunnels. They also wriggle through the soil, using their blunt heads to push earth aside.

Unlike other amphisbaenians, ajolotes sometimes come to the surface, generally after heavy rains. Above ground they are ambush hunters, lying in wait for lizards and other small animals. They use their forelimbs to drag their long bodies across the ground to grab their prey, which they generally drag underground to be eaten in safety.

Distribution: Baja California.
Habitat: Burrows.
Food: Worms and insects.
Size: 17–24cm (6–9.5in).
Maturity: Not known.
Breeding: Lays eggs.
Life span: 1–2 years.
Status: Common.

Ajolotes have long bodies with scales arranged in rings. They are unique among worm lizards because they still have forelimbs.

CROCODILIANS

Crocodilians are an ancient group of reptiles. They include crocodiles, alligators, caimans and gharials. They all live in or near water. Most crocodilians in North and South America belong to the alligator and caiman group. In fact only one type of alligator – the Chinese alligator – lives outside of the Americas. American crocodiles tend to be larger than their alligator and caiman cousins, and most are very rare.

American alligator

Alligator mississippiensis

Distribution: South-eastern United States.
Habitat: Swamps and rivers.
Food: Birds, fish and mammals.
Size: 2.8–5m (9.25–16.5ft).
Maturity: 5–10 years.
Breeding: Eggs laid in nest of mud and vegetation during spring.
Life span: 40 years.
Status: Common.

Young American alligators feed on insects, small fish and frogs. As they get bigger, they begin to take larger prey, such as turtles and water birds. Adults feed on land as well as in water. They are opportunistic feeders, attacking anything that comes within reach. They even leap up to snatch birds perching on low branches.

During cold weather, American alligators become dormant in burrows dug into mud banks. In dry periods, they will travel long distances to find water, sometimes ending up in swimming pools.

During courtship the female makes a mound of vegetation and mud above the high waterline and lays her eggs in a hole in the top. When she hears calling from hatchlings, she breaks open the nest and carries her young to the water. The young stay with the mother for about a year.

Unlike other crocodilians, the fourth teeth on either side of the lower jaw are not visible in alligators, fitting into sockets in their upper jaws.

Black caiman

Melanosuchus niger

Black caimans are the largest alligators in the Americas. When young they rely heavily on aquatic crustaceans for food, such as crabs and crayfish. They eat fish, such as catfish and piranhas, and often take large rodents called capybaras that live along the banks of rivers. At night, adults may hunt on land, taking advantage of their excellent hearing and sense of sight to track large animals, which may include livestock and even humans.

Breeding takes place during the dry season, presumably to reduce the chance that the eggs become submerged while they incubate. The females build nest mounds that are about 1.5m (5ft) high. The nest mounds are built in a variety of places, some concealed, others in the open. Each female digs a conical hole in her nest and lays 30–65 eggs in the top. They hatch about three months later, at the beginning of the wet season.

Distribution: Northern South America.
Habitat: Rivers and flooded forests.
Food: Fish, capybaras and other aquatic vertebrates.
Size: 4–6m (13.25–20ft).
Maturity: 5–10 years.
Breeding: Eggs laid in nest during dry season.
Life span: 40 years.
Status: Lower risk.

As their name suggests, black caimans have dark bodies. They have grey-brown bands on their lower jaws. The young have yellow or white bands on their flanks, which fade as they age.

Spectacled caiman

Caiman crocodilus

Distribution: Central America and northern South America.
Habitat: Areas of still water.
Food: Fish, wild pigs and water birds.
Size: 1.5–2.5m (5–8.25ft).
Maturity: 4–7 years.
Breeding: Eggs laid in nests during wet season.
Life span: 40 years.
Status: Common.

Spectacled caimans live in a wide range of habitats from rivers to coastal wetlands. They prefer stiller waters than the black caimans that share parts of their range, and consequently they have taken up residence in many reservoirs.

Spectacled caimans rarely come out of the water, only attacking land animals when they come to the water's edge. They spend the day floating on the surface and hunt mainly at night. During periods of drought, they aestivate – enter a period of dormancy to avoid desiccation – in cool burrows dug deep into mud.

The breeding season coincides with the wet season in May and June. The dominant males get the best territories and attract most females. Females lay eggs in mounds of vegetation that they build on banks or rafts of plants. Several females may lay eggs in a single nest, which they guard together. The young live in large groups called crèches.

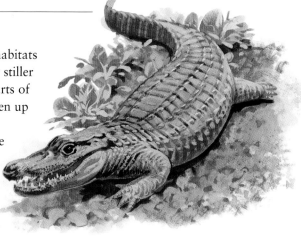

Spectacled caimans are smaller than most crocodilians. They get their name from ridges of bone located on their snouts between their eyes. The ridges appear to join the eyes together, looking similar to the frames of a large pair of glasses.

Orinoco crocodile (*Crocodylus intermedius*): 4–7m (13.25–23ft)
Orinoco crocodiles live in the middle and lower parts of the Orinoco River. The crocodiles also live in the wetland created when the river floods the grassland on either side. The crocodiles eat birds and land animals as well as fish. The females lay their eggs in holes dug into sandbars during periods of low water – in January and February. The eggs hatch as the rains arrive about 70 days later. The young are protected by their mothers for up to three years.

Cuvier's dwarf caiman (*Paleosuchus palpebrosus*): 1.2–1.6m (4–5.25ft)
This small caiman lives in South America, from Paraguay to Colombia. It inhabits freshwater rivers and flooded forests. It spends the day in burrows and feeds on small aquatic and terrestrial animals. Its short, curved teeth are particularly good at crushing shellfish.

Cuban crocodile (*Crocodylus rhombifer*): 3.5m (11.5ft)
This rare crocodile lives in the swamps of Cuba. It mainly eats fish and turtles, but will take small mammals if the opportunity arises. Its broad, back teeth can crush turtle shells. Cuban crocodiles are very agile on land. Some scientists believe that they may have once preyed upon giant ground sloths, which are now extinct.

American crocodile

Crocodylus acutus

American crocodiles live in fresh water, such as rivers and lakes, but will venture out into coastal waters, especially near estuaries and in lagoons, where the water is brackish. The crocodiles cope with the salty water by taking long drinks of fresh water when possible and removing salt from the body through glands on their faces – secreting crocodile tears in the process.

During periods of drought, the crocodiles burrow into mud and do not feed until the water returns. Feeding takes place at night and they may come on to land to prey on livestock. They have also been known to attack humans.

Most females lay their eggs in holes dug in the ground, but they may build nest mounds in areas where the soil is likely to become waterlogged and thus chill the incubating eggs. Nesting takes place in the dry season. Between 30 and 60 eggs are laid, which hatch three months later as the rainy season begins. The mother guards her nest until the hatchlings have dispersed.

Distribution: Southern Florida, Mexico, Central America and northern South America.
Habitat: Rivers and brackish water.
Food: Fish, turtles and birds.
Size: 4–5m (13.25–16.5ft).
Maturity: 5–10 years.
Breeding: Eggs laid in dry season.
Life span: 40 years.
Status: Vulnerable.

Unlike those of the alligators, the American crocodile's long fourth teeth are visible, sticking out of the lower jaw when the mouth is closed. American crocodiles often exceed the size of other crocodilians in North and South America.

SNAKES

Snakes are legless reptiles that have adapted to living in most habitats on Earth. They are not found in the polar regions or high up in mountains. In the oceans, they are found in some tropical seas. All snakes are hunters of live prey particular to their chosen habitat. Familiar snakes of the Americas include the rattlesnakes and the green anaconda.

Green anaconda

Eunectes murinus

Distribution: Northern South America.
Habitat: Wetlands and flooded forests.
Food: Birds, caimans, deer and capybaras.
Size: 6–10m (20–33ft); 250kg (550lb).
Maturity: 6 years.
Breeding: 4–80 young born from mother.
Life span: 25 years.
Status: Common.

Green anacondas are the world's heaviest snakes, if not the longest. They are not venomous snakes but kill by constriction, squeezing their prey in coils of their massive bodies.

Green anacondas spend most of their time in shallow water, being most common in open wetlands. Their eyes and nostrils are positioned on top of their heads, so that they can lie hidden underwater with only their heads at the surface. Anacondas are ambush predators: they wait for prey to come to the water's edge to drink, then they strike with lightning speed. Their bodies are powerful enough to squeeze the life out of a horse or a fully grown black caiman. Anacondas can kill humans, but only occasionally do so.

Male anacondas have claw-like spurs on their lower bodies, which they use to stimulate females. A single female may be tangled up with several males during mating. Like other boas, anacondas do not lay eggs but give birth to live young.

Compared to their huge bodies, green anacondas have small heads. Their bodies are covered in smooth olive scales and they have black ovals on their backs. The males are smaller than the females. The young, born live from the mother, measure about 66cm (26in) at birth.

Emerald tree boa

Corallus caninus

Emerald tree boas spend their entire lives away from the ground, gripping tree branches with their coils. The snake's bright leaf-green body has flashes of white running across its back that help it blend in with the forest foliage. This camouflage keeps the snake safe from forest raptors, such as owls and eagles.

Tree boas hang from sturdy branches and wait for small birds to fly by or small mammals to pass beneath them. The snake's eyes have vertical pupils. Just like small cats, this makes them better at sensing the movements of small prey in the gloom of the forest. Tree boas also have heat-sensitive pits on their snouts, which allow them to detect the body heat of prey moving near them. The snake waits, ready to pounce, with its upper body in an S-shape. When a prey animal comes close enough, the tree boa lunges forward and grabs it in its mouth. The snake's backward-curved teeth stop victims from struggling free.

During mating, the male entwines his tail with the female's. The female gives birth to between 3 and 15 young. The young snakes are red or orange for the first year of their lives.

Distribution: Northern South America.
Habitat: Rainforest.
Food: Birds and mammals.
Size: 1.5–2m (5–6.5ft).
Maturity: Not known.
Breeding: Young born live.
Life span: 40 years.
Status: Common.

The emerald tree boa has a long, slender body with a prehensile tail that is used for gripping branches. The snake's camouflaged body is reinforced down each side, like a girder, so it is powerful enough to reach across open spaces between branches.

Rosy boa (*Charina trivirgata*): 60–110cm (24–43in)
Rosy boas live in the deserts of the south-western United States and northern Mexico. Compared to other boas, their heads are less broad in proportion to their bodies. They have smooth scales that form red and cream stripes along their bodies. Rosy boas burrow under rocks and slither in crevices looking for prey.

Boa constrictor (*Boa constrictor*): 1–4m (40–160in)
Boa constrictors occur in a range of colours and patterns. Their coloration often depends on where they live, since they are equally at home in the branches of rainforest and among the grasses of open savannah. These boas have also become a common sight in many South American cities.

Red pipesnake (*Anilius scytale*): 70–90cm (28–35in)
This unusual snake uses its cylindrical body to tunnel underground, where it preys upon other subterranean animals, such as rodents and other snakes. Although it is hidden from view much of the time, the red pipesnake has striking red and black bands on its body. This pattern mimics the colours of highly venomous coral snakes, so predators stay away, fearing they may receive a deadly bite.

Kingsnake

Lampropeltis getulus

Kingsnakes are constrictors, killing their prey by squeezing them to death. They are very active hunters, slithering into rodent burrows and climbing through bushes to catch their diverse prey. Kingsnakes appear to be immune to the venom of other poisonous snakes, which they include on their menu. Kingsnakes are able swimmers and patrol riverbanks in search of frogs and small aquatic mammals.

As well as threatening many animals, kingsnakes also have several enemies of their own, from large birds of prey to raccoons and other carnivores. If cornered, a kingsnake will try to bite its attacker. If captured, the kingsnake's final defence is to smear its captor with foul-smelling faeces.

Kingsnakes live in a variety of climates and may be active during the day or night. They hibernate during cold periods, which may last for several months at the northern extent of their range.

The males bite their mates on the backs of their necks to restrain them during mating. About 12 eggs are laid under rotting vegetation.

Kingsnakes have different coloured bodies in different parts of their range. For example, Mexican kingsnakes are black, while those found in the deserts of Arizona have yellow bodies with black spots.

Distribution: Southern United States and northern Mexico.
Habitat: All land habitats.
Food: Birds, lizards, frogs and other snakes.
Size: 1–2m (3.25–6.5ft).
Maturity: Not known.
Breeding: Eggs laid in rotting vegetation.
Life span: 25 years.
Status: Common.

Texas thread snake

Leptotyphlops dulcis

The Texas thread snake, or Texas blind snake as it is also known, spends most of its life burrowing through the ground. Its body is well adapted for this lifestyle, being equipped with smooth scales and a blunt head for shoving earth out of the way.

The snakes feed on worms and other invertebrates that they come across, using their keen sense of smell to locate them. They also tunnel into the nests of ants and termites. When they enter a nest, the snakes begin to release the same chemical pheromones used by the insects themselves. This fools the normally aggressive insects into thinking the snakes belong there. The invading reptiles are free to slither about and feast on insect eggs and larvae. Texas thread snakes will come to the surface at night, especially after heavy rains, when the soil beneath is waterlogged.

After mating, the female lays only a handful of eggs and stays close to them while they incubate, often coiling around them. The thread snake family number 80 species in all.

The long, thin body of the Texas thread snake is covered in smooth, silvery scales. Even the snake's eyes are covered in thin scales.

Distribution: Southern United States and northern Mexico.
Habitat: Underground.
Food: Insects and spiders.
Size: 15–27cm (6–11in).
Maturity: Not known.
Breeding: Female incubates eggs in coils.
Life span: Not known.
Status: Common.

Sidewinder

Crotalus cerastes

Sidewinders are named for their unusual method of locomotion. The snakes move sideways across loose ground, such as sand. Many snakes that live in similar habitats also "sidewind". This is a form of locomotion that involves a wave-like undulation of the snake's body, so that only two points are in contact with the ground at any given moment. The snake progresses in a sideways direction across the ground compared to the orientation of the body, leaving parallel S-shaped tracks in the sand.

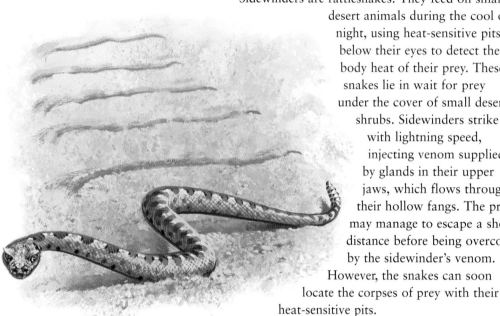

Sidewinders are rattlesnakes. They feed on small desert animals during the cool of night, using heat-sensitive pits below their eyes to detect the body heat of their prey. These snakes lie in wait for prey under the cover of small desert shrubs. Sidewinders strike with lightning speed, injecting venom supplied by glands in their upper jaws, which flows through their hollow fangs. The prey may manage to escape a short distance before being overcome by the sidewinder's venom. However, the snakes can soon locate the corpses of prey with their heat-sensitive pits.

Distribution: South-western United States and north-western Mexico.
Habitat: Desert.
Food: Lizards and rodents.
Size: 45–80cm (18–32in).
Maturity: Not known.
Breeding: Live young born in late summer.
Life span: Not known.
Status: Common.

Sidewinders have wide bodies so that they do not sink into sand. Their tails are tipped with rattles that increase in length as the snakes age. Their heads are flattened and triangular.

Western diamondback rattlesnake

Crotalus atrox

Distribution: Southern United States and northern Mexico.
Habitat: Grassland and rocky country.
Food: Vertebrate prey including small mammals, birds and lizards.
Size: 2m (6.5ft).
Maturity: 3–4 years.
Breeding: Young born live.
Life span: Not known.
Status: Lower risk.

Western diamondbacks are the largest and most venomous rattlesnakes in North America. The snake's rattle comprises dried segments – or buttons – of skin attached to the tail. The rattle is used to warn predators that the snake gives a poisonous bite. Although it will readily defend itself when cornered, the diamondback would prefer to conserve venom, and enemies, including humans, soon learn to associate the rattle with danger.

Like all rattlesnakes, diamondbacks are not born with a rattle. Instead they begin with just a single button, which soon dries into a tough husk. Each time the snake moults its skin, a new button is left behind by the old skin. The rattle grows in this way until it contains around ten buttons that give the characteristic noise when shaken.

Western diamondbacks have very potent venom. They kill more people each year than any other North American snake, although this number rarely reaches double figures. The venom is extremely effective at tackling prey. It can kill even large prey, such as hares, in seconds. Like other rattlesnakes, diamondbacks can sense body heat using pits on their faces.

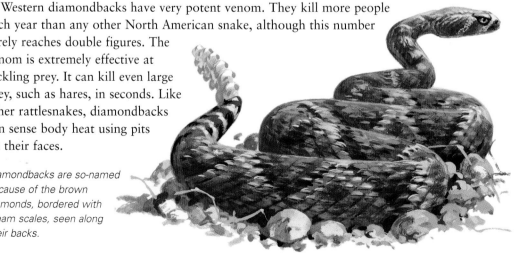

Diamondbacks are so-named because of the brown diamonds, bordered with cream scales, seen along their backs.

Western coral snake

Micruroides euryxanthus

Distribution: South-western United States and northern Mexico.
Habitat: Desert.
Food: Snakes and lizards.
Size: 60–90cm (24–35in).
Maturity: 1–2 years.
Breeding: Lay eggs in summer.
Life span: Not known.
Status: Common.

As they are relatives of cobras and mambas, western coral snakes have a similarly potent venom. Their bright bands serve as a warning to potential predators that the snakes are very dangerous. The venom will kill most small animals. One in ten humans who leave a bite untreated are overcome by the toxins.

Coral snakes spend a lot of time underground. Their thin, cylindrical bodies covered in smooth scales are ideal for this tunnelling lifestyle, and their rounded heads are used for burrowing through soft soil. However, the snakes also venture into the burrows of other animals to seek out resting snakes and lizards, their main source of food. They rarely come to the surface during the day, but may emerge to hunt in the cool of night. Western coral snakes mate in early summer and the females produce eggs about a month later. They are the only venomous snakes in the Americas to lay eggs rather than bear live young.

The western coral snake, with its brightly banded body, is typical among American coral snakes. Many non-venomous snakes mimic the colours of coral snakes to deter predators.

Milksnake (*Lampropeltis triangulum*): 0.4–2m (1.3–6.5ft)
Milksnakes are found ranging from Colombia to southern Canada. They are not venomous, but are among several species that mimic the red, yellow and black banded coloration of coral snakes. They are nocturnal hunters, preying upon small rodents and amphibians. Females lay eggs in nests constructed under rocks, in tree stumps and other secluded spots.

Corn snake (*Elaphe guttata*): 1–1.8m (3.25–6ft)
Corn snakes belong to the rat snake group. They live in the south-eastern United States and are found in several colour forms. Corn snakes hunt on the ground, up trees and among rocks. The are not venomous but will rise up when threatened as if to strike. They kill their prey – mainly small rodents – by constriction.

Common lancehead (*Bothrops atrox*): 1–1.5m (3.25–5ft)
Lanceheads, or fer-de-lance snakes, are pit vipers. Like rattlesnakes, they have heat-sensitive pits on their faces. They are named for their arrow-shaped heads, typical among vipers. Lanceheads are among the most dangerous snakes in South America. Others have more potent venom, but lanceheads are often found living alongside people, feeding on rats and other rodents. Like many other vipers, male lanceheads tussle with each other over females.

Common garter snake

Thamnophis sirtalis

The common garter snake has one of the widest ranges of any North American snake. At one extreme, the common garter lives on the southern shores of Hudson Bay in eastern Canada and survives the long and icy subarctic winters. At the other end of its range, it lives in the humid, subtropical swamps of Florida.

Garter snakes are closely associated with water. They are able swimmers but feed on animals found in and out of water. Garter snakes are active hunters and generally have to pursue their victims. They seek out meals by poking their small heads into nooks and crannies and flushing out prey. Their long bodies allow them to move with great speed, and their large eyes are suited to tracking prey on the move.

Garter snakes hibernate in burrows, and many snakes may crowd into a suitable hole. Mating takes place soon after hibernation. In northern regions with short summers, the pressure to mate quickly is very strong, while in the south the snakes have a longer breeding season.

Distribution: Southern Canada to Florida.
Habitat: Close to water.
Food: Worms, fish and amphibians.
Size: 65–130cm (25–51in).
Maturity: Not known.
Breeding: Mate after hibernation.
Life span: Not known.
Status: Common.

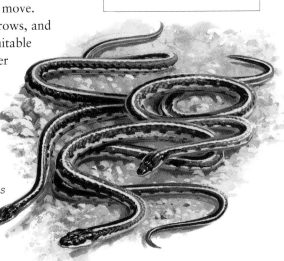

Common garter snakes have long bodies and small heads. They are found in a variety of colours, which provide camouflage in different habitats.

CATS

Cats belong to the Felidae *family of mammals. They fall into two main groups. The* Panthera *genus contains the big cats, such as lions and tigers, while* Felis *comprises the small cats, including the domestic cat. Most American cats belong to the second group, with the jaguar being the only big cat found on both continents. Today most are rarely seen, and some are threatened with extinction.*

Cougar

Felis concolor

Extremely strong and agile, cougar adults are able to leap over 5m (16.5ft) into the air. Once they make a kill, their victims are dragged into secluded places and eaten over several days.

Cougars are also known as pumas, panthers or mountain lions, and have the most widespread distribution of any American species. They live in nearly all habitats, from mountainsides of the Canadian Rockies to the jungles of the Amazon and the swamps of Florida.

The cougar is the largest of the small cats in America, males reaching over 2m (6.5ft) long. They patrol large territories, moving during both day and night and taking shelter in caves and thickets. A cougar's preferred food is large deer, such as mule deer or elk. They stalk their prey before bringing it down with a single bite to the throat, or ambush it from a high vantage point. Cougars live alone, and mark their territories with their scent and by scraping visual signals in the soil and on trees.

Distribution: North, Central and South America from southern Canada to Cape Horn.
Habitat: Any terrain with enough cover.
Food: Deer, beavers, raccoons and hares.
Size: 1–2m (3.25–6.5ft); 60–100kg (135–220lb).
Maturity: 3 years.
Breeding: Every 2 years; litters of 3 or 4 cubs.
Life span: 20 years.
Status: Some subspecies endangered.

Margay

Felis wiedii

Distribution: Central America and Amazon Basin.
Habitat: Tropical forest.
Food: Birds, eggs, lizards, frogs, insects and fruit.
Size: 46–79cm (18–31in); 2.5–4kg (5.5–9lb).
Maturity: 1 year.
Breeding: Single cub or twins born once a year.
Life span: 10 years.
Status: Endangered.

Margays are small cats that live in the lush forests of Central and South America. These small, slender cats spend nearly all of their lives in the treetops, rarely touching ground. They are active at night, searching through the branches for food, which ranges from small tree-dwelling mammals, such as marmosets, to insects and fruit.

Margays are very acrobatic climbers. They use their long tails to help them balance, and their broad, padded feet give them a good grip on flimsy branches. Margays are unique among cats because they can twist their hind feet right round so they face backwards.

Like most cats, margays live alone, defending large territories from intruders. They do, of course, pair up briefly with mates for breeding, but the males leave the females before litters are born. Breeding takes place throughout the year and most litters have one or perhaps two cubs.

Margays can climb down tree trunks headfirst like squirrels, or hang upside down with the claws on their reversed hind feet embedded in tree bark.

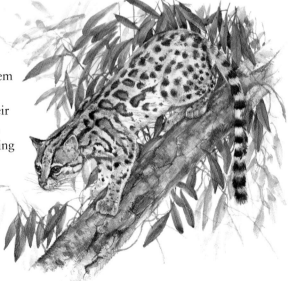

Jaguar

Panthera onca

The jaguar is the only big cat in the Americas. It is smaller in length than the cougar, but much bulkier and heavier. Jaguars are usually a tawny yellow with dark rings, but they can also be black.

Jaguars prefer to live in areas with plenty of water for at least part of the year, although they will stray on to grasslands and into deserts in search of food. They live alone, taking refuge in secluded spots during the day and stalking prey at night. Despite being expert climbers, they hunt on the ground and drag their kills to hideaways before devouring them.

Female jaguars defend smaller territories than males, and a male's territory may overlap those of two or three females. The cats advertise their presence by scenting landmarks with urine or faeces and by scraping marks on tree trunks and rocks. When a female is ready to breed, she will leave her home range and be courted by outside males. Litters usually stay with their mother for about two years.

Distribution: South-western United States, Mexico, Central and South America to northern Argentina.
Habitat: Forests and swamps.
Food: Capybaras, peccaries, caimans and tapirs.
Size: 1.1–1.9m (3.5–6.25ft); 36–158kg (80–350lb).
Maturity: 3 years.
Breeding: Litters of 1–4 cubs born every 2 or 3 years.
Life span: 22 years.
Status: Lower risk.

Pampas cat (*Felis colocolo*): 57–70 cm (23–28in); 2–3kg (4.5–6.5lb)
The pampas cat is a small cat with a long coat of yellowish or brown striped fur. This rare species lives in the South American treeless grasslands known as pampas, most of which are in Argentina. Pampas cats hide during the day in the tall grasses of the pampas, but may hide in one of the rare trees in the region. At night the cat feeds on guinea pigs and ground birds.

Bobcat (*Felis rufus*): 65–100cm (25–40in); 4.1–15.3kg (9–33lb)
Bobcats live across the southern half of North America. They are found from semi-deserts to mountain forests, making their dens in tree hollows and rock crevices. Bobcats hunt at night, patiently stalking prey over ground before attacking with a deadly pounce. Territories are marked with the scent from faeces, urine and a gland above the anus. Mating takes place in late winter or early spring, with litters of up to six cubs staying with their mother until the next winter.

Jaguarundi (*Felis yagouaroundi*): 55–77cm (22–30in); 4.5–9kg (10–20lb)
The jaguarundi is a small forest cat with a grey-brown coat found in the lowlands of Central and South America. Unlike most cats, jaguarundis are crepuscular – they hunt in the twilight of dawn and dusk when prey are disorientated by the changing light levels. Their diet consists mainly of birds and small rodents. Reports suggest that some jaguarundis live in pairs in parts of their range, but they otherwise appear to be solitary animals.

Ocelot

Felis pardalis

Ocelots are medium-sized small cats found across most of the American tropics. These agile hunters are most common in the dense jungles of the Amazon Basin, but are also found high on the slopes of the Andes and in the dry shrublands of northern Mexico.

An ocelot's typical day is spent sleeping in the cool of a shady thicket or on a leafy branch, but at night the cat comes out to hunt. Ocelots eat a wide range of animals, including rodents, snakes and even young deer and peccaries if the opportunity arises.

Ocelots are largely solitary animals, although males will maintain social links with numbers of females in their local areas. They communicate with quiet mews, which become loud yowls during courtship. In the heart of the tropics, ocelots breed all year round, while at the northern and southern extremes of their range, they tend to mate during the late summer and fall.

Ocelots used to be hunted for their fur. The cats are now protected from hunting but are still threatened by deforestation.

Distribution: Mexico to northern Argentina.
Habitat: Tropical forest.
Food: Rodents, rabbits, birds, snakes and fish.
Size: 55–100cm (22–40in); 11.5–16kg (25–35lb).
Maturity: 18 months.
Breeding: Litters of 2–4 born once a year.
Life span: 15 years.
Status: Lower risk.

DOGS

Domestic dogs belong to the Canidae *family, which they share with similar animals, such as wolves (from which they are descended), foxes and jackals. Most types of wild canid live in large family groups called packs. Dog societies are very complex because the animals must cooperate to survive. They hunt together and take it in turns to care for the young.*

Maned wolf

Chrysocyon brachyurus

The maned wolf lives in areas of swamp and open grassland in central South America, east of the Andes. Its name comes from a dark swathe of hair on its nape and along its spine. The hairs in this mane stand erect when the animal is threatened.

Maned wolves form monogamous pairs throughout their lives. Males and females share territory and have dens hidden inside thick vegetation. Most of the time they stay out of each other's way, hunting alone at night. The pair only spend time together during the breeding season – at the end of winter. Both parents help to raise the litter, regurgitating food at the den for the young to feed on.

Unlike other wolves, which run down their prey, maned wolves stalk their victims more like foxes. Despite having very long legs, maned wolves are not great runners. Instead, their height allows them to peer over tall grasses looking for prey.

Maned wolves have fox-like coloration, with a reddish-brown coat of longish fur. These canids are omnivorous, supplementing their diet with fruit.

Distribution: Central and eastern Brazil, eastern Bolivia, Paraguay, northern Argentina and Uruguay.
Habitat: Grassland.
Food: Rodents, other small mammals, birds, reptiles, insects, fruit and other vegetable matter.
Size: 1.2–1.3m (4–4.5); 20–23kg (44–50lb).
Maturity: 1 year.
Breeding: Monogamous pairs produce litters of 2–4 cubs.
Life span: 10 years.
Status: Lower risk.

Grey wolf

Canis lupus

Grey wolves howl to communicate with pack members over long distances. Each individual can be identified by its howl.

All domestic dogs are descended from grey wolves, which began living alongside humans many thousands of years ago. Grey wolves are the largest dogs in the wild, and they live in packs of about ten individuals. A pack has a strict hierarchy, with a male and female "alpha pair" in charge. The alpha dogs bond for life and are the only members of the pack to breed. The rest of the pack is made up of the alpha pair's offspring.

In summer, pack members often hunt alone for small animals such as beavers or hares, while in winter, the pack hunts together for much larger animals. Grey wolves are strong runners and can travel 200km (125 miles) in one night. They generally detect prey by smell and chase them down, taking turns to take a bite at the faces and flanks of their victims until they collapse from exhaustion.

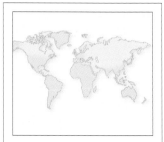

Distribution: Canada and some locations in the United States and Europe, and across most of Asia.
Habitat: Tundra, pine forest, desert and grassland.
Food: Moose, elk, musk ox and reindeer.
Size: 1–1.6m (3.25–5.25ft); 30–80kg (66–175lb).
Maturity: 22 months.
Breeding: Once per year.
Life span: 16 years.
Status: Vulnerable.

Kit fox

Vulpes macrotis

Distribution: Western United States.
Habitat: Desert and scrub.
Food: Rodents, pikas, insects and fruit.
Size: 38–50cm (15–20in); 1.9–2.2kg (4–5lb).
Maturity: 1 year.
Breeding: Litters of 4–5 cubs.
Life span: 15 years.
Status: Vulnerable.

Kit foxes live in the dry desert and scrub areas of the high plateaux and valleys beside the Rocky Mountains in the United States. They generally live in breeding pairs, but social bonds are quite loose and pairs often split. The female does not leave her den – in a disused burrow – while she is suckling her litter of four or five cubs. During this time she relies on the male for food, which is generally small rodents and rabbits, insects and fruit.

After three or four months, the young are strong enough to travel with their parents to other dens in their territory. A kit fox family's territory overlaps widely with those of other groups in the area. The size of the territory depends on the climate. Desert territories have to be large to supply enough food for the family. The kit fox is very similar in appearance and behaviour to the swift fox (*Vulpes velox*) which lives on the great plains farther east. It is possible that hybridization takes place where the ranges of these two dogs overlap.

The kit fox's large ears are lined with blood vessels that radiate heat to cool the animal down in hot desert climes.

Hoary fox (*Dusicyon vetulus*): 59–64cm (23–25in); 4kg (9lb)
Hoary foxes live in south-central Brazil. They have short coats of yellow and black hairs. They inhabit sparsely wooded savannahs, taking shelter in burrows deserted by other animals, such as armadillos. The foxes do hunt down small mammals and birds, but a lot of their diet is made up of insects, such as grasshoppers. For this reason, their grinding molar teeth are wider than those of other dogs.

Crab-eating fox (*Dusicyon thous*): 60–70cm (24–28in); 6–7kg (13–15lb)
Crab-eating foxes live in the woodlands and grasslands of western South America that exist in the highlands around the Amazon Basin. They feed on both coastal and freshwater crabs as well as insects, fruit and carrion. Crab-eating foxes are nocturnal and they locate crabs in the dark by listening for rustling noises among thick vegetation. This species lives in pairs and may breed at any time of the year.

Coyote (*Canis latrans*): 75–100cm (30–40in); 8–20kg (18–44lb)
Coyotes live across the whole of North America, from the deserts of Mexico to the barren tundra near the Arctic. These largely solitary dogs look a little like small grey wolves. Coyotes are active in the dark, and especially at dawn and dusk, but they do sometimes hunt during the day. Coyotes are the fastest runners in North America, reaching speeds of 64kph (40mph). This helps them catch swift jackrabbits – their favourite food.

Bush dog

Speothos venaticus

Bush dogs are unusual members of the dog family, looking more like weasels or mongooses than other dogs. They live in wetlands and flooded forests in highly social packs of about ten dogs. Pack members hunt together, chasing ground birds and rodents. Like other pack dogs, their victims are often much bigger than an individual dog, for example capybaras, agoutis and rheas. They are thought to be expert swimmers, diving into water as they chase prey.

Bush dogs are diurnal – active during the day – and keep together by making high-pitched squeaks as they scamper through the dense forest. As night falls, the pack retires to a den in a hollow tree trunk or abandoned burrow. Little is known about the social system within the packs, but it is likely that there is a system of ranking.

Litters of two or three young are produced in the rainy season. Females only become ready to breed once they come into contact with males.

Distribution: Northern South America, east of the Andes.
Habitat: Forests and swampy grasslands.
Food: Ground birds and rodents.
Size: 57–75cm (22–30in); 5–7kg (11–15lb).
Maturity: 1 year.
Breeding: Litter of 2–3 cubs born in rainy season.
Life span: 10 years.
Status: Vulnerable.

A whole pack of bush dogs squeezes into one den to spend the night.

BEARS

The world's largest land carnivore, the Kodiak bear, lives in North America. It is a huge, hairy animal that can grow to 3m (10ft) tall. Despite their immense size and strength, bears are generally not the vicious predators many people think they are. Most eat more plant food than meat, and they are usually shy beasts, preferring to stay away from humans.

Polar bear

Ursus maritimus

Distribution: Arctic Ocean to southern limits of floating ice, and Hudson Bay.
Habitat: Ice fields.
Food: Seals, reindeer, fish, seabirds and berries.
Size: 2–2.5m (6.5–8.25ft); 150–500kg (330–1100lb).
Maturity: 6 years.
Breeding: 1–4 cubs born every 2–4 years.
Life span: 30 years.
Status: Vulnerable.

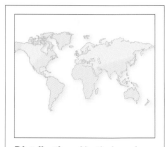

Polar bears have proportionally longer necks than other types of bear so that they can lunge after seals and other aquatic prey.

Polar bears are semi-aquatic animals. They live on the fringes of the vast ice fields that surround the North Pole, where they feed on seals and other marine animals. The bears may cover large distances in search of food, sometimes coming far inland or swimming for miles across open water. Their feet have hairy soles to keep them warm and give them a good grip on the ice. Their forefeet are also very broad, making them good paddles in water.

The bears' snow-white coats help them blend into their surroundings and stay hidden from their prey. A polar bear's staple food is the ringed seal. The bears either wait beside holes in the ice for seals to surface, or sneak up on them across the ice. Bears sometimes dig down into seal dens beneath the surface snow and eat new-born pups.

Polar bears put on a lot of weight in summer because they have less opportunity to feed in winter. They often take shelter from extreme weather in underground dens. Pregnant females sleep inside large dens for long periods during the winter months, before giving birth to their pups in spring. The young stay with their mothers for two years.

Brown bear

Ursus arctos

Brown bears live in many parts of the northern hemisphere, and although they belong to a single species, they look rather different from place to place. For example, the brown bears in Europe and Asia are smaller and darker than their American cousins. In North America, there are two races of brown bear: Kodiaks and grizzlies.

Brown bears make their homes in cold places, such as northern forests, mountains and barren tundra. They feed on a range of fruits, plants and small animals. Only grizzlies regularly attack larger animals, such as deer and even smaller black bears.

Brown bears are generally solitary animals, although they may gather in groups around large food supplies, such as schools of salmon beneath waterfalls. As winter approaches, the bears dig themselves dens for semi-hibernation. Although they sleep during most of the winter, they often come out of the den for short periods between sleeps. Mating takes place in early summer. The female gives birth in spring, and her cubs stay with her for at least two years.

Brown bears have humps between their powerful shoulders, and longer claws than most other bears.

Distribution: North America, Siberia, Europe and Caucasus Mountains.
Habitat: Tundra, alpine meadows and forests.
Food: Salmon, grasses, roots, mosses, bulbs, insects, fungi, rodents, deer, mountain sheep and black bears.
Size: 1.7–3m (5.5–10ft); 100–700kg (220–1,540lb).
Maturity: 6 years.
Breeding: 1–4 cubs born every 3–4 years.
Life span: 25–30 years.
Status: Endangered in some places.

American black bear

Ursus americanus

Distribution: Alaska, Canada and patchily throughout parts of the United States from New England to Tennessee, Florida, Mississippi and western states into northern Mexico.
Habitat: Forests.
Food: Fruits, nuts, grass, roots, insects, fish, rodents and carrion.
Size: 1.3–1.8m (4.25–6ft); 100–270kg (220–594lb).
Maturity: 6 years.
Breeding: 1–5 cubs born every 2 years.
Life span: 25 years.
Status: Lower risk.

American black bears are the smallest bears in North America. They live in the conifer forests of Canada and a few wilderness areas as far south as Mexico. They share these forests with grizzly bears and are sometimes eaten by them. Their main defence against this is to climb trees out of the reach of the less agile grizzly.

Black bears are most active at night. Three-quarters of what they eat is plant matter, with small animals, such as fish and rodents, making up the rest. Like other bears, black bears semi-hibernate through the winter in dens under fallen trees or in burrows. Although they sleep heavily, they often wake through the winter, going on excursions during breaks in the severe winter weather.

Although black bears generally forage for food alone, they will congregate around a large source of food. In general they stay away from each other, especially unknown bears. In the middle of summer, males and females come together for short periods. The male leaves soon after mating and cubs are born at the end of winter, while the mother is still in her winter den. The young stay with their mother until at least two years old, usually when they are driven away by the aggression of males courting their mother.

American black bears vary in coloration from black to dark or reddish-brown and pale tan. They differ from grizzlies in several respects; for example, they have shorter fur and they lack a shoulder hump. They also have shorter legs and claws, which helps them to climb trees with far more adeptness than grizzlies, and so escape these predators. They vary in size according to the quality of food available.

Spectacled bear

Tremarctos ornatus

Distribution: Northern Andes Mountains, including Colombia, Ecuador, Peru, Bolivia and into Chile.
Habitat: Tropical mountain forest and alpine grassland.
Food: Fruit, epiphytes, bamboo hearts, corn, rodents and insects.
Size: 1.2–1.8m (4–6ft); 60–175kg (132–385lb).
Maturity: Not known.
Breeding: 2 cubs born every 2–3 years.
Life span: 25 years.
Status: Vulnerable.

The spectacled bear is the only species of bear in South America. It lives mainly in the lush, high-altitude forests clothing the slopes of the Andes Mountains from Colombia southward as far as northern Chile.

Spectacled bears are active at night, especially during the twilight hours. During the day they shelter in caves, under tree roots or on tree trunks. They are expert climbers and spend a great deal of time foraging in trees. Once up trees, the bears often build feeding platforms from broken branches. They use these platforms to reach more food.

The spectacled bear's food is mainly fruit, and it will travel through the forest collecting ripe fruits. During periods when ripe fruit is unavailable, the bears eat epiphytes – plants that grow on other plants – called bromeliads, feasting on the soft edible hearts of the plants.

Being a tropical species, breeding occurs all year round. Pairs stay together for a few weeks after mating, but the cubs are born seven months later. The cubs stay with their mother for at least two years before being chased away by adult males seeking to mate with their mother.

Spectacled bears are so named because of the large white circles or semicircles of whitish fur around their eyes.

SMALL CARNIVORES

Most small carnivores belong to the Mustelidae *family. The mustelids are a diverse group, including otters, martens and badgers, which are adapted to aquatic, arboreal and subterranean lifestyles respectively. The world's largest and most successful mustelids live in the Americas, where they are found from the icy north to the humid tropics.*

Striped skunk

Mephitis mephitis

The striped skunk is well known for the foul-smelling spray it produces to ward off attackers. This spray comes out of two tiny apertures inside the anus. The discharge, known as musk, is squirted in spray form or as a directed arc of droplets.

The skunk will only spray when it has exhausted all other defensive tactics. These include arching its back, holding its tail erect and stamping its feet. If these fail, the skunk will twist its body into a U-shape – so its head and tail are facing the attacker – and release its musk. The musk, which can be smelled by humans over a mile away, causes discomfort to the eyes of an enemy.

Striped skunks are most active at night, foraging for food under the cover of thick vegetation. They spend the day in sheltered places, such as disused burrows. During the winter, skunks hibernate in their dens, staying underground for between two to three months. Mating takes place in springtime. Litters of up to ten young are born in summer.

The striped skunk is characterized by the broad white stripes that extend from the top of its head to the tip of its tail.

Distribution: North America.
Habitat: Woods, grasslands and deserts.
Food: Rodents, other small vertebrates, insects, fruit, grains and leaves.
Size: 28–30cm (11–12in); 0.7–2.5kg (1.5–5.5lb).
Maturity: 1 year.
Breeding: 1–10 young born every summer.
Life span: 6 years.
Status: Common.

American mink

Mustela vison

American mink are small carnivores that live close to water, where they feed on small aquatic animals. They originally came from North America, but were brought to Europe and Asia to be farmed for their fine fur. They have since escaped into the wild and are now a common pest. They are also competition for the similar, but very rare, European mink.

Mink prefer to live in areas with plenty of cover. Their river-bed dens are generally deserted burrows made by other river mammals, but mink will dig their own when necessary.

Mink are active at night and dive into water to snatch their prey. They live alone and will defend their own stretches of riverbank against intruders. A litter of up to five young is born two months after mating inside dry, underground nests lined with fur, feathers and leaves. In autumn the young begin to fend for themselves.

Mink are known for their luxurious fine fur, which is used for clothing. Several domestic varieties of mink have been bred, each with different-coloured fur.

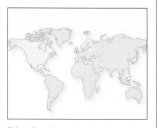

Distribution: North America. Introduced to northern Europe.
Habitat: Swamps and near streams and lakes.
Food: Small mammals, fish, frogs and crayfish.
Size: 33–43cm (13–17in); 0.7–2.3kg (1.5–5lb).
Maturity: 1–1.5 years.
Breeding: 5 young born in late spring.
Life span: 10 years.
Status: Common.

Wolverine

Gulo gulo

Wolverines are giant relatives of the weasels. As well as the conifer forests of North America, they are found in northern Europe and Siberia, where they are known as gluttons due to their catholic feeding habits.

Wolverines are generally nocturnal, but will forage by day if they need to. Their diet varies throughout the year. In summer, they feed on small animals, such as rodents and ground-living birds, and readily feast on summer fruits. In winter, when most other carnivores are hibernating, wolverines may tackle bigger prey, such as deer. Their wide feet act as snowshoes, allowing them to walk over deep snow, in which hapless deer are defenceless and unable to make their escape.

Wolverines mate in early summer and young are born in underground dens the following spring. They leave their mothers in the autumn.

Wolverines have large heads and heavily built bodies with dense coats of hairs of different lengths to prevent winter snow and ice from getting too close to the skin, causing heat loss.

Distribution: Canada, northern United States, Scandinavia and Siberia.
Habitat: Tundra and conifer forest.
Food: Carrion, eggs, rodents, berries, deer and sheep.
Size: 65–105cm (25–41in); 10–32kg (22–70lb).
Maturity: 2–3 years.
Breeding: Litter of 2–4 born in early spring every 2 years.
Life span: 10 years.
Status: Vulnerable.

Spotted skunk (*Spilogale putorius*): 12–35cm (5–14in); 0.2–1kg (0.5–2.2lb)
This small skunk lives throughout most of North America. It has a unique pattern of white stripes and spots on its rump. Like the larger American skunks, spotted skunks spray foul-smelling musk. They spend the day under cover, sometimes hiding in trees. They do not hibernate, and eat a mixed diet including plants, insects and rodents. Spotted skunks mate in autumn and give birth the following spring to four or five young.

Black-footed ferret (*Mustela nigripes*): 38–50cm (15–20in); 0.7–1kg (1.5–2.2lb)
This extremely rare carnivore lives in just a few dry prairies in Wyoming, USA. Black-footed ferrets live in the burrows – called towns – of prairie dogs. The ferrets rest during the day and then travel around the town at night, preying on the resident prairie dogs. Mating takes place in spring and the young are born six weeks later.

Greater grisón (*Galictis vittata*): 47–55cm (18–22in); 1.4–3.3kg (3–7lb)
The greater grisón is one of only a few South American mustelids. It ranges from southern Mexico to central Peru and south-eastern Brazil, making its home in both forest and open country. Grisóns have grey backs with a thin white stripe extending down the middle. They make their dens in burrows abandoned by viscachas and other large rodents, and appear to be active during both the day and night. Grisóns feed on small mammals, birds, eggs, lizards and frogs. Breeding takes place throughout the year.

American badger

Taxidea taxus

American badgers are tough animals that live in the open country in the Great Plains region of North America. They are expert burrowers and use this skill to dig out their preferred foods – rodents, such as prairie dogs and ground squirrels. They rest in their burrows during the day and come out to feed at night. During the coldest weeks of the year, American badgers do not hibernate, but sleep underground for several days at a time.

They may bury some of their food for later or even dig holes big enough for them and their prey to fit into. American badgers and coyotes are known to hunt together in teams. The coyotes sniff out the buried prey and the badgers dig them out. Both parties then share the food.

Mating occurs in summer and early autumn, and births take place in the following spring. The young leave home after two months.

American badgers have a single white stripe running from the nose along the back. Northern-race badgers have the stripe to their shoulders, while on those of the south race it runs all the way along the back.

Distribution: Central and southern North America.
Habitat: Dry, open country.
Food: Rodents, birds, reptiles, scorpions and insects.
Size: 40–70cm (16–28in); 4–12kg (9–26.5lb).
Maturity: Females 4 months; males 1.3 years.
Breeding: 1–5 young born in spring.
Life span: 14 years.
Status: Lower risk.

Sea otter

Enhydra lutris

Sea otters live in the cold coastal waters around the northern Pacific Rim. They do not need to come on to land to survive, but often do. Unlike other marine mammals, sea otters do not have thick blubber under their skins for insulation. Instead, they rely on a layer of air trapped by their soft fur to insulate them against the cold. Pollution, such as oil in the water, can reduce the fur's ability to trap air, and otters may die of hypothermia as a result.

The otters spend a minute or two at a time underwater, collecting food such as shellfish and urchins. They then float on their backs to feed. They smash the hard shells against stones to get at the soft meat inside, using their chests as tables.

Sea otters are active during the day. At night they wrap themselves in kelp before going to sleep to prevent themselves from floating away. They sometimes put their forepaws over their eyes while sleeping.

Sea otters live alone and only tolerate each other when mating. Breeding takes places all year round. Pups are carried on the mother's chest until they are two months old, when they begin to feed themselves.

Distribution: Northern Pacific coasts from California to Japan.
Habitat: 20m (60ft) deep water.
Food: Fish and shellfish, such as sea urchins, abalones, crabs and molluscs.
Size: 1–1.2m (3.25–4ft); 15–45kg (33–99lb).
Maturity: Females 4 years; males 6 years.
Breeding: Single pup every 1–3 years.
Life span: 20 years.
Status: Threatened.

Sea otter fur comprises 100,000 hairs per 1sq cm (0.15sq in), making it the densest of any mammal. This keeps the animal warm in the cold ocean. The hind feet are webbed and flipper-shaped.

Giant otter

Pteronura brasiliensis

The giant otter is the largest mustelid in the world, although it is not as heavy as the sea otter. This semi-aquatic mammal inhabits the tropical river basins of South America. It lives in groups of about six, each communicating with chirping sounds. Generally, the group comprises an adult pair and their offspring of various litters. Each group controls its own stretch of stream, preferring those areas with plenty of cover.

The giant otter swims at high speed by waving its tail and body up and down, using its webbed feet to steer. On land it is far less agile, and is often seen sitting grooming itself. Giant otters are diurnal – only active during the day. They catch prey in their mouths and hold it in their forepaws to eat it on the shore. During the dry season, the otter groups are restricted to small areas of water, but when the rains come to flood the forest, the otters can roam over larger areas. Little is known about the mating habits of giant otters, other than that the young stay with their parents for a few years before reaching adulthood.

Distribution: Central America and South America from Venezuela to Argentina.
Habitat: Slow-moving rivers and creeks in forests and swamps.
Food: Fish, fish eggs, crabs, birds and small mammals.
Size: 0.8–1.4m (2.5–4.75ft); 22–34kg (48–75lb).
Maturity: Not known.
Breeding: 1–3 young produced every year.
Life span: 15 years.
Status: Vulnerable.

The giant otter's fur has a velvety appearance, more like the pelt of a seal than an otter. Its feet are large and have thick webbing, and the tail is flattened into a flipper-like shape.

North American river otter

Lutra canadensis

Distribution: North America.
Habitat: Rivers and lakes.
Food: Amphibians, fish, crayfish and aquatic insects.
Size: 60–110cm (24–43in); 3–14kg (6.5–30lb).
Maturity: 2–3 years.
Breeding: 1–5 young born every year.
Life span: 20 years.
Status: Lower risk.

North American river otters rarely stray far from the banks of shallow rivers. They live alone or in pairs, but often play with other individuals in the area. This play strengthens social ties. Each of the otters has an individual scent which it uses to mark its territory. River otters communicate with each other through sounds such as whistles, growls, chuckles and screams.

North American river otters are known for their boundless energy, and they must eat frequently. They catch fish in their mouths and detect other prey by feeling with their whiskers along the bottoms of streams. Unlike many other otters which chew their food, the river otter's prey is gulped down immediately.

Mating takes place in March and April. The young are born almost a year later. The females give birth in dens close to the water's edge. They drive the males away soon after the birth of their young, but the dog otters return later to help raise the offspring. The young depart at the age of one year.

River otters have streamlined bodies with dark fur, thick tails and short legs with webbed feet.

Patagonian weasel (*Lyncodon patagonicus*): 30–35cm (12–14in); weight not known
This mustelid has grey-brown fur, with broad white stripes running from the head to the shoulders. The weasel's body is similar to that of a grisón, except that the tail is shorter. The Patagonian weasel lives in the pampas – grasslands of Argentina and southern Brazil. Little is known about the behaviour of this species, but its large cutting teeth suggest that it is highly predaceous.

Tayra (*Eira barbata*): 56–68cm (22–27in); 4–5kg (9–11lb)
This unusual species is only found in central Mexico and on the island of Trinidad. Its coat is short and varies from grey to black. Typical among mustelids, the tayra has a slender body, short limbs and a long tail. This carnivore is found in dense forest, living in small groups on the ground, preying on rodents and small deer. When it is being chased by predators, it has been known to run up trees and leap through the branches before coming back down at another location.

American pine marten (*Martes americana*): 32–45cm (13–18in); 0.3–1.3kg (0.5–3lb)
The American pine marten lives in the cold northern forests of Canada and high-altitude areas of the United States. It has a dark coat and a long slender body. Pine martens spend the day in nooks and crannies in the forest, and move through the trees and along the ground in search of food during the night. Their diet includes small mammals, carrion, fruit and insects.

Fisher

Martes pennanti

The fisher, or pekan, lives in the thick forests of North America. Despite its name, it feeds on small land animals, such as mice and porcupines. Fishers have no permanent dens, but take shelter in hollow trees, holes in the ground and even abandoned beaver lodges.

They are active during the day and night, and despite being expert climbers, spend most of their foraging time on the ground. When they come across suitable prey animals, they rush forward and kill them with bites to the back of the neck. Larger animals are killed with repeated bites to the face.

Males seek out mates during the spring breeding season and litters are born about ten months later. As with many mustelids, the fertilized eggs do not begin to grow immediately inside the females. Their development is delayed for several months so that they are born at the right time of year. Unusually, births always take place in trees.

Distribution: Canada and northern United States.
Habitat: Conifer forest.
Food: Birds, rodents, carrion.
Size: 49–63cm (19–25in); 1.3–3.2kg (3–7lb).
Maturity: 1–2 years.
Breeding: 3 young born every spring.
Life span: 10 years.
Status: Lower risk.

Fishers have dark fur that is coarser than that of most mustelids. Nevertheless, they are still hunted by humans for their fur.

RACCOONS AND RELATIVES

Raccoons and their relatives belong to a family of mammals called the Procyonidae. Procyonids are small opportunistic feeders and scavenging animals. Many live in trees, but the most successful – the raccoons – live mainly on the ground. Most procyonids live in the Americas, where they range from the cold northern forests of Canada to the humid, tropical swamps of the Amazon.

Common raccoon

Procyon lotor

Raccoons live in woodland areas and rarely stray far from water. They are more active at night than during the day. Periods of rest are spent in dens in tree hollows or other sheltered places. When on the move, raccoons will readily swim across streams and rivers and will climb into trees in search of food. They use their touch-sensitive hands to grab prey and then break it into mouth-sized pieces.

Raccoons do not hibernate in warmer parts of their range, although in cooler northern parts they may do so. In fact, they only semi-hibernate, popping out every now and then to feed during breaks in the severest weather.

Males are largely solitary but will tolerate the presence of females living in or near their territories. Mating takes place in spring, and young are born a couple of months later. The young stay with their mothers until the following spring.

The common raccoon is well known for its black "bandit" mask across the eyes and its tail ringed with black hoops. The animal's footprints look similar to those of a human infant.

Distribution: Southern Canada throughout the United States to Central America.
Habitat: Forests and brushland.
Food: Crayfish, frogs, fish, nuts, seeds, acorns and berries.
Size: 41–60cm (16–24in); 2–12kg (4.5–26.5lb).
Maturity: 1 year.
Breeding: 3 or 4 young born in summer.
Life span: 5 years.
Status: Common.

Olingo

Bassaricyon gabbii

Distribution: Central America to northern South America as far as Brazil.
Habitat: Tropical forest.
Food: Fruit, insects and small mammals.
Size: 35–48cm (14–19in); 0.9–1.5kg (2–3.5lb).
Maturity: 21 months.
Breeding: Single offspring.
Life span: 5 years.
Status: Lower risk.

Olingos live in the trees of tropical forests. They are active at night and spend the day in nests of leaves high up inside hollow trees. Equipped with long claws, olingos are expert climbers, and they rarely descend to the ground. They can also jump long distances through the treetops, using their long tails to keep them balanced.

An olingo's diet comprises mainly fruit, although it will seek out insects and small vertebrates, such as lizards, on occasion. Olingos live alone, although they are often found living alongside kinkajous – procyonids that are close relatives – as well as opossums and night monkeys.

They mark objects in their territories with urine, although it is not known whether this is to ward off intruders or to help them navigate in the darkness. Mating takes place all year round. Gestation lasts about ten weeks and generally results in a single offspring.

Olingos have thick, pinkish fur. These procyonids have long bodies with short limbs and flattened tails.

Ring-tailed coati

Nasua nasua

Distribution: Northern South America as far as Argentina.
Habitat: Woodland.
Food: Fruit, insects, rodents.
Size: 41–67cm (16–26in); 3–6kg (6.5–13lb).
Maturity: 2 years.
Breeding: 2–7 young born in rainy season.
Life span: 10 years.
Status: Common.

Coatis have long muzzles compared to raccoons and other procyonids. They use these to root out food from rocky crevices and from knots in trees. Coatis forage both on the ground and in trees. On the ground they hold their long tails erect, with the tips curled. In trees, coatis' tails are prehensile enough to function as a fifth limb. The tips curl around branches to provide support in more precarious locations.

Coatis are most active during the day. When there is plenty of fruit on the trees, coatis will eat little else. However, during seasons when fruit is less abundant, coatis comes down to the forest floor to forage for insects and rodents.

Coatis tend to congregate in bands of up to 20 females and young. Adult males live alone and are only allowed into bands during the breeding season, which is the time when there is plenty of fruit available. When fruit is not as easy to find, male coatis may try to eat smaller members of their band, and consequently are expelled by the adult females.

Like all coatis, this species has a long and pointed muzzle with an articulated tip. Ring-tailed coatis have long, coarse fur, and tails banded with white stripes.

Cacomistle (*Bassariscus astutus*): 30–42cm (12–16in); 0.8–1.3kg (1.75–3lb)
Also called ringtails, cacomistles have small cat-like bodies and bushy black and white striped tails. They live in rocky areas from Oregon to Kansas, and southward to southern Mexico. They seldom stray far from water and are most active at night, foraging mainly for insects, rodents and fruit. Being agile climbers, they move up and down cliffs with ease. Like those of many other climbing animals, a cacomistle's hind feet can twist around 180 degrees. This allows the animals to climb down trees and rocks head-first, with the claws on the hind feet clinging to the surface behind them.

Mountain coati (*Nasuella olivacea*): 35–45cm (14–18in); 2kg (4.5lb)
Mountain coatis closely resemble other coatis, but tend to be smaller and have shorter tails. They are very rare and live in the tropical forests on the slopes of the Andes Mountains in South America. They feed on insects, fruit and small vertebrates, which they find among the trees and on the ground.

Crab-eating raccoon (*Procyon cancrivorus*): 45–90cm (18–35in); 2–12kg (4.5–26lb)
Crab-eating raccoons, or mapaches, live in swamps or by streams across most of South America, east of the Andes Mountains and north of Patagonia. This species has much shorter hair and a more slender body than most of its raccoon cousins. They search the water for food at night, detecting prey – shellfish, fish and worms – with their touch-sensitive paws.

Kinkajou

Potos flavus

Kinkajous are almost entirely arboreal (tree-living). Thanks to their long claws and prehensile tails, they are very agile climbers. Kinkajous are nocturnal and spend the day in dens inside hollow trees. On the hottest days they emerge from their stifling dens to cool off in the open on branches.

At night, kinkajous race around the trees in search of fruit. After searching through one tree, they will cautiously move to the next before beginning to forage again. They use their long tongues to reach the soft flesh and juices inside the fruit.

Kinkajous tend to return to the same roosting trees each dawn. They travel alone or in breeding pairs. However, groups of kinkajous may form in trees that are heavy with fruit. Kinkajous leave their scent on branches, probably as a signal to potential mates. They also give shrill calls to communicate with partners. Mating takes place all year round, and single offspring are born after four months.

Distribution: Mexico to central Brazil.
Habitat: Forests.
Food: Fruit, insects and small vertebrates.
Size: 40–76cm (16–30in); 1.4–4.6kg (3–10lb).
Maturity: 1.5–2.5 years.
Breeding: Single offspring.
Life span: 15 years.
Status: Endangered.

Kinkajous have soft and woolly fur, with rounded heads and stockier bodies than most of their relatives. They are sometimes mistaken for African primates called pottos.

SQUIRRELS AND RELATIVES

Squirrels and their close relatives, such as beavers, marmots and gophers, are all types of rodent, so they are related to rats and mice. The squirrel family numbers over 350 species in two main groups: the ground squirrels that dwell on or under the ground, and the arboreal species – tree and flying squirrels. American squirrels include three ground-dwellers: the woodchuck, beaver and prairie dog.

Grey squirrel

Sciurus carolinensis

Distribution: Eastern North America. Introduced to parts of Europe.
Habitat: Woodlands.
Food: Nuts, flowers and buds.
Size: 38–52cm (15–21in); 0.3–0.7kg (0.5–1.5lb).
Maturity: 10 months.
Breeding: 2 litters born each year with 2–4 young per litter.
Life span: 12 years.
Status: Common.

Grey squirrels are native to the open woodlands of eastern North America. They have also been introduced into parts of Europe, where they have out-competed the smaller red squirrels for food and breeding sites.

Grey squirrels feed primarily on the nuts and buds of many woodland trees. In summer, when they are most active just after dawn and before dusk, grey squirrels also eat insects. In winter, when most animals of their size are hibernating, grey squirrels spend their days eating stores of food which they buried throughout the previous summer. Grey squirrels may make dens in hollow trees, but are more likely to make nests, or dreys, from twigs and leaves in the boughs of trees.

There are two breeding seasons each year: one beginning in midwinter, the other in midsummer. Males begin to chase females through the trees a few days before they are receptive to mating. When females are ready, their vulvas become pink and engorged. Litters of three are born six weeks later.

Grey squirrels have, as their name suggests, greyish fur, although many individuals have reddish patches. Their tails, which have many white hairs, are bushier than those of most other squirrels.

Woodchuck

Marmota monax

Woodchucks are the largest squirrels in North America. Their powerful legs have curved claws, which are used for digging.

Woodchucks are also called groundhogs or whistlepigs – the latter because of the shrill alarm call they make when threatened. Unlike most other squirrels, they eat the green parts of plants rather than the seeds and buds. They also eat bark and small twigs. Their natural habitat is the edge of forests or other open areas where there is plenty of cover. With the growth of agriculture, woodchucks have increased in number, making use of hedges beside open fields. They live alone, unlike most other ground squirrels.

In winter, woodchucks hibernate by using subcutaneous fat reserves they have put on over summer. Their winter sleep is much deeper than most squirrels. Mating takes place soon after hibernation ends. Female woodchucks have a single litter every year and males mate with more than one female. Young woodchucks are thrown out of their mother's burrow after a few months.

Distribution: Southern Canada southward through eastern North America.
Habitat: Woodland or open areas that have plenty of ground cover.
Food: Plant leaves and stems.
Size: 45–65cm (18–26in); 2–5kg (4.5–11lb).
Maturity: 2 years.
Breeding: 3–5 young born in May.
Life span: 6 years.
Status: Common.

Northern pocket gopher

Thomomys talpoides

Pocket gophers have robust, tubular bodies with short legs. Their forefeet have long claws and their tails are naked at the tip. Male gophers are much larger than females.

Pocket gophers spend a great deal of their time burrowing. They feed on the underground parts of plants, such as roots, tubers and bulbs. The gophers access their food by digging temporary feeding tunnels out and up from deeper and more permanent galleries, located 1–3m (3.25–10ft) underground. Gophers keep their burrow entrances blocked with earth most of the time, and rarely appear above ground during the day. At night they may move around on the surface.

Gophers carry food in pouches inside their cheeks to storage or feeding sites in their burrow systems. They do not drink water, and so get all of their liquid from plant juices.

Only during the mating season will a male be allowed into a female's burrow. Litters are born just 18 days after mating, which generally takes place in summer.

Distribution: Western North America from Canada to Mexico.
Habitat: Burrows under desert, prairie and forest.
Food: Roots, bulbs and leaves.
Size: 11–30cm (4.5–12in); 50–500g (0.1–1.1lb).
Maturity: 1 year.
Breeding: 1–10 young born in summer.
Life span: 2 years.
Status: Common.

Flying squirrel (*Glaucomys volans*): 21–70cm (8–28in); 50–180g (0.1–0.4lb)
Flying squirrels range over eastern and central North America, from Quebec to Honduras. Their bodies resemble those of other squirrels, except that they have loose folds of skin along the sides of their bodies and attached to their elongated arms and legs. This membrane is used for gliding from tree to tree.

Prairie dog (*Cynomys ludovicianus*): 28–33cm (11–13in); 0.7–1.4kg (1.5–3lb)
This species of prairie dog, and others like it, live in open grasslands from western Canada to Mexico. They are not true dogs, but ground squirrels that make a barking call. They live in colonies inhabiting communal burrows called towns. In frontier times, one huge town in west Texas was estimated to contain 400 million prairie dogs. Today these rodents are much rarer. They have been exterminated in many places, partly because the holes they make can injure the domesticated livestock that graze throughout their grassland habitat. They can also be pests of cereal crops.

Eastern American chipmunk (*Tamias striatus*): 13–19cm (5–7.5in); 70–140g (0.15–0.2lb)
These rodents live in the eastern part of North America. They live in woodland and bushy habitat, feeding on nuts, seeds, mushrooms and fruit during the daytime. Eastern American chipmunks retire to burrows at night. They are solitary animals, sleeping through the winter in their burrows, waking frequently to feed on caches of food made during the autumn. Chipmunks carry spare food in cheek pouches.

American beaver

Castor canadensis

Beavers are among the largest of all rodents. Family groups of beavers live in large nests, called lodges, in or near forest streams or small lakes. Beavers eat wood and other tough plant foods, which have to be soaked in water before being eaten.

They use their large front teeth to gnaw through the bases of small trees. Sections of these logs are transported back to the lodge via a system of canals dug into the forest. If necessary, beavers will also dam a stream with debris to make a pool deep enough to store their food. A beaver colony may maintain a dam for several generations. The lodge has underwater entrances so beavers can swim out to their food supply even when the pool is frozen.

Distribution: North America.
Habitat: Streams and small lakes.
Food: Wood, leaves, roots and bark.
Size: 60–80cm (24–32in); 12–25kg (26–55lb).
Maturity: 1.5–2 years.
Breeding: 2–4 young born each spring.
Life span: 24 years.
Status: Locally common.

A beaver has webbed hind feet, a flattened tail for swimming and large front teeth for gnawing through wood. Its fur is coated with oil to keep it waterproof.

OTHER RODENTS

As well as squirrels, the Rodentia *order includes rats, mice and other small mammals, such as guinea pigs. Rodents are such a successful group partly because of their dentistry. They have large spaces between their incisor teeth at the front and the molars farther back, so that they can suck their cheeks in and close off their throats. This allows them to gnaw through wood or soil without swallowing it.*

North American porcupine

Erethizon dorsatum

North American porcupines are nocturnal animals that spend most of the night looking for food on the ground. However, they occasionally climb slowly into trees to find food. They cannot see very well, but have sensitive noses for detecting danger.

During the daytime, porcupines rest in hollow trees, caves or disused burrows. They regularly move from den to den throughout the year. They do not hibernate and keep feeding throughout the winter, but they will stay in their den during periods of harsh weather.

Porcupines live solitary lives, but do not defend territories, although they may drive away other porcupines from trees laden with food. If cornered by predators, porcupines turn their backs on their attackers and thrash around with their spiky tails. The barbed quills penetrate the attacker's skin and work their way into the body.

In early winter, males seek out females and shower them with urine before mating. The males are chased away by the females after mating. They give birth to their litters in summer.

Porcupines have sharp, barbed quills (thickened hairs) on their rumps and short tails for use in defence.

Distribution: North America, including Alaska and Canada, south to northern Mexico.
Habitat: Forest and brush.
Food: Wood, bark and needles in winter; buds, roots, seeds and leaves in summer.
Size: 64–80cm (25–32in); 3.5–7kg (7.5–15lb).
Maturity: 2.5 years.
Breeding: Single young born in summer.
Life span: 18 years.
Status: Common.

Capybara

Hydrochaerus hydrochaeris

Capybaras are the largest rodents in the world. They live in herds of about 20 individuals, feeding by day on the banks of rivers and in swampy areas. Although they are well suited to being in water, with eyes and nostrils high on the head and webbed hind feet, capybaras do not feed for long periods in water. They tend to use water as a refuge from predators and as a means of keeping cool on hot days. If startled, capybaras gallop into water and may swim to the safety of floating plants. When they surface, only their eyes and nostrils are visible.

Capybaras do not have permanent dens, but sleep in waterside thickets. Each herd contains several adults of both sexes as well as their offspring, all conforming to a hierarchy. A single male leads the herd. Only he can mate with the females in the herd. Fights often break out between the other males as they attempt to improve their rank.

Capybaras have bodies similar to guinea pigs, except that they are much bigger and more heavy-set. The males possess large sebaceous (oil) glands on their short rounded snouts.

Distribution: Central America to Uruguay.
Habitat: Thickly vegetated areas around fresh water.
Food: Grass, grains, melons and squashes.
Size: 1–1.3m (3.25–4.25ft); 27–79kg (59–174lb).
Maturity: 15 months.
Breeding: 5 offspring born throughout the year.
Life span: 10 years.
Status: Common.

Pygmy mouse

Baiomys taylori

Pygmy mice are the smallest rodents in the Americas, little more than the size of a person's thumb. They live in areas where plants, logs and rocks provide them with plenty of cover. The mice create networks of runs among undergrowth and under rocks, leaving piles of droppings at junctions. These may act as signposts or be signals to other mice in their network. Pygmy mice are most active at dawn and dusk, but will also feed throughout the day.

At night they sleep in nests made from plants and twigs. They do not live in groups as such, but will tolerate the presence of other mice close by. Pygmy mice can breed at a young age. Females can become pregnant after just a month of life. They breed throughout the year, often producing several litters per year. Both parents care for the young, which are born in nests inside shallow dips dug into the ground or in secluded cavities under logs or rocks.

The pygmy mouse's ears are smaller and rounder than most mice. It has black and brown hairs on its back with lighter red and brown fur underneath.

Distribution: South-western United States to central Mexico.
Habitat: Dry scrub.
Food: Stems, leaves, insects and seeds.
Size: 5–8cm (2–3in); 7–8g (0.015–0.017lb).
Maturity: Females 28 days; males 80 days.
Breeding: Several litters of 1–5 young each year.
Life span: 2 years.
Status: Common.

Mara (*Dolichotis patagonum*): 73–80cm (29–32in); 8–16kg (18–36lb)
The mara is a large rodent with long, thin legs, which make it look rather like a small deer. This species lives in the pampas of central and southern Argentina. Maras prefer to live on open grassland or in dry scrub. They dig their own burrows, using sharp claws on their forefeet. They stay in their burrows throughout the night and browse on plants throughout the day. Maras may travel in small groups, although they separate at night.

Chinchilla (*Chinchilla brevicaudata*): 22–38cm (9–15in); 500–800g (1.1–1.8lb)
Chinchillas are rare rodents that live in the Andes Mountains, ranging between Peru, Bolivia and Chile. Chinchillas are hunted illegally for their thick and soft blue-grey fur. They live in barren uplands, sheltering in crevices among rocks. They are active at dawn and dusk, eating any alpine plants that grow around them. Where they exist in large enough numbers, they live in colonies of up to 100 individuals. They produce two litters of two or three young each year.

Muskrat (*Ondatra zibethicus*): 22–33cm (9–13in); 0.7–1.8kg (1.5–4lb)
Muskrats live over most of North America, excluding the far north, and they are also found across Europe and warmer parts of Siberia. They are semi-aquatic animals, with oily, waterproof fur, webbed hind feet and scaly tails, used for steering while swimming. They live in small groups along riverbanks and in marshes. Muskrats are nocturnal, eating water plants and small aquatic animals. They dig burrows into riverbanks, which they access through underwater entrances, or they make domed nests from grass when living in more open wetlands.

Guinea pig

Cavia aperea

Guinea pigs, or cavies as they are also known, are most active in the twilight hours – around dawn and dusk. At these times, most predators are less active because their eyes cannot cope with the rapidly changing light levels. Guinea pigs are found in a wide range of habitats and altitudes, even living high up in the Andes Mountains.

Guinea pigs generally rest underground or in thickets. They may dig their own burrows, but are more likely to take over holes made by other animals. When on the move, these rodents follow well-trodden paths to areas where food is available.

Guinea pigs live in small groups of fewer than ten individuals. Many groups may crowd around a large supply of food, forming a temporary mass of rodents. The groups have hierarchies, with single males and females ruling over the others. Contenders for the top positions in the group may fight each other to the death. Breeding takes place throughout the year.

Although domestic guinea pigs often have long, soft coats of many colours and patterns, wild specimens have shorter and coarser fur, generally made up of grey, brown and black hairs.

Distribution: Colombia to Argentina, excluding the Amazon Basin.
Habitat: Grassland, swamp and rocky areas.
Food: Plants.
Size: 20–40cm (8–16in); 0.5–1.5kg (1–3.5lb).
Maturity: 3 months.
Breeding: Up to 5 litters per year.
Life span: 8 years.
Status: Common.

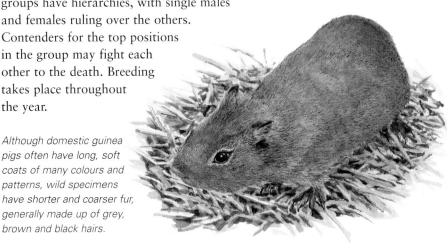

BATS

Bats are grouped together in the Chiroptera *order of mammals. They are the only mammals that can truly fly. Their wings are made from thin membranes of skin stretched between elongated arms and legs. Most bats are active at night and "see" the world through sound. They emit high-pitched calls and interpret the echoes that bounce back to build up pictures of their surroundings.*

Common vampire bat

Desmodus rotundus

Within their range, vampire bats are found in most types of habitat where there are large animals to feed upon, and they have become common in areas where livestock is being raised. They feed on the blood of animals such as cattle and donkeys and sometimes domestic poultry.

They begin to feed soon after nightfall, flying silently from their roosts in caves and hollow trees. Vampire bats will travel several kilometres to find blood. Once they locate suitable host animals, they lick the target area – usually on the neck or leg – and bite off hairs or feathers to clear a patch of skin. Then the bat cuts away a circle of skin with its long teeth and laps up the blood flowing from the wound.

Vampire bats swallow about 20ml (7fl oz) of blood each day. They return to their roosts to digest their food during the day. Roosts may contain as many as 2,000 bats. Single males mate with small groups of females. They need to guard them, however, because they are often usurped by other males. Births of single young take place in spring or autumn.

Vampire bats have dark upper bodies with grey undersides. Their upper front teeth are very long and pointed, and their limbs are adapted for walking along the ground.

Distribution: Mexico to Uruguay.
Habitat: Caves, hollow trees and disused buildings.
Food: Blood.
Size: 7–9cm (3–3.5in); 15–50g (0.03–0.1lb).
Maturity: 10 months.
Breeding: Single birth in spring or autumn.
Life span: 10 years.
Status: Common.

Tent-building bat

Uroderma bilobatum

Tent-building bats have four white stripes on their faces, with pointed "nose leaves". Up to 20 females may share a tent.

Tent-building bats live in areas with enough palm or banana trees for them to roost in. They make tents from the broad fronds by nibbling through the central, supportive ribs so that the fronds flop down over them. The tents shelter the bats from the sun and wind while they sleep during the day. The fronds eventually die and fall off the trees because their vascular systems have been damaged by the bats. Consequently, the bats build themselves new shelters every two or three months.

Tent-building bats eat mainly fruit, which they chew up, drinking the juice. They also alight on flowers to grab insects, and will eat any nectar and pollen available. Males roost alone or in small groups, while females rest in groups of 20 or more. Breeding takes place at all times of the year. Nursing mothers leave their single young in their tents while they go on their nightly foraging trips.

Distribution: Southern Mexico and northern South America to Brazil.
Habitat: Palm or banana forests.
Food: Fruit, pollen, nectar and insects.
Size: 5.5–7.5cm (2–3in); 13–21g (0.03–0.04lb).
Maturity: Not known.
Breeding: Single young born throughout the year.
Life span: Not known.
Status: Common.

Velvety free-tailed bat

Molossus ater

Velvety free-tailed bats are nocturnal insect-eaters, tracking their prey by echolocation. Echolocation is a system in which the bats bounce chirps of ultrasound off objects and listen to the echoes to build an image of their surroundings.

They live in damp forests, but will venture out into more open country to find food. They roost by day in tree hollows, in rock overhangs or under palm fronds. At dusk, the bats set off in search of food, which they store in pouches inside their cheeks. When the pouches are full, the free-tailed bats return to their roosts to digest their food.

These bats sometimes use their mobile tails as feelers by crawling backwards along the ground, waggling their tails from side to side. With wings adapted for twisting and turning in pursuit of prey, free-tailed bats are not very good at taking off from the ground. Instead, they take to the wing by climbing up trees and dropping into the air.

Velvety free-tailed bats are so-named because of their soft fur and because, unlike most bats, they do not have membranes of skin joined to the sides of their tails.

Distribution: Northern Mexico to Argentina in South America.
Habitat: Forests and open woodland.
Food: Insects.
Size: 5–9.5cm (2–4in); 10–30g (0.02–0.04lb).
Maturity: 1 year.
Breeding: Single offspring produced up to 2 times per year.
Life span: Not known.
Status: Common.

Ghost bat (*Diclidurus albus*): 5–8cm (2–3in); 20–35g (0.04–0.07lb)
This species of bat ranges from southern Mexico to Peru and northern Brazil. Ghost bats have white or grey fur and are found in tropical forests, seldom far from running water. They roost by day under large palm leaves, and pursue moths and other insects by night. Ghost bats live largely solitary lives, but do congregate at roosts, especially during the breeding season in late summer.

Fishing bulldog bat (*Noctilio leporinus*): 10–13cm (4–5in); 60–80g (0.13–0.17lb)
The males of this species of bat, which lives in Central America, have bright orange fur, while the females are dull grey or brown. They have pointed muzzles with heavily folded lips and long hind legs with well-developed claws. These claws are used for catching fish. Fishing bulldog bats hunt over ocean surf as well as lakes and rivers. They even follow flocks of pelicans and snatch small fish disturbed by the birds.

New World sucker-footed bat (*Thyroptera discifera*): 3.5–5cm (1.5–2in); 40–60g (0.08–0.13lb)
This species ranges from Nicaragua to Peru and northern Brazil. Its name refers to the suction cups located on short stalks on the soles of its forefeet. The bats use these suckers to hang from smooth leaves in their rainforest habitat. Unusually for bats, which generally hang upside down, sucker-footed bats roost upright.

Pallid bat

Antrozous pallidus

Pallid bats prefer to live in areas with plenty of rocky outcrops, in dry scrubland or forest terrain in western North America. They roost in caves and hollow trees during the day and do not emerge until well after dark. They go on two foraging trips each night, returning to their roosts in between to digest their food. They hunt for food on the wing, frequently descending to about 2m (6.5ft) above the ground before taking a long glide over the terrain. This behaviour is suited to locating slow-moving and ground-based prey, such as beetles and crickets.

Some pallid bats may migrate from cooler parts of their range to warmer areas in winter. Others hibernate during the coldest months. Pallid bats live in large social groups. They call to one another as they return to the roosts after feeding, and communicate as they jostle for position inside their roosting sites. During the summer, males live in male-only roosts. Mating takes place in autumn, soon after that year's young have dispersed from their mothers' roosts. Births, usually of twins, take place in summer.

Pallid bats have creamy to yellow fur, with whitish patches on their undersides. Their ears are very large in proportion to their heads.

Distribution: Western North America from British Colombia to Mexico.
Habitat: Forests and arid scrubland.
Food: Insects, spiders and lizards.
Size: 6–8.5cm (2.5–3.5in); 17–28g (0.04–0.06lb).
Maturity: 1 year.
Breeding: Twins born in summer.
Life span: 9 years.
Status: Vulnerable.

HOOFED ANIMALS

Hoofed animals walk on the tips of their toes. Their hooves are made from the same material as fingernails and claws – keratin. Walking on tiptoes makes their legs very long, and most hoofed animals are fast runners because of this. Hoofed mammals belong to two groups: Perissodactyla *includes horses, zebras, rhinoceroses and tapirs, while* Artiodactyla *includes pigs, sheep, antelope, deer and cattle.*

Brazilian tapir

Tapirus terrestris

Brazilian tapirs, also known as South American tapirs, spend the day in forests of dense vegetation. At night they emerge into more open country, where they browse on vegetation. They prefer to spend part of the night in water or mud, and are surprisingly agile swimmers given their size. When on land, they walk with their snouts close to the ground. Each night, a tapir will follow one of several well-trodden trails to a favourite watering hole.

Tapirs spend most of their lives alone. They are fairly aggressive towards one another at chance meetings. They alert each other to their presence by giving shrill whistling sounds and marking the ground with their urine. Brazilian tapirs breed all year round, but most mate during the rainy season, which means that their young are born just before the rains begin in the following year.

Tapirs have rounded bodies that are wider at the back than at the front. This helps them charge through thick vegetation when in danger. They have short hairs on their bodies and narrow manes on their necks. Their noses are long and flexible. Young tapirs have red fur patterned with yellow and white stripes and spots.

Distribution: From Colombia and Venezuela southward to northern Argentina.
Habitat: Woodland or dense grassy habitats with a source of water.
Food: Water plants, fruit and buds.
Size: 1.8–2.5m (6–8.25ft); 180–320kg (396–704lb).
Maturity: 3–4 years.
Breeding: 1 or 2 young born in rainy season.
Life span: 35 years.
Status: Lower risk.

Guanaco

Lama guanicoe

Guanacos have long limbs and necks for reaching food in trees and shrubs. They have brown, woolly fur on their upper bodies and necks, while their undersides have white hair.

Guanacos are considered the wild relatives of domestic llamas and alpacas. They are distant cousins of the camels of Africa and Asia. Like camels, guanacos have adapted to living in dry areas, although their preferred habitat – alpine grassland – is not as hot as the habitats of most camels.

Like their domestic relatives, guanacos are fast runners. They have more haemoglobin (oxygen-carrying pigment) in their red blood cells than any other mammal. This allows them to survive at altitude.

Guanacos mainly graze on grass, but they also pluck leaves from shrubs. They live in herds of about 15 individuals. Each herd is controlled by one adult male. Once a young guanaco reaches adulthood, it is chased away by the dominant male.

Distribution: Southern Peru to eastern Argentina and southern Chile.
Habitat: Dry, open areas.
Food: Grass.
Size: 1.2–2.5m (4–8.25ft); 100–120kg (220–264lb).
Maturity: Females 2 years; males 4 years.
Breeding: Single young born in spring.
Life span: 28 years.
Status: Vulnerable.

Bighorn sheep

Ovis canadensis

Bighorn sheep are named after the massive spiral horns of the males, which may be up to 1.1m (3.5ft) long. The females have smaller, less curved horns.

Bighorn sheep are the most common type of wild sheep in North America. They are excellent climbers and are often found on steep rocky outcrops or high cliffs. They seek refuge in steep areas from predators, such as cougars, which are not agile enough to keep up with their sure-footed prey.

Flocks of bighorn sheep can contain up to 100 individuals. They head up to high meadows in summer before retreating to the valleys when the winter snows come.

Male bighorn sheep generally stay together in separate groups from the ewes and lambs. The rams have strict hierarchies based on the size of their horns. Fights are highly ritualized, with the adversaries butting their horns together. Ewes prefer to mate with rams with large horns and will refuse the courtship of others.

Distribution: South-western Canada to northern Mexico.
Habitat: Alpine meadows and rocky cliffs.
Food: Grass and sedge.
Size: 1.2–1.8m (4–6ft); 50–125kg (110–275lb).
Maturity: 3 years.
Breeding: 1–3 young born in spring.
Life span: 20 years.
Status: Lower risk.

Collared peccary (*Tayassu tajacu*): 0.75–1m (2.5–3.25ft); 14–30kg (31–66lb)
Collared peccaries, or javelines as they are also known, are relatives of wild boars and pigs. They have white collars around their necks and the rest of their bodies are covered in grey fur. They range from the south-western United States to northern Argentina. Peccaries root out bulbs and tubers with their snouts and also eat snakes and small invertebrates. Like many pigs, they appear to be immune to rattlesnake bites.

Muskox (*Ovibos moschatus*): 1.9–2.3m (6.25–7.5ft); 200–410kg (440–900lb)
Muskoxen are large cattle-like animals that live on the barren tundra of the Canadian Arctic. Males are larger than females, and both sexes have curved horns and coats of thick, dark brown hair that hang almost to the ground. Their name is derived from the strong smell of the bulls during the mating season in summer.

Vicuña (*Vicugna vicugna*): 1.25–1.9m (4–6.25ft); 36–65kg (79–143lb)
Vicuñas are related to guanacos and camels. They live in the high Andes Mountains of Peru, Bolivia and Chile. They are smaller than guanacos and have tawny coloured coats. Some biologists have suggested that alpacas are a cross between domestic llamas and vicuñas, although this theory is contestable. Vicuñas have teeth more like those of rodents than other hoofed animals. Their lower incisors grow throughout the animal's lifetime. The teeth are constantly being worn away by the tough alpine grasses that make up the vicuña's diet.

American bison

Bison bison

Although rare, the American bison has been saved from extinction. Once, herds of over a million individuals grazed the vast prairies of western North America. They were almost wiped out by hunters in the 19th century where the grasslands were cleared to make way for agriculture.

Bison often rub their shoulders and rumps against boulders and tree trunks, and they enjoy taking mud and dust baths. This behaviour scratches off fly larvae and other parasites that live on their hides.

Mature bulls move in separate groups from the cows. In the mating season, in late summer, the males join the females. They fight for the females by ramming each other head-on. After mating, a bull will guard his mate for several days to prevent other rival males from mating with her.

Male bison are larger than females. Both sexes have sharp, curved horns, which stick out from the shaggy, brown hair on their heads.

Distribution: Patches of western Canada and central United States.
Habitat: Prairie and woodland.
Food: Grass.
Size: 2.1–3.5m (7–11.5ft); 350–1000kg (770–2200lb).
Maturity: 1–2 years.
Breeding: Single young born in spring every 1 or 2 years.
Life span: 40 years.
Status: Lower risk.

DEER

Deer are a group of hoofed mammals that are found across the northern hemisphere. They belong to the Cervidae family of mammals. In form and habit, deer resemble the horned antelopes of Africa, which are actually more closely related to sheep and cattle. However, instead of horns, deer grow antlers. In most species, only males have them, and unlike horns, which remain for life, antlers are shed annually.

Moose

Alces alces

Male moose are almost twice the size of females. The males sport huge antlers – nearly 2m (6.5ft) across – and have flaps of skin hanging below their chins, called dewlaps.

Moose are the largest deer in the world. They live in the cold conifer forests that cover northern mountains and lowlands. As well as in North America, moose live across northern Europe and Siberia, but are known as elk there.

Moose plod through the forests and marshes, browsing on a wide range of leaves, mosses and lichens. They often feed in the shallows of streams and rivers, nibbling on aquatic vegetation. These large deer have even been seen diving underwater to uproot water plants. In summer, they are most active at dawn and dusk. In winter, they are active throughout the day. They paw the snow to reveal buried plants and twigs. Although moose may gather together to feed, they spend most of the year alone. In the autumn mating season, males fight each other for females.

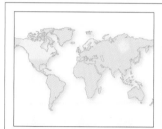

Distribution: Alaska, Canada, northern United States, Siberia and northern Europe. Introduced to New Zealand.
Habitat: Marsh and Woodland.
Food: Leaves, twigs, moss and water plants.
Size: 2.4–3.1m (8–10.5ft); 200–825kg (440–1815lb).
Maturity: 1 year.
Breeding: 1–3 young born in spring.
Life span: 27 years.
Status: Common.

White-tailed deer

Odocoileus virginianus

White-tailed deer, or Virginia deer as they are called in the United States, prefer areas with tall grasses or shrubs to hide in during the day. When the deer spot predators, they raise their white tails to expose the white patches on their rumps. This serves as a visual warning to other deer that danger is near. If pursued, the deer bound away, reaching 60kph (40mph).

White-tailed deer live in matriarchies, with each small group being controlled by a single adult female, which is the mother of the rest of the group. The adult males live alone or in small bachelor herds. In the autumn mating season, males mark plants with scent produced by glands on their faces, and urinate in depressions scraped into the ground. The males fight with their antlers – rut – for the right to court females.

White-tailed deer have brown fur on their upper parts and white undersides. The white fur extends under the tail, which gives the species its name. The males shed their antlers in midwinter and grow new ones in spring.

Distribution: North, Central and South America from southern Canada to Brazil.
Habitat: Shrublands and open woodland.
Food: Grass, shrubs, mushrooms, twigs, lichens and nuts.
Size: 0.8–2.1m (2.5–7ft); 50–200kg (110–484lb).
Maturity: 1 year.
Breeding: 1–4 young born in summer.
Life span: 10 years.
Status: Common.

Pronghorn

Antilocapra americana

Despite appearances, pronghorns are not true deer. They are the sole members of a separate group of hoofed animal called the *Antilocapridae*. Unlike true deer, pronghorns do not have antlers, but have horns like antelope, although they are forked like those of a deer.

Pronghorns are the fastest land mammals in the Americas. They have been recorded racing along at 72kph (45mph).

In late autumn, pronghorns gather into large herds of 1,000 or more. They spend the winter in these herds and split into smaller single-sex groups when spring arrives. In October, older males compete for small territories, which they use to attract groups of females. Once females have entered the territories, the males will not allow other males near them.

Pronghorns get their name from the prongs sticking out halfway up their backward-curving horns. Male pronghorns are slightly larger than the females. The males also have black masks on their faces.

Distribution: Southern Canada to northern Mexico.
Habitat: Grassland and desert.
Food: Grass, leaves and cacti.
Size: 1–1.5m (3.25–5ft); 36–70kg (79–154lb).
Maturity: Females 18 months; males 3 years.
Breeding: 1–3 young born in spring.
Life span: 10 years.
Status: Common.

Red brocket deer (*Mazama americana*): 72–140cm (27–54in); 8–25kg (17–55lb)
Red brocket deer range from eastern Mexico to northern Argentina. They have whorls of hair on their faces and stout bodies covered in reddish-brown hair. The males have simple spike-like antlers. This species lives in woodland and dense forests. They may be active at all times of the day or night, feeding on grasses, vines and the new shoots of plants. These shy deer tend to freeze when they spot danger, blending into the thick vegetaion.

Pampas deer (*Ozotoceros bezoarticus*): 1.1–1.4m (3.5–4.75ft); 25–40kg (55–88lb)
As their name suggests, pampas deer live on the open grasslands – or pampas plains – in the south-eastern part of South America. They have dark red or brown coats. Males have forked antlers and glands on their hooves that produce a strong scent. Pampas deer graze on young grass shoots throughout the day. In late summer and autumn the males fight for access to females, and most births occur in the spring.

Huemul (*Hippocamelus antisensis*): 1.4–1.65m (4.75–5.5ft); 45–65kg (99–143lb)
Huemuls live in the rugged hill country high in the Andes of Peru, Chile, Bolivia and Argentina. They have coarse coats and black Y-shaped markings on their faces. Huemuls spend the summer high on the mountains, grazing on the grasses and sedges growing in alpine meadows. In winter, they climb down to lower altitudes. Mating takes place in the drier winter season and fawns are born at the end of the rains.

Southern pudu

Pudu pudu

Southern pudus live in the wet forests on the slopes of southern Andes Mountains. They are the smallest of all deer, being only a little bigger than maras – the long-legged rodents that live in the same region.

Pudus are mainly nocturnal in their behaviour, although they are sometimes spotted feeding during the day. They move through the dense forest slowly, picking off the ripest fruits and most succulent leaves and buds. They try not to draw attention to themselves and stay well hidden as much as possible. If attacked, they run away in zigzag paths and often seek refuge in the branches of trees.

Pudus live alone, patrolling small territories and only occasionally encountering other members of their species. Being so small, pudus can reach maturity much more quickly than other deer. They are ready to breed after just six months of life. Births take place in spring, and by the following autumn that year's fawns are ready to take part in the breeding activity, which occurs at that time.

Southern pudus have grey and brown fur. They have short, thick legs and the males have small spikes for antlers.

Distribution: Southern Chile to south-western Argentina.
Habitat: Humid forest.
Food: Tree and shrub leaves, vines, bark, fruit and flowers.
Size: 60–85cm (23–33in); 5–14kg (11–30lb).
Maturity: 6 months.
Breeding: Single young in spring.
Life span: 10 years.
Status: Vulnerable.

NEW WORLD MONKEYS

These monkeys are so-called because the Americas comprise the New World. They are the only primates that live in the Americas, and most live in South America, with only a few species ranging as far north as Central or Meso America and Mexico. New World monkeys differ from Old World monkeys in two ways: they have flattened noses with more broadly spaced nostrils, and most have prehensile tails.

Pygmy marmoset

Cebuella pygmaea

Distribution: Upper Amazon Basin.
Habitat: Rainforest.
Food: Fruit, buds, insects and sap.
Size: 11–15cm (4.5–6in); 100–140g (0.22–0.3lb).
Maturity: 1.5–2 years.
Breeding: 1–3 young born throughout the year.
Life span: 10 years.
Status: Common.

Pygmy marmosets are the smallest monkeys in the world. They live in the low plants that grow beneath tall trees in tropical forests. They clamber among the thick vegetation in search of food throughout the day, being most active in the cooler hours at the beginning and end of each day.

Pygmy marmosets eat fruit, flower buds and insects, but their preferred food is the sweet, sticky sap from certain trees. Their lower canine teeth are specially shaped for gouging holes in tree bark, causing the sap to leak out from the wood beneath. A tree used by a group of pygmy marmosets will be covered in wounds where the animals repeatedly bite through the bark.

Like all monkeys, pygmy marmosets live in complex societies. They live in family groups, with two parents and eight or nine offspring. Families sleep together, huddled on branches. Breeding pairs may mate at any time, but most produce small litters – usually twins – in December or June.

Pygmy marmosets have grey-brown fur and tails ringed with red-brown stripes. Their tails are prehensile and can be wrapped around branches. They move cautiously through the treetops to avoid attack by large birds of prey.

Brown capuchin

Cebus apella

Capuchins are sometimes called ring-tails. This is because they often curl the tip of their semi-prehensile tail into a ring. Capuchins are among the most intelligent and adaptable of all monkeys. They are found in a wide range of habitats, from dense jungles to towns and cities. Some even live on the seashore, where they collect crabs. Some capuchins break open hard nuts by pounding them with stones – an example of animals using tools.

This species lives in troops of about 12 monkeys. Most troops have a single adult male, who fathers all the children. The monkeys chatter and squeak a great deal, telling each other of their location and warning of danger. Without a set breeding season, capuchin mothers give birth to their single babies at any time of the year. Each baby initially clings to its mother's chest, then rides on her back until it becomes more independent.

Like some other capuchin species, brown capuchins have a cap of dark hair on the top of their heads, with thick tufts or "horns" above the ears.

Distribution: From Colombia to Paraguay.
Habitat: Rainforest.
Food: Fruit, nuts, flowers, bark, gums, insects and eggs.
Size: 30–56cm (12–22in); 1.1–3.3kg (2.5–7.25lb).
Maturity: Females 4 years; males 8 years.
Breeding: Single young born throughout the year.
Life span: 30 years.
Status: Lower risk.

Humboldt's woolly monkey (*Lagothrix lagotricha*): 50–69cm (20–27in); 5.5–11kg (12–24lb)

Woolly monkeys live in the high forests on the slopes of Andes Mountains and Mato Grosso in Brazil. They have very heavyset bodies compared to other tree-living monkeys, with thick black fur. They spend much time at the tops of the tallest trees that protrude from forest canopies, although they do climb down to the ground more often than most monkeys. On the ground, they may walk on their hind legs using their heavy tails to keep them upright. They eat mainly fruit and insects, but can survive on leaves and seeds when necessary.

Golden lion tamarin (*Leontopithecus rosalia*): 20–33cm (8–13in); 600–800g (1.3–1.7lb)

This extremely rare monkey lives in just one small area of coastal forest near Rio de Janeiro, Brazil. The long, silky, golden mane around the head and shoulders has earned the golden lion tamarin its English name. These monkeys feed on fruit, insects and small vertebrates during the day, before retiring to holes in trees to sleep. They live in family groups of four or five, the male helping to raise his offspring. Golden lion tamarins breed during the wettest part of the year, which is during the warm southern summer. Most offspring are born as twins.

Squirrel monkey

Saimiri boliviensis

Squirrel monkeys live in many types of forest. They spend most of their time in trees, rarely coming down to the ground. However, some populations of squirrel monkeys have made their homes in areas cleared of trees for agriculture. These monkeys tend to live close to streams for reasons of safety. Squirrel monkeys form complex social groups, or troops, which are larger than those of any other monkey species in the Americas. In pristine rainforests, the troops can number up to 300 individuals.

Males do not help in raising the young and during the mating season – the dry part of the year – they establish hierarchies by fighting each other. Only the dominant males get to mate with the females, which give birth to single young. Soon after giving birth, the new mothers chase away the breeding males, which reform their bachelor subgroups. Adolescent males, too old to stay with their mothers, eventually join these subgroups, having fought their way in.

Distribution: Central America to Upper Amazon Basin.
Habitat: Tropical forest, close to streams.
Food: Fruit, nuts, flowers, leaves, gums, insects and small vertebrates.
Size: 26–36cm (10–14in); 0.75–1.1kg (1.65–2.4lb).
Maturity: Females 3 years; males 5 years.
Breeding: Single young born from June–August.
Life span: 20 years.
Status: Lower risk.

Squirrel monkeys have black, hairless snouts and helmets of dark fur around their pale faces. Their ears are covered in pale fur. The rest of the body is more brightly coloured, in hues of pale yellow and red, and the mobile tail has a black tip. The body is slender in shape.

Black-handed spider monkey

Ateles geoffroyi

Spider monkeys are the most agile of the American primates, not least because their long prehensile tails function as a fifth limb. The animals can pick up food or hold on to branches with their tails. It is not unusual to see one of these monkeys hanging from its tail alone.

Spider monkey troops live high up in forest canopies, and almost never visit the ground. They are most active early in the morning, taking the rest of the day to relax and digest tough plant food.

Troops generally contain about 30 individuals, with both sexes in equal numbers. However, larger groups of more than 100 have been reported. The males in the troops defend large territories by regularly patrolling the perimeters, while females and young tend to stay close to the centre. Males tend to stay in the troops they were born into, while females move to other troops in the area. Breeding occurs all year round. Spider monkeys reportedly have a unique defensive strategy: when potential predators approach – including humans – the monkeys drop heavy branches on top of them.

Spider monkeys have very long prehensile tails and similarly long legs, hence their name. This allows them to be extremely agile in the treetops.

Distribution: Mexico to Colombia.
Habitat: Tropical forest.
Food: Fruit, seeds, buds, leaves, insects and eggs.
Size: 38–63cm (15–25in); 6–8kg (13.2–17.6lb).
Maturity: 4–5 years.
Breeding: Single young born throughout the year.
Life span: 30 years.
Status: Vulnerable.

Red howler monkey

Alouatta seniculus

Howlers are large monkeys that live in the trees of tropical forests. They are known for the roaring howls that fill South American forests. The monkeys have very wide jaws, which allow them to open their mouths wide and make such loud calls.

Howler monkeys roar first thing in the morning before setting off to look for food. Although they eat fruits, such as figs, when they are available, howler monkeys rely for long periods on just leaves. Few other monkeys have such an unvaried, indigestible diet. After a rest in the middle of the day, the monkeys feed some more before travelling back to their sleeping trees while howling to each other again.

Howler monkey troops contain about eight or nine individuals. Larger troops form when there are more fruits available. Males compete with each other to join troops, and the victors may kill the young of the males they depose. The howling call is thought to be a mechanism for locating nearby troops. These monkeys breed all year round. The young ride on their mothers' backs for up to a year. Both males and females leave their mothers' troops when they are sexually mature and join others.

Distribution: Northern South America.
Habitat: Rainforest and mangroves.
Food: Leaves and figs.
Size: 55–92cm (22–36in); 4–10kg (8.75–22lb).
Maturity: 4–5 years.
Breeding: Single young born throughout the year.
Life span: 20 years.
Status: Endangered.

Howler monkeys typically have reddish-brown hair, although some have a more yellowish or dusky coloration. Their strong prehensile tails have naked patches on their undersides to help them grip branches. The males are larger than the females and generally have darker hair. The loud calls of these monkeys, especially by the males, are made possible by a specialized larynx in the throat, which amplifies the sound.

White-faced saki

Pithecia pithecia

Distribution: Northern South America from Venezuela to north-eastern Brazil.
Habitat: Tropical forest.
Food: Fruit, honey, leaves, mice, bats and birds.
Size: 30–70cm (12–28in); 0.7–1.7kg (1.5–3.75lb).
Maturity: 2–3 years.
Breeding: Single young born in the dry season remain with their parents until they are mature.
Life span: 14 years.
Status: Common.

White-faced sakis live high up in trees. They feed during the daytime and almost never come down to the ground. Although they do occasionally leap from tree to tree, sakis are not the most agile of monkeys. They climb down trunks backwards and generally run along thick branches on all fours. Sometimes, however, sakis have been seen walking on their hind legs with their arms held above their heads.

A lot of the saki's diet consists of vegetable matter and fruit. However, these monkeys do also catch small vertebrate animals, such as birds and bats. The sakis rip their victims apart with their hands before skinning and eating the pieces of flesh. The monkeys have sharp teeth that are useful for biting into forest fruits and slicing up meat.

A saki group is based around a pair of breeding adults. The rest of the group, which may contain up to five individuals, will generally be the chief pair's offspring of different ages. The breeding pair produce a single baby once a year. Most births occur in the dry season at the end of the year.

Only male white-faced sakis have the white faces after which they are named. The females have black or dark brown faces. Most saki monkeys have broad, round faces with hooded eyebrows.

Night monkey

Aotus lemurinus

Night monkeys, which are also known as douroucoulis, are the only nocturnal monkeys in the world. These rare monkeys live in most types of forest except those close to water. Biologists used to think there was a single species, but it is now known that there are several living across South America.

The large eyes of these monkeys collect enough light for them to see in the gloom. Night monkeys can only see in monochrome (black and white), but this still allows them to run and jump through the trees even on the darkest nights. By day, they rest in nests made from dry leaves and twigs.

Night monkeys live in family groups, with one adult pair and two or three of their young. Family members warn each other of approaching danger, such as tree snakes or birds of prey, with long "wook" alarm calls. The monkeys have loose sacs of skin under their chins, which they inflate to amplify these calls. At night these visual signals are ineffective, so night monkeys rely on scent as well as calls to communicate with other monkeys and nearby groups. The scent comes from their urine and glands on their chests, which the monkeys rub on branches.

Night monkeys have large eyes which give them good night vision. Their thick, woolly fur gives them a rounded appearance, and their tails, which are not prehensile, are thickened and furry at their tips.

Distribution: Central and South America from Panama southward to Brazil, but patchily distributed.
Habitat: Forests.
Food: Fruit, nuts, leaves, bark, flowers, gums, insects and small vertebrates.
Size: 24–37cm (9.5–14.5in); 0.6–1kg (1.25–2.25lb).
Maturity: 2 years.
Breeding: Single young born throughout the year.
Life span: 18 years.
Status: Vulnerable.

Titi monkey (*Callicebus molloch*): 24–61cm (9.5–24in); 0.5–0.75kg (1–1.75lb)
Titi monkeys live in most forested parts of northern South America. They exhibit a variety of fur colours, ranging from grey to red to gold. Their tails are long and bushy, but not prehensile. The monkeys tend to live in the lower trees near riverbanks. They often climb down to the shrub plants near to the ground to feed on fruit, leaves, birds' eggs, and invertebrates. They live in family groups dominated by single pairs of adults.

Black-bearded saki (*Chiropotes satanas*): 32–51cm (12.5–20in); 2–4kg (4.5–8.75lb)
As its name suggests, the black-bearded saki has a very long, thick beard on its elongated chin. Its head, beard and tail are black, and its shoulders, back, hands and feet are reddish-brown to black. This species lives in Guyana, Venezuela and Brazil, north of the Amazon. The black-bearded saki eats fruit, the seeds of unripe fruit, leaves, flowers and a few insects. It lives in troops of up to 30 individuals.

Muriqui (*Brachyteles arachnoides*): 46–63cm (18–25in); 12–15kg (44–33lb)
The muriqui, or woolly spider monkey, is the largest New World monkey. This extremely rare monkey lives in the coastal forests of south-eastern Brazil – an area which has been heavily deforested. Little is known about muriqui society. The animals are thought to live in promiscuous groups, where all adults freely mate with each other.

Bald uakari

Cacajao calvus

Uakaris only live in tropical rainforests that are flooded or filled with many slow-flowing streams, and consequently they are very rare. They are active during the day, running on all fours through the tops of large trees. They mainly feed on fruit, but will also eat leaves, insects and small vertebrates. Although they are quite agile, uakaris rarely jump from branch to branch. They almost never come down to the ground.

Uakaris live in large troops of 10–30 individuals. In areas where forests have not been damaged by human activity, groups of over 100 have been reported. Uakari troops often get mixed in with those of other monkeys, such as squirrel monkeys, during daytime feeding forays.

Each troop has a hierarchical structure, which is maintained by fighting among both sexes. The dominant males control access to females in a troop during the breeding season. Females give birth to single young every two years.

Distribution: Upper Amazon from Peru to Colombia.
Habitat: Beside rivers in flooded forests.
Food: Fruit, leaves and insects.
Size: 51–70cm (20–28in); 3.5–4kg (7.5–8.75lb).
Maturity: Females 3 years, males 6 years.
Breeding: Single young born in summer every 2 years.
Life span: 20 years.
Status: Endangered.

Bald uakaris have hairless, red faces fringed with shaggy fur, hence their name. The long fur on the body is pale but looks reddish-brown, and a few have white fur. Their clubbed tails are proportionally shorter than all other New World monkeys.

ARMADILLOS AND RELATIVES

Armadillos, anteaters and sloths belong to a group of mammals called the Xenarthra *(formerly named* Edentata, *meaning toothless). Most xenarths live in South and Central America. Only one, the long-nosed armadillo, lives as far north as Texas. These animals are taxonomically related to one another but do not share evident common physical characteristics, except for unique bones that strengthen their spines.*

Giant armadillo

Priodontes maximus

Like all armadillos, the giant armadillo has bands of bony plates running from side to side across its body to serve as armour. These plates are covered in leathery skin, and a few thick hairs stick out from between them.

The giant armadillo is the largest of all armadillos. It is nocturnal and shelters by day in burrows dug with the mighty claws on its forefeet. Most of the burrows are dug into the side of termite mounds. Giant armadillos also dig to get at their prey. They typically excavate termite mounds and ant nests, but they also dig out worms, subterranean spiders and occasionally snakes.

Unlike many other armadillos, giant armadillos cannot curl up completely to protect their soft undersides with their armoured upper bodies. Instead, these giants rely on their considerable size to deter predators. If they are attacked, giant armadillos try to dig themselves out of trouble. Armadillos live alone. They breed all year and mate when they chance upon one another on their travels. One or two young are born inside a large burrow after a four-month gestation.

Distribution: Venezuela to northern Argentina.
Habitat: Dense forest and grassland near water.
Food: Termites, ants, spiders and other insects, worms, snakes and carrion.
Size: 0.7–1m (2.25–3.25ft); 60kg (132lb).
Maturity: 1 year.
Breeding: 1–2 young born throughout the year.
Life span: 15 years.
Status: Vulnerable.

Long-nosed armadillo

Dasypus novemcinctus

Distribution: Southern United States to northern Argentina.
Habitat: Shaded areas.
Food: Arthropods, reptiles, amphibians, fruit and roots.
Size: 24–57cm (9.5–22.5in); 1–10kg (2.2–22lb).
Maturity: 1 year.
Breeding: 4 young born in spring.
Life span: 15 years.
Status: Common.

Long-nosed armadillos are found in a wide range of habitats, but always require plenty of cover. In the warmer parts of their range they feed at night. In colder areas they may be spotted during the day, especially in winter. These armadillos build large nests at the ends of their long burrows. The nests are filled with dried grasses. In areas with plenty of plant cover, long-nosed armadillos may also build their nests above ground.

Long-nosed armadillos search for their animal prey by poking their long noses into crevices and under logs. They also eat fallen fruit and roots. When threatened, the animals waddle to their burrows as fast as possible. If cornered, they will curl up into armoured balls.

Long-nosed armadillos forage alone, but they may share their burrows with several other individuals, all of the same sex. The breeding season is in late summer. Litters of identical same-sex quadruplets are born in the spring.

The long-nosed armadillo is also called the nine-banded armadillo because it typically has that number of plate bands along its back, although specimens can possess either eight or ten bands.

Three-toed sloth

Bradypus tridactylus

Distribution: Eastern Brazil.
Habitat: Coastal forest.
Food: Young leaves, twigs and buds.
Size: 41–70cm (16–29in); 2.25–5.5kg (5–12lb).
Maturity: 3.5 years.
Breeding: Single young born throughout the year.
Life span: 20 years.
Status: Endangered.

Three-toed sloths spend most of their lives hanging upside down from trees. They are very inactive creatures, but they do climb down to the ground once or twice a week to excrete or move to other trees.

Three-toed sloths feed by pulling on flimsy branches with their forelegs, to bring them close to their mouths. They spend long periods waiting for their tough food to digest. Because they are so inactive, sloths have a lower body temperature than other mammals – sometimes as low as 24°C (75°F). Their fur is sometimes tinged with green because algae are growing in it. The sloths may absorb some of the algal nutrients through their skin, and it also provides useful camouflage from predators.

Sloths have very simple societies. They live alone and females only produce offspring every two years. Mating can occur throughout the year though, with both partners still hanging upside down. Mothers give birth in this position too, and the young cling to the hair on their mothers' breasts.

Three-toed sloths have long grey hairs that project in the opposite direction to those of other mammals, so that they point downwards when the animals are upside down. This ensures that rainwater runs off. They climb using their strong, hook-like claws.

Pichi (*Zaedyus pichiy*): 26–34cm (10–13in); 1–2kg (2.2–4.4lb)
The pichi is a small armadillo that lives on the grasslands of southern Argentina and the alpine meadows of the Chilean Andes. Its head, body and tail are armoured and have long hairs growing out from behind each plate. When threatened, a pichi draws its legs under its body so that the serrated edges of its armour dig into the ground. It anchors itself in its burrow in this way. Pichis probably hibernate in colder parts of their range. Between one and three young may be born at any time of the year.

Northern tamandua (*Tamandua mexicana*): 47–77cm (18–30in); 2–7kg (4.4–15.5lb)
Tamanduas are sometimes called lesser anteaters. They range from southern Mexico to northern Peru. Their fur is short and thick, and varies in colour. Tamanduas have long snouts with extremely small mouths, and long, curved claws. Lacking teeth – like all anteaters – their insect food is ground up using muscular gizzards inside their stomachs. They feed on ants, termites and bees, searching for them both on the ground and in trees.

Two-toed sloth (*Choloepus hoffmanni*): 54–74cm (21–29in); 4–8.5kg (8.8–19lb)
Two-toed sloths live in the rainforests of northern South America. Unlike their three-toed cousins they have only two digits on each forefoot, but their hind feet have three. Like other sloths, this species lives a slow, nocturnal life, hanging from high branches. It eats leaves, fruit and twigs. Algae grow on its long fur, camouflaging it from predators.

Giant anteater

Myrmecophaga tridactyla

Giant anteaters live wherever there are large ant nests or termite mounds in abundance. They use their powerful claws to rip the colonies apart, then they use their sticky tongues to lick up the insects and their eggs and larvae. A single giant anteater can eat over 30,000 ants or termites in one day.

Despite being powerful diggers, giant anteaters shelter in thickets, not burrows, because of their awkward shape. They spend most of their time alone searching for food, with their long noses close to the ground. While on the move, they curl their forelimbs under their bodies so that they are actually walking on the backs of their forefeet and their claws do not hinder them.

Females often come into contact with one another, but males keep their distance. Breeding can take place all year.

Distribution: Belize to northern Argentina.
Habitat: Grasslands, forests and swamps.
Food: Ants, termites and beetle larvae.
Size: 1–1.2m (3.25–4ft); 18–39kg (40–89lb).
Maturity: 2.5–4 years.
Breeding: Single young born throughout the year.
Life span: 25 years.
Status: Vulnerable.

Giant anteaters have powerful digging claws on their forelimbs and incredibly long tongues – often over 60cm (24in) – inside their snouts. They have white stripes along their flanks and a long, bushy tail.

RABBITS

Rabbits, hares and pikas belong to the mammal order Lagomorpha. *Most of the lagomorphs that live in the Americas are found north of Mexico. Unlike their cousins in Europe, most American rabbits do not dig burrows. Like hares, they generally shelter above ground. The only rabbit to dig its own burrow is the pygmy rabbit, which is also the smallest rabbit in the world.*

Pika

Ochotona princeps

The pikas of North America live in areas of scree – fragments of eroded rock found beneath cliffs or mountain slopes. They shelter under the rocks and feed on patches of vegetation that grow among the scree. Pikas may forage at all times of the day or night, but most activity takes place in the early mornings or evenings.

During the winter, pikas survive by eating "ladders" of grass and leaves that they have collected during the late summer. These ladders are piles made in sunny places, so that the plants desiccate into alpine hay. Like most of their rabbit relatives, pikas eat their primary droppings so that their tough food is digested twice, in order to extract all of the nutrients.

Adult pikas live alone and defend territories during the winter. In spring, males expand their territories to include those of neighbouring females. Most females produce two litters during each summer. When preparing for winter, the females chase their mates back to their own territories and expel their mature offspring.

Pikas are small relatives of rabbits. They do not have tails, and their rounded bodies are covered in soft red and grey fur. Unlike those of a rabbit, a pika's hind legs are about the same length as its forelegs.

Distribution: South-western Canada and western United States.
Habitat: Broken, rocky country and scree.
Food: Grass, sedge, weeds and leaves.
Size: 12–30cm (5–12in); 110–180g (0.25–0.4lb).
Maturity: 3 months.
Breeding: 2 litters born during summer.
Life span: 7 years.
Status: Common.

Snowshoe hare

Lepus americanus

Like most hares, snowshoe hares do not dig burrows. Instead they shelter in shallow depressions called forms, which they scrape in soil or snow. Snowshoe hares are generally nocturnal, and rest in secluded forms or under logs during the day. When dusk arrives, the hares follow systems of runways through the dense forest undergrowth to feeding sites. They maintain these runways by biting away branches that block the way and compacting the winter snow.

In summer, the hares nibble on grasses and other green plant material. They survive the long winter by supplementing their diet with buds, twigs and bark. Over several years, the overall population of snowshoe hares can rise and fall dramatically. At the low points there may be only two animals per square kilometre. At the peak there may be as many as 1,300 in the same area.

Snowshoe hares are more social than other hares. During the spring breeding season, the male hares compete with each other to establish hierarchies and gain access to mates. Conflicts often result in boxing fights – hence "mad March hares".

Distribution: Alaska, Canada and northern United States.
Habitat: Conifer forest.
Food: Grass, leaves, buds and bark.
Size: 40–70cm (16–27in); 1.35–7kg (3–15lb).
Maturity: 1 year.
Breeding: 4 litters per year.
Life span: 5 years.
Status: Common.

Female snowshoe hares are a little larger than the males. In summer their fur is grey, but in areas with heavy winter snow, they grow white fur as camouflage from predators.

Eastern cottontail

Sylvilagus floridanus

Cottontail rabbits do not dig burrows, although they may shelter in disused ones dug by other animals. Generally they shelter in thickets or forms – shallow depressions made in tall grass or scraped in the ground. Cottontails forage at night, grazing mainly on grasses, but also nibbling small shrubs. Unlike hares, which rely on their speed to outrun predators, cottontails freeze when under threat, blending into their surroundings. If they have to run, they follow zigzag paths, attempting to shake off their pursuers.

In warmer parts of their range cottontails breed all year round, but only in summer farther north. Males fight to establish hierarchies, with the top males getting their choice of mates. A pregnant female digs a shallow hole, which is deeper at one end than the other. She lines the nest with grass and fur from her belly. Once she has given birth, she crouches over the shallow end and her young crawl up from the warm deep end to suckle.

Distribution: Eastern Canada and United States to Venezuela.
Habitat: Farmland, forest, desert, swamp and prairie.
Food: Grass, leaves, twigs and bark.
Size: 21–47cm (8–18in); 0.8–1.5kg (1.75–3.3lb).
Maturity: 80 days.
Breeding: 3–7 litters each year.
Life span: 5 years.
Status: Common.

Females cottontails are larger than the males. The name "cottontail" is derived from their short rounded tails, which have white fur on their undersides. Their upper bodies are covered in grey, brown and reddish hairs.

Volcano rabbit (*Romerolagus diazi*): 27–31cm (10–12in); 370–600g (0.8–1.3lb) This is a very rare and unusual rabbit species, found only on the slopes of two volcanoes in central Mexico. Volcano rabbits share many similarities with pikas, being small and rounded and lacking tails. These small-eared lagomorphs live in small colonies in rocky areas, feeding on tender herbs. Volcano rabbits shelter in burrows by day and follow networks of runways through tall grasses when feeding at night.

Pygmy rabbit (*Brachylagus idahoensis*): 21–27cm (8–11in); 200–450g (0.4–0.9lb) These rabbits live on an arid plateau in the north-west of the United States. Pygmy rabbits are related to cottontails, but they are about half the size. They dig burrows under thickets of sagebrush – the only North American rabbit to do so – and move through a network of runways above ground. They eat the sagebrush and are most active at dawn and dusk.

Swamp rabbit (*Sylvilagus aquaticus*): 45–55cm (18–22in); 1.5–2.5kg (3.3–5.5lb) Swamp rabbits live in the wetlands around the Mississippi Delta and other rivers in the southern United States. Unlike most rabbits, the males and females of this species are about the same size. Swamp rabbits build nests of dead plants and fur at ground level. They maintain territories by calling to intruders and marking their areas with scent. They breed all year round. Female swamp rabbits may produce up to 40 young per year.

Jackrabbit

Lepus californicus

Jackrabbits are actually a type of hare and so share many of the hare's characteristics, from long ears to large, hairy hind feet. Jackrabbits live in dry areas with only sparse plant cover. This has benefited the species in the past. Overgrazing of the land by cattle in the arid south-west United States and Mexico has created an ideal habitat for jackrabbits.

Unlike other hares, jackrabbits make use of burrows. They do not dig their own, but they will modify underground shelters made by tortoises trying to escape the heat of the day.

Distribution: South-western United States to northern Mexico.
Habitat: Dry grasslands.
Food: Grass.
Size: 40–70cm (16–28in); 1.35–7kg (3–15lb).
Maturity: 1 year.
Breeding: 3–4 litters each year.
Life span: 5 years.
Status: Common.

Female jackrabbits are larger than males. They have grey fur with reddish and brown flecks. Their undersides are paler, and their tails and the tips of their huge ears are black. Like other hares, male jackrabbits indulge in frenzied fights during the breeding season.

MARSUPIALS

Marsupials are a group of mammals that brood their young in pouches on their bellies, rather than in wombs, like placental mammals. The overwhelming majority of marsupials are found in Australia and New Guinea, but several species live in the Americas. However, fossil evidence has led zoologists to believe that marsupials first evolved in South America, and spread to Australasia from there overland.

Water opossum

Chironectes minimus

Water opossums have short waterproof coats with a grey and black pattern. Their hind feet are webbed, and both sexes have pouches opening to the rear.

Water opossums, or yapoks, live beside bodies of fresh water in tropical forests. They make dens in burrows in the banks of streams or lakes, with entrances just above water level. Unusually, both sexes have pouches. A female can close her pouch using a ring of muscles to keep her developing young dry while she is underwater. A male's pouch is always open and he uses it to protect his scrotum while in water or when moving quickly through forest.

Water opossums are superb swimmers. They use their hind feet to propel themselves through the water. However, they also forage on land or in trees. They spend the night in their dens, but may rest in bundles of leaves in secluded places on the forest floor between daytime feeding forays. Most births take place between December and January. After their birth, the young spend a few more weeks in the pouch until they are fully developed.

Distribution: Central and South America from southern Mexico to Belize and Argentina.
Habitat: Freshwater streams and lakes.
Food: Crayfish, shrimp, fish, fruit and water plants.
Size: 27–40cm (10.5–16in); 600–800g (1.25–1.75lb).
Maturity: Not known.
Breeding: 2–5 young born in summer.
Life span: 3 years.
Status: Lower risk.

Virginia opossum

Didelphis virginiana

Distribution: United States, Central America and northern South America.
Habitat: Moist woodlands or thick brush in swamps.
Food: Plants, carrion, small vertebrates and invertebrates.
Size: 33–50cm (13–20in); 2–5.5kg (4.5–12lb).
Maturity: 6–8 months.
Breeding: 2 litters per year.
Life span: 3 years.
Status: Lower risk.

Virginia opossums generally live in forested areas that receive plenty of rain. However, the species is very adaptable and is making its home in new places across North America. Many survive in more open country beside streams or in swamps, while others make their homes in people's sheds and barns.

Virginia opossums are most active at night. By day they rest in nests of leaves and grass, hidden away in crevices, hollow trees and sometimes in burrows. By night, the marsupials hunt for food. They are good climbers, using their prehensile tails to cling to branches.

Virginia opossums do not hibernate, but they do put on fat as the days shorten with the approach of autumn. They rely on this fat to keep them going during the periods of harshest winter weather, when they cannot get out to feed. In the very coldest parts of their range, these marsupials sometimes suffer frostbite on their naked tails and thin ears.

Mating takes place in both late winter and spring. The young are only 1cm (0.4in) long and underdeveloped when born. Over 20 are born, but the mother can only suckle 13 at once, so the weaker babies die.

Virginia opossums have white faces, often with darker streaks. Their bodies are covered in shaggy coats of long grey and white hairs, but their tails are almost naked.

INSECTIVORES

Insectivores, or insect-eaters, belong to the Insectivora *order of mammals. The first mammals to develop their young in uteruses belonged to this group, and most insectivores still resemble these small, primitive animals. However, insectivores have evolved to live in a wide range of niches, including subterranean, terrestrial, aquatic and arboreal habitats.*

Giant mole shrew

Blarina brevicauda

Giant mole shrews live in most land habitats within their range, but they are hard to spot. They use their strong forepaws and flexible snouts to dig deep burrows in soft earth and, when on the surface, they scurry out of sight beneath mats of leaves or snow. However, they do climb into trees in search of food on occasion.

These small mammals feed at all times of the day and night. They rest in nests of grass and leaves made inside their tunnels or in nooks and crannies on the surface. Giant mole shrews will eat plant food, but they also hunt for small prey, such as snails, mice and insects. Their saliva contains a venom which paralyzes their prey. In the mating season, which takes place between spring and autumn, their territories expand so that they overlap those of members of the opposite sex.

Distribution: Central Canada to south-eastern United States.
Habitat: All land habitats.
Food: Insects, small vertebrates, seeds and shoots.
Size: 12–14cm (5–5.5in); 15–30g (0.03–0.06lb).
Maturity: 6 weeks.
Breeding: Litters of 5–7 young born throughout summer.
Life span: 2 years.
Status: Common.

Giant mole shrews have stout bodies with long, pointed snouts covered in sensitive whiskers. Their eyes are very small because they spend most of the time underground, and their ears are hidden under thick coats of grey hairs.

Star-nosed mole

Condylura cristata

Distribution: Eastern Canada to south-eastern United States.
Habitat: Muddy soil near water.
Food: Aquatic insects, fish, worms and crustaceans.
Size: 10–12cm (4–5in); 40–85g (0.08–0.19lb).
Maturity: 10 months.
Breeding: 2–7 young born in summer.
Life span: Not known.
Status: Endangered.

Star-nosed moles live in waterlogged soil. They dig networks of tunnels into the soil, which generally reach down as far as the water table. They push the mud and soil out of the entrances of the tunnels, making molehills in the process. The moles construct nests at the ends of tunnels, which are lined with dry grass.

Star-nosed moles are expert swimmers. They search for food at the bottom of streams and pools, using their sensitive snouts to feel their way and detect prey. In winter, star-nosed moles use tunnels with underwater entrances to get into ponds that are iced over. They feed in water during both the day and night, but they are only really active above ground during the hours of darkness.

Most births take place in early summer. The young already have the star of rays on their snouts. Breeding pairs of males and females may stay together throughout the winter and breed again the following year.

Star-nosed moles are named after the curious fleshy rays that radiate around each nostril. These rays are sensitive feelers used in the darkness below ground. Their fur is dark and dense, and is coated with water-repelling oils.

DOLPHINS AND WHALES

Whales and dolphins belong to the Cetacea order of mammals, so they are called the cetaceans. They fall into two broad groups: baleen whales and toothed whales. Instead of teeth, baleen whales have horny plates lined with bristles for filter-feeding, and they include the rorquals and right whales. The toothed whales hunt down prey, and they include dolphins, porpoises, orcas (killer whales) and sperm whales.

Amazon river dolphin

Inia geoffrensis

Distribution: Amazon and Orinoco River Basins.
Habitat: Dark, slow-moving river water.
Food: Small fish.
Size: 1.7–3m (5.5–10ft); 60–120kg (132–264lb).
Maturity: Not known.
Breeding: Single calf born between April and September.
Life span: 30 years.
Status: Vulnerable.

Amazon river dolphins live in the wide rivers of the Amazon Basin. During the rainy season, they move into flooded areas of forest and up swollen streams into lakes. They may become isolated in pools when waters recede, but most are able to survive by eating the river fish that are trapped with them.

Dolphins live in small groups. They are thought to defend the areas around them and will stay in an area as long as there is enough food. They breathe at least once a minute, through the nostrils on the tops of their heads. They dive down to the bottom of rivers to search for food, using their bristled snouts to root through mud and weeds.

Like other dolphins, Amazon river dolphins may use echolocation to find their way in the murky river waters. They sometimes feed in the same areas as giant otters. It may be that the hunting behaviour of otters drives fish out of the shallows towards the dolphins.

When young, Amazon river dolphins have metallic blue and grey upper bodies with silvery bellies. As they age, their upper bodies gradually turn pinkish. They have long snouts with sensitive bristles covering them.

Vaquita

Phocoena sinus

Most vaquitas have dark grey or black upper bodies, with paler undersides. Like other porpoises, vaquitas have blunt faces without the beak-like snouts of dolphins.

Vaquitas live in the upper area of the Gulf of California, near the mouth of the Colorado River. No other marine mammal has such a small range, and consequently vaquitas are extremely rare and may become extinct.

Vaquitas used to be able to swim up into the mouth of the Colorado. However, in recent years so much water has been removed from the river for irrigation and for supplying cities that the Colorado is little more than a trickle where it reaches the ocean. This has probably changed the composition of the Gulf waters, too. The vaquita population was also affected by the fishing industry in the Gulf. Fishermen drowned many vaquitas in their nets by accident, and their activities have also reduced the amount of fish available for the porpoises to eat.

Biologists know little about the lives of vaquitas. They probably spend most of their time alone, locating their prey close to the sea floor using echolocation. Births probably take place all year round.

Distribution: Gulf of California in the eastern Pacific.
Habitat: Coastal waters and mouth of the Colorado River.
Food: Fish and squid.
Size: 1.2–2m (4–6.5ft); 45–60kg (99–132lb).
Maturity: Not known.
Breeding: Not known.
Life span: Not known.
Status: Critically endangered.

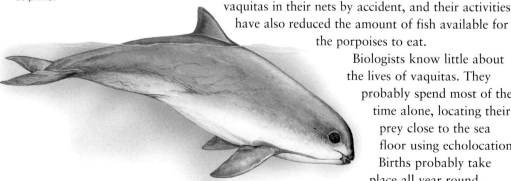

Risso's dolphin

Grampus griseus

Risso's dolphins live in small groups of about ten individuals. The groups move to warm tropical waters in winter and head back toward the poles in summer. The dolphins are often seen leaping out of the water as members of a school play with one another.

Risso's dolphins feed in deep water. They dive down to catch fast-swimming squid and fish. Like other dolphins, they probably use echolocation to locate their prey in the dark depths. They produce clicking noises that bounce off objects in the water. The dolphins can hear each other's clicks and echoes, and groups may work together to track down shoals of fish or squid. In areas where there is plenty of food, dolphin schools congregate so that thousands of the leaping mammals may be seen together.

Distribution: All tropical and temperate seas.
Habitat: Deep ocean water.
Food: Fish and squid.
Size: 3.6–4m (12–13.25ft); 400–450kg (880–990lb).
Maturity: Not known.
Breeding: Single young born once per year.
Life span: 30 years.
Status: Common.

Risso's dolphins have very blunt faces, lacking the beaks of typical dolphins. They have dark grey bodies, which are often scarred by attacks from other dolphins and large squid. Older dolphins may have so many scars that their bodies look almost white.

Spectacled porpoise (*Australophocaena dioptrica*): 1.8–2m (6–6.5ft); 115kg (253lb)
Spectacled porpoises live in coastal waters around South America and New Zealand. Their backs are black, while their undersides, including most of their faces, are white. They have black "spectacles" around their eyes. They are thought to feed on fish and squid, sometimes diving deep below the surface to catch their prey.

La Plata dolphin (*Pontoporia blainvillei*): 1.3–1.75m (4.25–5.75ft); 20–61kg (44–134lb)
These small dolphins live in the coastal waters of south-eastern South America. They are sometimes seen in the wide mouth of the Rio de la Plata in Uruguay – hence their name – but do not appear to swim up any other rivers. Their bodies are grey and they have long slender beaks that curve slightly downwards. They probe the bottom with their snouts, feeding on fish, squid and shrimp.

Tucuxi (*Sotalia fluviatilis*): 1.4–1.9m (4.5–6.25ft); 40–53kg (88–116lb)
These dolphins live in coastal waters from the Caribbean to Brazil and in the rivers of the Amazon Basin, right up to the foothills of the Andes Mountains on the western side of South America. They have grey upper bodies and pinkish undersides. Tucuxis feed mainly on fish and shrimp.

Beluga

Delphinapterus leucas

Beluga means white in Russian, so these whales are sometimes called white whales. However, they should not be confused with white sturgeon – large fish that produce beluga caviar. Belugas also have a nickname – sea canaries – because they call to each other with high-pitched trills.

Belugas live in the far north, where days are almost absent or very short for much of the year. Some beluga pods (schools or groups) spend all their time in one area of ocean, such as the Gulf of St Lawrence. Other pods are always on the move. The pods are ruled by large males, and all pods spend their winters away from areas of thick ice, which may mean being farther or nearer to land depending on where they are. In summer, they enter river estuaries and shallow bays.

They navigate using a well-developed sonar system, thought to be controlled by their melons, which are large sensory organs on top of their heads. Most calves are born in late summer, and their mothers will mate again in early summer a year or two later.

Distribution: From Arctic Ocean to Gulf of Alaska and Gulf of St Lawrence.
Habitat: Deep coastal waters and mouths of large rivers.
Food: Fish, squid, octopuses, crabs and snails.
Size: 3.4–4.6m (11.25–15.25ft); 1.3–1.5 tonnes (2860–3300lb).
Maturity: Females 5 years; males 8 years.
Breeding: Single calf born every 2–3 years.
Life span: 25 years.
Status: Vulnerable.

Adult beluga whales are almost completely white, helping them to hide among ice floes. Younger whales begin life with dark bodies, which gradually become yellow and brown before fading to white.

Orca

Orcinus orca

Distribution: Throughout the world's oceans.
Habitat: Coastal waters.
Food: Seals, other dolphins, fish, squid, penguins and crustaceans.
Size: 8.5–9.8m (28–32.25ft); 5.5–9 tonnes (12,000–20,000lb).
Maturity: Females 6 years; males 12 years.
Breeding: Single young born generally in autumn every 3–4 years.
Life span: 60–90 years.
Status: Lower risk.

Orcas have black upper bodies and white undersides. They also have grey patches behind their dorsal fins and white patches along their sides and above the eyes. These "whales" are really the largest members of the dolphin family.

Orcas are also known as killer whales. They are expert hunters, being armed with up to 50 large, pointed teeth, and they catch prey in all areas of the ocean. Although orcas have been detected 1km (0.6 mile) below the surface, they prefer to hunt in shallow coastal waters and often swim into bays and mouths of rivers to snatch food near the shore.

Orcas typically live in pods of five or six individuals. Generally each pod is run by a large male, although larger groups have several adult males. Females and their young may split off into subgroups. Like other toothed whales and dolphins, orcas produce click sounds that are used for echolocation. The whales also communicate with each other using high-pitched screams and whistles. Orcas have several hunting techniques. They break pack ice from beneath, knocking their prey into the water, or they may rush into shallow water to grab prey from the shore. It is reported that they may crash on to the shore to drive prey into the surf where other members of the pod pick them off. Orcas breed throughout the year, although most mate in the early summer and give birth in the autumn of the following year.

Humpback whale

Megaptera novaeangliae

Humpbacks spend their summers feeding far from shore, in the cold waters near the poles. They feed by taking in huge mouthfuls of sea water. Their baleen plates then strain out any fish or krill from the water. Pairs of humpbacks also corral schools of fish by blowing curtains of bubbles around them. The fish will not swim through the bubbles and crowd together as the whales rush up from beneath with their mouths wide open.

As winter approaches, the whales stop feeding and head to warmer, shallow waters near coasts or groups of islands. For example, populations of humpbacks spend the winter near Baja California and the Hawaiian islands. During the winter the whales do not feed; instead they concentrate on reproduction. The males produce songs which are repeated over and over for days on end. The songs probably attract receptive females that are not caring for calves that year, and also help rival males keep away from each other. Pregnant females stay feeding for longer than the other whales, and arrive in the wintering grounds just in time to give birth.

Humpback whales are so called because of their dorsal fins, which may be swelled into humps by deposits of fat. Humpbacks have the longest pectoral (arm) fins of any whale – about a third as long as their bodies. These baleen whales have throat grooves which expand to enlarge the throat size as the feeding whale gulps water.

Distribution: All oceans.
Habitat: Deep ocean water.
Food: Small fish and krill.
Size: 12.5–15m (41–49.5ft); 30 tonnes (66,000lb).
Maturity: 4–5 years.
Breeding: Single young born every 2 years.
Life span: 70 years.
Status: Vulnerable.

Grey whale

Eschrichtius robustus

Grey whales spend their lives on the move. In autumn they swim from Arctic waters down the western coast of North America, mating on the way, to spend the winter in bays along the coast of Mexico. The young that were conceived during the previous year are born in these bays in late January and February, and soon after, the whales set off to spend the summer in the food-rich waters of the Arctic.

A similar migration takes place down the eastern coast of Asia, but these whales are relatively few in number. Grey whales spend a good deal of time playing in shallow water during the winter. They leap out of the water and may become stranded for a few hours as they wait for the tide to rise. While on the move, they "spyhop" – protrude their heads above the surface so that they can look around.

Grey whales are baleen whales that feed on the seabed. They drive their heads through the sediment to stir up prey. They then suck in the disturbed water and strain the animals from it. Most feeding takes place in the summer, and whales may fast for the remaining six months of the year.

Distribution: Northern Pacific Rim.
Habitat: Shallow coastal water.
Food: Amphipods (small crustaceans).
Size: 13–15m (43–49.5ft); 20–37 tonnes (44,000–81,000lb).
Maturity: Females 17 years; males 19 years.
Breeding: Single young born every 2 years.
Life span: 70 years.
Status: Endangered

Grey whales do not have dorsal fins, but a series of small humps along their backs. They are often covered in white barnacles.

Bowhead whale (*Balaena mysticetus*): 11–13m (36.25–43ft); 50–60 tonnes (110,000–132,000lb)
Bowhead whales live in the Arctic Ocean. They have huge curved jaws with more baleen plates than any other whale. Adults have black bodies with pale patches on their lower jaws. Bowheads live among ice floes. They feed on tiny floating crustaceans, such as krill and copepods. They can eat 1.8 tonnes (3,960lb) in one day.

Blue whale (*Balaenoptera musculus*): 25–30m (82.5–100ft); 100–160 tonnes (220,000–352,000lb)
The blue whale is the largest animal to have ever existed. It has a blue-grey body, with spots along its back and a pale pleated throat. Blue whales live alone, ploughing between subtropical waters and those near the poles. The populations of the northern and southern hemispheres never meet. They eat krill – tiny floating crustaceans – and can gulp down 6 tonnes (13,200lb) of them in a single day. Their pleated throats distend to four times their normal size as the whales take in mouthfuls of krill-laden water.

West Indian manatee

Trichechus manatus

Despite appearances, manatees are not cetaceans. Neither are they related to seals – pinnipeds. These marine mammals belong to the *Sirenia* order, as do the dugongs – similar animals from South-east Asia. Sirenians evolved to live in water separately from whales and seals. In fact, they are believed to be more closely related to elephants than other sea mammals. Like elephants, they are vegetarian, not carnivorous.

Manatees live in both salt and fresh water, although they spend more time in freshwater habitats. They rarely stray far from land, and may travel far up rivers to sources of warm water during winter.

Manatees feed both during the day and night. They use their dextrous lips to pluck water plants, such as water hyacinths. Although they do not actively seek them out, manatees' vegetarian diets are supplemented by the aquatic invertebrates, such as snails and insect larvae, living on the water plants. The single young is born after about a year's gestation.

Distribution: Coast of Florida to Brazil.
Habitat: Estuaries and shallow coastal water.
Food: Water plants and aquatic invertebrates.
Size: 2.5–4.5m (8.25–15ft); 500kg (1100lb).
Maturity: 8–10 years.
Breeding: Single young born every 2–3 years.
Life span: 30 years.
Status: Vulnerable.

Manatees have wrinkled grey-brown skin with a sparse covering of fine hairs. Their fore-flippers have nails on their upper surfaces and their upper lips, which are very manoeuvrable, have moustaches of thick bristles.

SEALS AND RELATIVES

Seals, sea lions and walruses are pinnipeds – they belong to the Pinnipedia *order of mammals. They are descended from carnivorous, terrestrial ancestors. However, it seems that seals may be only distantly related to sea lions and walruses, despite their similar appearances. Like other sea mammals, pinnipeds have a thick layer of blubber under their skin, which keeps them warm while swimming in cold water.*

Californian sea lion

Zalophus californianus

Californian sea lions spend the year moving up and down the Pacific coast of North America. In autumn and winter, most males move north to feed off the coast of British Columbia. The females and young stray less far from the breeding grounds and probably head south at this time.

The sea lions are seldom far from the shore at any time of the year. They generally go on foraging trips at night, although they are often active during the day as well. Each trip can last for several hours.

During the summer breeding season, the sea lions congregate on flat beaches in the central area of their range. Most choose sandy habitats, but will use open, rocky areas if necessary. The males arrive first and fight each other for control of small territories on the beaches and in the water. They can only hold their territories for a few weeks before having to swim away and feed.

Californian sea lions have less heavyset bodies than most sea lions because they live in warmer climes. They are fast swimmers, reaching speeds of 40kph (25mph).

Distribution: Pacific coast of North America and Galápagos Islands.
Habitat: Ocean islands and coastline.
Food: Fish, squid and seabirds.
Size: 1.5–2.5m (5–8.25ft); 200–400kg (440–880lb).
Maturity: Females 6 years; males 9 years.
Breeding: Single pup born each year.
Life span: 20 years.
Status: Vulnerable.

South American sea lion

Otaria flavescens or *byronia*

South American sea lions do not travel very far from their breeding sites during the non-breeding season, although they may spend long periods out at sea. These sea lions sometimes feed in groups, especially when they are hunting shoals of fish or squid.

The breeding season begins at the start of the southern summer. Adults arrive on beaches or flat areas of rock at the beginning of December. Males arrive a few weeks before the females, and defend small patches of the beach. The females give birth to the young they have been carrying since the year before. After a few weeks of nursing their pups, the females become receptive to mating again. As the numbers of females increases, males stop controlling territories and begin to defend groups of females. Unsuccessful males without harems of their own gang together on the fringes of the beaches and charge through the females to mate with them.

Male South American sea lions have dark brown bodies with brown manes on their heads and necks. The females are less heavyset and have paler bodies and no manes.

Distribution: South Pacific and Atlantic waters off the South American coast from northern Peru to Brazil.
Habitat: Coastal waters and beaches.
Food: Fish, squid and crustaceans.
Size: 1.8–2.5m (6–8.25ft); 150–350kg (330–770lb).
Maturity: Females 4 years; males 6 years.
Breeding: Single pup born in January.
Life span: 20 years.
Status: Vulnerable

Walrus

Odobenus rosmarus

Walruses live among the ice floes of the Arctic Ocean. These huge sea mammals are well known for their long tusks, which they use to stab opponents during fights. Walruses also use their tusks to "haul out", or pull themselves on to floating ice, and sometimes hook themselves to floes so that they can sleep while still in the water.

Walruses use their whiskered snouts to root out prey and blast away sediment with jets of air squirted from the mouth. They tackle shelled prey by holding them in their lips and sucking out the soft bodies.

Walruses live in large herds, sometimes of many thousands. In winter they feed in areas of thin sea ice, avoiding thick, unbroken ice, which they cannot break through from beneath. In summer, when the ice recedes, they spend more time on land.

Walruses have long tusks growing out of their upper jaws. Males, which are twice the size of females, also have longer tusks. Their bodies are reddish-brown and sparsely covered in coarse hairs. Males have two air pouches inside their necks, which they use to amplify their mating calls.

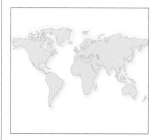

Distribution: Coast of Arctic Ocean.
Habitat: Pack ice.
Food: Worms, shellfish and fish.
Size: 2.25–3.5m (7.5–11.5ft); 400–1,700kg (880–3,740lb).
Maturity: Females 6 years; males 10 years.
Breeding: Single young born once per year.
Life span: 40 years.
Status: Vulnerable.

Southern elephant seal (*Mirounga leonina*): 2–9m (6.5–30ft); 400–5,000kg (880–11,000lb)
Southern elephant seals are the largest pinnipeds in the world. The males are four to five times the size of the females and have inflatable trunk-like noses, with which they amplify their bellowing calls. Elephant seals live in the waters around Antarctica and South America, where they dive for fish and squid. They congregate on flat beaches to breed in winter. The males arrive first and take up positions. They may stay on the beaches for the next two months without feeding. The females arrive a few weeks later and give birth. After giving birth, the females spread out and the males battle to mate with harems of females along the beaches. On a smaller beach, all the females may be controlled by a single bull, known as a beach master.

Steller's sea lion (*Eumetopias jubatus*): 2.4–3m (8–10ft); 270–1,000kg (594–2,200lb)
Steller's sea lions are the largest sea lions. They live along the coast of the northern Pacific Ocean, from Japan to California. Adult males have huge necks, made even chunkier by coarse manes. The females are about a third of their size. Steller's sea lions often rest on rocky coasts, but they feed on fish, squid and shellfish out at sea. Females give birth to single pups in early summer.

Hooded seal

Cystophora cristata

Hooded seals rarely approach land, preferring to spend their whole lives among the ice floes in the cold Arctic Ocean. Apart from during the breeding season, hooded seals live alone. They dive down to depths of more than 180m (590ft) to catch shoaling fish and bottom-living creatures.

When the breeding season arrives in spring, the seals congregate on wide ice floes. The females take up widely spaced positions on the ice, preparing to give birth to the young conceived the year before. Meanwhile, males compete for access to small groups of females. The victors stay near the females as they nurse their new-born calves, chasing away any intruders while inflating their nasal balloons.

Hooded seal pups are suckled for only four days – the shortest time of any mammal – after which the mothers abandon them.

Distribution: Waters around Greenland.
Habitat: Drifting ice floes.
Food: Octopuses, squid, shrimp, mussels and fish.
Size: 2–2.7m (6.5–9ft); 145–300kg (320–660lb).
Maturity: Females 3 years; males 5 years.
Breeding: Single pup born in March.
Life span: 30 years.
Status: Common.

Hooded seals are so named because the males possess elastic sacs or hoods on the tops of their heads. The hoods are connected to their noses and can be inflated with air to amplify their calls while sparring with rival males. Female seals also have hoods, but they are not inflatable.

ANIMALS OF EUROPE AND AFRICA

Europe and Africa are separated by the Mediterranean Sea, and although the divide is only a few short miles in some places, the two continents are very different, both in terms of climate and their animal life. Europe is not actually a continent at all; it is a large peninsula stretching from the Ural Mountains to the Atlantic Ocean on the western side of the huge Asian landmass. Africa also used to be joined to Asia. It is now cut off entirely by the man-made Suez Canal, but many animals found in Africa also live in parts of Asia. Europe's wildlife might seem ordinary compared to many other parts of the world; many of the animals that once roamed free there, such as lions and bears, are now extinct or at least very rare. Africa, on the other hand, is well known for its wildlife. It is home to the largest land animal of all, the African elephant, as well as the great apes and many other diverse species.

Above from left: Fire salamanders, mandrill, lion.

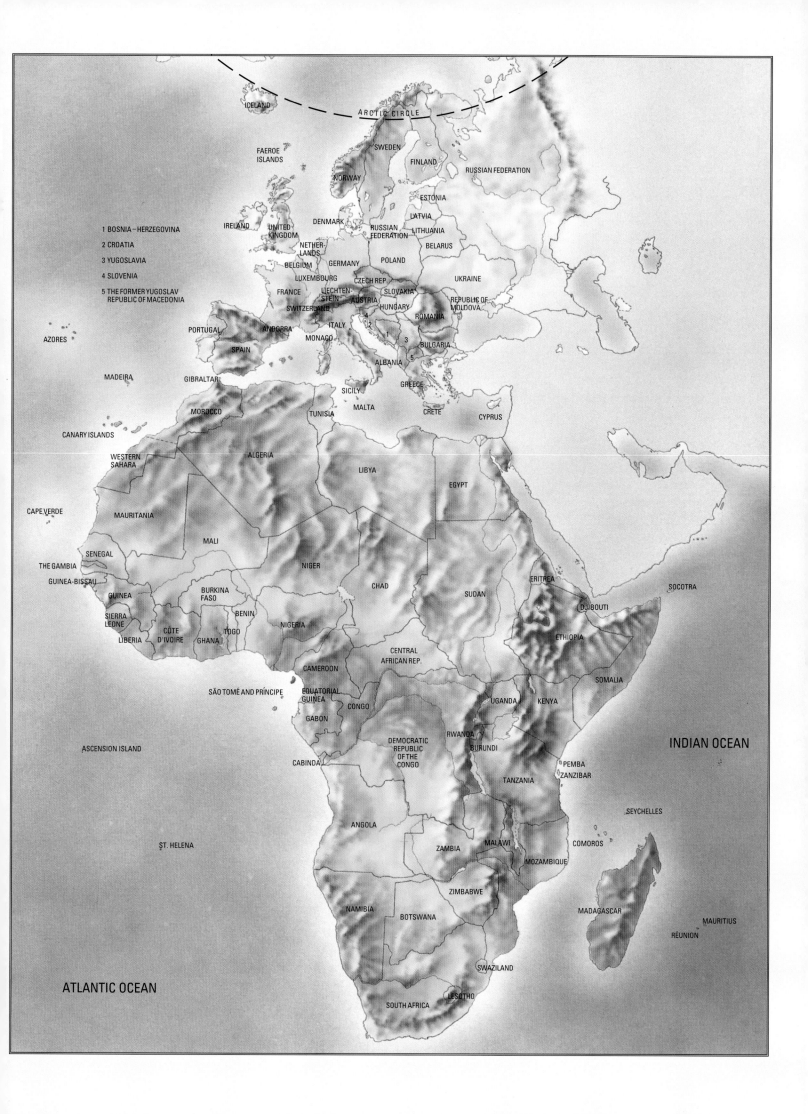

SALAMANDERS AND RELATIVES

Of the living amphibians, salamanders and newts are the most similar to ancestral amphibians, known from fossils. Salamanders typically have rougher skin than newts and are better able to survive out of water because they have glands to keep their skins moist. They are also frequently brightly coloured and armed with toxins to repel predators.

Olm

Proteus anguinus

The olm is the world's largest cave-dwelling vertebrate. It lives in the dark, in bodies of cold, underground water. The olm has dull white, sometimes pinkish skin and three tufted, bright red gills on each side of its neck. Its tail is long and eel-like. The olm's gills are filled with blood, allowing the animal to breathe underwater. Oxygen in the water is transferred to the blood via the surface of the gills.

The olm's eyes are reduced to tiny black dots under the skin, leaving it virtually blind. Newly born young have more fully developed eyes than the adults, but these disappear after a year. The olm has a powerful sense of smell and can also find food, communicate and move around by detecting weak electric signals emitted by prey, other olms or inanimate objects such as rocks and pebbles.

Olms have tiny legs for the size of their bodies, with only three stumpy toes on their front legs and two on their back legs. Their snouts are broad and help them to burrow into mud or fine sand to find food, usually freshwater crustaceans.

Olms have elongated bodies, white or pink skin, three pairs of external gills and tiny, skin-covered black eyes that can only perceive light and shadow. Olms were once more common, but numbers have dropped because of water pollution and widespread capture for the pet trade.

Distribution: Slovenia through to Bosnia-Herzegovina.
Habitat: Underground lakes and streams.
Food: Freshwater crustaceans.
Size: 25–30cm (10–12in).
Maturity: Very little information. Thought to be 16–18 years.
Breeding: Females normally give birth to 2 larvae. If the water is warm enough up to 80 eggs may be laid instead.
Life span: 100 years.
Status: Rare.

Fire salamander

Salamandra salamandra

Fire salamanders have poison glands in their skins that are surrounded by special muscles. These are particularly concentrated on their backs. When the muscles contract, they squeeze toxins from the glands. The salamanders can squirt their poison up to 2m (6.5ft). The poison irritates the skin and may affect the nervous systems of any animals that it touches. It can even kill certain predators by paralyzing their lungs, thus stopping them from breathing.

Females are able to store sperm from males for up to two years. They carry 10–40 live young around in their bodies. These are born with their legs well developed, but they still possess larval gills. Some females have been found carrying only four or five young, but these were born fully developed, without gills. By having fewer young, a female is able to provide her offspring with more food. Being so far developed means the young can continue to grow and survive on land, where it is relatively safe.

The fire salamander has a bright yellow and black pattern that warns all would-be predators that it carries toxins. The underside is dark grey with fewer markings. Female fire salamanders are larger than males.

Distribution: Central and southern Europe, Middle East and north-west Africa.
Habitat: Forested, hilly or mountainous country, not far from water.
Food: Invertebrates such as slugs, worms, flies, beetles and centipedes.
Size: 14–17cm (6–7in).
Maturity: Change into adults 2 or 3 months after birth.
Breeding: 10–40 young develop inside female and born after 8 months.
Life span: 20 years.
Status: Common.

Great crested newt

Triturus cristatus

Great crested newts have dark backs, while their bellies are orange or red with large black blotches or spots. The males are more colourful than the females, with tall crests along their backs during the breeding season.

During the breeding season, male great crested newts become brightly coloured, particularly on their bellies. They also develop high toothed crests along their backs and white bands along the sides of their tails. The male newts also have thicker skins than the females at this time.

The newts hibernate on land during the winter. They return to the water around mid-March, and the males develop their breeding livery two or three weeks later. Once the breeding season is over, their crests and outer skins are absorbed into their bodies. Young great crested newts hatch in water as tadpoles. As they develop, they feed on fish, other tadpoles, worms and aquatic insects. The adults feed on larger prey, including newts, frogs and older tadpoles. They locate their prey in the mud at the bottom of their pond, using smell and sight.

Great crested newts are afforded protection by their skins. If threatened, their skins release a white, creamy fluid which is an irritant to the eyes, nose and mouth of predators.

Distribution: England, Scotland, central Europe from France to Urals, and southern Scandinavia to Alps.
Habitat: Spend most of the year in weedy ponds.
Food: Small aquatic invertebrates and vertebrates, including other amphibians.
Size: 11–16cm (4.5–6.5in).
Maturity: Tadpoles change into newts after 8–16 weeks. Reach adult size after 2 years.
Breeding: 200–300 eggs laid between April and mid-July.
Life span: 27 years.
Status: Vulnerable.

Palmate newt (*Triturus helveticus*): 9cm (3.5in)
The palmate newt lives in western Europe, from Scotland to north-west Spain and Portugal. The males have webbed feet, yellow bellies and thin filaments of skin that extend 5mm (0.2in) from the tips of their tails. The females are much duller and lack the tail filaments. They hibernate under logs and stones from November through to March, when they return to water to breed and spend the summer months.

Spectacled salamander (*Salamandrina terdigitata*): 10cm (4in)
The spectacled salamander is found in Italy. It is the only European salamander to have four toes on all four feet. Most others have four on their front feet and five on their back feet. The females are able to store sperm from the males, enabling them to produce young as soon as spring arrives, giving them the best chance of survival. They find mates when there is more time later in the year, and so prepare for the following season.

Marbled newt (*Triturus marmoratus*): 9–11cm (3.5–4.5in)
The marbled newt is found in south-west France, Spain and Portugal. It has a green back, interrupted by a black marbling effect and a grey belly. Both males and females develop orange-red stripes along their backs, from neck to tail. The females keep this stripe when they return to water to breed. During this time, the males lose their red stripes and develop crests, along with silver bands on their tails. When threatened, their tails are erected and swayed from side to side.

Sharp-ribbed newt

Pleurodeles waltl

The sharp-ribbed newt has special rib bones that are able to inject poison into a predator by protruding through special pores in its skin. When the poison enters the skin of a predator, it causes a great deal of pain. The newt will also head-butt a predator, exposing glands at the back of its head that exude a toxic fluid. It has similar glands on its tail, which it lashes to release the toxin.

This species lives permanently in water and will only leave a pool if the water level begins to fall. The newts have flattened bodies to help them slip under rocks and logs. Sharp-ribbed newts breed twice in a year, in early spring and again in midsummer. The males have much longer tails than the females, and during the mating season they develop special pads under their front legs to help grasp the females when transferring sperm.

Distribution: Spain, Portugal and Morocco.
Habitat: Entirely aquatic, in standing water such as ponds, lagoons, dams and irrigation systems.
Food: Invertebrates, small fish and carrion.
Size: 15–30cm (6–12in).
Maturity: 4 years.
Breeding: Female lays between 100 and 1,000 eggs depending on her size. Breeding takes place twice: once in the spring and again in midsummer.
Life span: Not known.
Status: Common.

The sharp-ribbed newt has a dark brown back. Along its sides it has dark blotches with lines of dull orange circles. These are the pores from which the ribs can protrude from its body. Its belly is generally much paler in colour.

FROGS AND TOADS

Throughout the world, there are over 4,000 species of frog and toad – more than ten times the number of salamanders and newts. Frogs are often recognized by their long legs, hopping motion and smooth, often brightly coloured skins. Toads, on the other hand, are often dark brown, warty amphibians that walk rather than hop. However, many frogs and toads are difficult to distinguish from one another.

African clawed toad

Xenopus laevis

Distribution: Southern Africa.
Habitat: Muddy pools.
Food: Small worms, crustaceans, fly larvae and tadpoles of own species.
Size: 6–9cm (2.5–3.5in).
Maturity: Females 15–18 months; males 12 months.
Breeding: Spawn from August–December.
Life span: Over 20 years.
Status: Common.

Today, chemical tests are used to tell whether women are pregnant. However, African clawed toads were once commonly used in hospitals as pregnancy tests. Pregnant women produce a particular hormone, which is released into their urine. If this hormone is present in the urine when injected into female toads, then the toads spontaneously lay eggs. In nature, eggs are laid singly and may be attached to water plants or rocks.

From the head along the toad's sides there are a few rows of small stitch-like lines. Each line is a little depression containing minute hairs that detect vibrations in the water. This helps to tell the toad where it is, the location of other toads or predators, and occasionally food.

African clawed toads like to hang just below the water surface, waiting for food to swim by. They are the only South African amphibians to feed and breed in the water for their whole lives. If their pools dry up, they bury themselves in the mud and wait for the rainy season to arrive.

The African clawed toad is very flat, with small upward-facing eyes. Its skin is very slimy and generally coloured brown, green or grey, with darker spots or blotches on its back. Its belly is a yellowish-white colour.

Cape ghost frog

Heleophryne purcelli

The Cape ghost frog is a small frog with dull green skin, covered in black-brown spots bordered with yellow. Its eyes are a coppery colour.

Cape ghost frogs live in very fast-flowing mountain streams. They have well developed toe pads for clinging to wet rocks in these torrential habitats. Their large hind feet are also webbed, to help them swim against the current. Male Cape ghost frogs also have pads along the insides of their front legs and, prior to the mating season, they develop small spines around the rims of their lower jaws. These modifications help them grasp females and prevent them from being washed away while mating.

The females lay their large eggs under stones or in gravel in shallow backwaters, alongside the main channels of streams. Their tadpoles are long and flat. They, too, must cling on to rocks to avoid being washed away by the torrents. They attach themselves to smooth rocks with their large sucker-like mouths. The tadpoles feed on microscopic algae that grow on the surfaces of the rocks. They use their long, muscular tails to fight against the currents for periods while grazing.

Distribution: South Africa.
Habitat: Fast-flowing streams in mountain areas.
Food: Algae.
Size: 3.5–5cm (1.5–2in).
Maturity: 2 years.
Breeding: Summer.
Life span: Not known.
Status: Common.

Tomato frog (*Dyscophus antongilii*): 5–10cm (2–4in)
Tomato frogs have orange-red backs, yellowish undersides, green eyes and sometimes black spots on their throats. The females are a brighter red than the males. They live in the lowlands of Madagascar, in swamps and shallow pools. Breeding occurs during the rainy season in stagnant or very slow-moving water. Females lay 1,000–1,500 small black and white eggs on the water's surface. The tadpoles are very quick to hatch and do so only 36 hours later, changing into adults after about 45 days.

Mountain ghost frog (*Heleophryne rosei*): 3.5–5cm (1.5–2in)
The mountain ghost frog is extremely rare and restricted to an area only 7–8sq km (1.5sq miles) in size on Table Mountain in South Africa. It has specific breeding requirements and needs areas that have water all year round. The tadpoles take a long time to grow and need at least two seasons before they change into adults.

African "hairy" frog (*Trichobatrachus robustus*): Length not known
The African "hairy" frog lives in western Africa. It gets its name from special hair-like filaments that develop on the male frog's legs and sides. The filaments are full of blood vessels and grow when the frog needs more oxygen to breathe. The species has lungs that are much smaller than the lungs of other frogs of a similar size. This means that when the males become very active as they jostle over females to mate with, they require more oxygen. The filaments act as external lungs, providing them with extra oxygen.

African bullfrog

Pyxicephalus adspersus

To avoid drying up, the African bullfrog can wrap itself in a cocoon. This is made from many layers of dead skin, and looks like plastic film. The frog can survive in this cocoon for two or three months, getting all the moisture it needs by absorbing water from its bladder. When the rains finally arrive, the cocoon softens and splits open. The frog scrambles out and eats the cocoon.

The male guards its eggs and tadpoles in a shallow puddle. Sharp upper teeth and two horny spikes at the tip of the lower jaw help ward off intruders. If the puddle is in danger of drying out, the male digs an escape channel for transferring the tadpoles to water. When the tadpoles develop, they can be aggressive and cannibalistic.

Distribution: Tropical areas across central Africa.
Habitat: Temporary bodies of water and small lakes in open or bush country.
Food: Insects and other invertebrates, reptiles, amphibians, birds and rodents.
Size: Up to 20cm (8in); 2kg (4.5lb).
Maturity: 1–2 years.
Breeding: Female lays up to 4,000 eggs in temporary pools. Tadpoles change into striped froglets but lose their stripes over time.
Life span: More than 20 years.
    Status: Not known.

African bullfrogs are generally olive green, with lighter coloured throats and bellies to help them blend in with their surroundings. Juveniles have obvious stripes, which later fade as they get older.

Goliath bullfrog

Conraua goliath

Goliath bullfrogs are the largest frogs in the world, and can grow to more than 30cm (12in) in length. They live in only a few rivers in western Africa and are at risk from disappearing altogether because the rainforests where they live are being cleared for growing crops and grazing cattle. The construction of human settlements and dams built across rivers are also problems for the species because they destroy even more of their habitat.

Adult Goliath bullfrogs eat insects, crustaceans, fish and other amphibians, including newts, salamanders and smaller frogs. Their tadpoles, however, are plant-eaters and will only feed on certain species of water plant that are found near waterfalls and rapids in particular areas. The distribution of the water plants restricts the Goliath bullfrogs to a relatively small region of West Africa.

The Goliath bullfrog is silent, not having a vocal sac in its throat to make any sound. It is a shy species that is hunted by one local forest tribe, who eat them and keep the thigh bones as good-luck charms.

The Goliath bullfrog is a very dark coloured frog, mainly a blackish-green. The belly is a lighter pinkish-orange and the eyes are a coppery brown.

Distribution: Cameroon and Equatorial Guinea.
Habitat: Swiftly flowing rivers in dense rainforests.
Food: Small freshwater invertebrates, fish and other amphibians. Tadpoles eat plants.
Size: 30cm (12in); 3.3kg (7.25lb).
Maturity: Not known.
Breeding: Not known.
Life span: Not known.
Status: Vulnerable.

Common toad

Bufo bufo

The common toad often lives in very dry areas over most of the year. Its thick, loose skin and nocturnal habits help to protect it from drying out. Toads are eaten less commonly than frogs because of foul-tasting chemicals released by glands in their skins. If threatened, the common toad will also inflate its body and rise up on its legs, looking two or three times as big and more intimidating than usual.

Toads are particularly fond of ants, and use their sticky tongues to reach out and catch them. They have a good sense of smell, and this is thought to be very important in helping them to move long distances and find their breeding sites each year. They tend to come out of hibernation during February and March – usually a few weeks later than common frogs.

Rather than laying clumps of spawn, as frogs do, common toads release a long double strand of spawn that becomes entangled in pondweed and other vegetation. In warm weather, tadpoles metamorphose in about eight weeks.

Common toads are olive brown and covered in warts. They have copper-coloured eyes and walk rather than hop like frogs. The males are smaller and have fewer warts than the females, and only the males croak.

Distribution: Most of Europe, north-west Africa, Asia and parts of Oceania.
Habitat: Damp areas of deciduous woodland, scrub, gardens, parks and fields. In the breeding season, they live in ponds, lakes, ditches and slow-moving rivers.
Food: Insects and their larvae, spiders, slugs and worms. Larger toads sometimes prey on slow worms, small grass snakes and harvest mice, which are swallowed alive.
Size: 8–15cm (3–6in).
Maturity: 4 years.
Breeding: 600–4,000 eggs laid.
Life span: 40 years.
Status: Common.

European common frog

Rana temporaria

European common frogs are found in a variety of habitats, including fields and woodland close to water. Their diet is eclectic, including insects, molluscs and worms. Male common frogs have swellings on their first fingers to help them grasp the females when mating. Sometimes two or three males may try to mate with one female. Occasionally she will die in this situation through drowning or being squashed by their combined weight.

Spawning can take place as early as December or January but it is more usual in late February, March or April. Frogs flock to a traditional pond, lake or ditch, where hundreds or thousands may be swimming around. Males emit quiet croaks and can be seen jostling for the best females. While a female is releasing her 1,000–4,000 eggs, the male, directly on top, will spread his sperm over all them.

After spawning, the ponds become quiet again, as the frogs leave to live on land. They do so until the autumn, when they hibernate under logs and rocks. When it is very cold, they will rest in the water, usually in amongst thick vegetation.

Common frogs are variable in colour, but generally have a greenish-brown body colour with darker blotches and dark masks on their faces.

Distribution: Widespread throughout Europe, including Turkey and Russia.
Habitat: Live in meadows, gardens and woodland. Breed in puddles, ponds, lakes and canals. Prefer areas of shallow water.
Food: Insects, snails, slugs and worms, caught with long, sticky tongues. Tadpoles are herbivorous and feed on algae.
Size: 6–10cm (2.5–4in).
Maturity: 3 years.
Breeding: 1,000–4,000 eggs laid.
Life span: 12 years.
Status: Common in most of range.

European tree frog

Hyla arborea

European tree frogs are bright green frogs. They are able to change colour, and when they first come out from hibernation, in the spring, they are grey-brown. They are excellent climbers, living in shrubs and trees throughout southern Europe. They have sucker pads on the ends of their toes to help them grasp branches. The green skin helps to keep them hidden among the leaves.

Tree frogs are most active during the night, particularly if it has been raining. They leap around, catching a variety of night-flying flies and moths. In late spring, the males sit by the edges of ponds or on plants overhanging the water, croaking to attract females. When the males call, they inflate vocal sacs, which produce their distinctive sound. When full of air, the sacs are as big as the frogs. The song produced is similar to the bark of a dog or the quack of a duck. When a number of males croak together throughout the night, they can be heard as far as several kilometres away.

The European tree frog is lime green on top and white underneath. It has a somewhat contorted appearance because the skin on its head is fused to its skull.

Distribution: Europe, below 800m (2,650ft) above sea level.
Habitat: Scrub and open woodland with shrubs.
Food: Flies and moths.
Size: 3–4.5cm (1.25–2in).
Maturity: Not known.
Breeding: 800–1,000 eggs laid in small clumps during late April or May.
Life span: 20 years.
Status: Declining.

Fire-bellied toad (*Bombina bombina*): 3–5cm (1.25–2in)
From above, fire-bellied toads are well camouflaged by their dull, mottled colours. They have black or dark brown warty skins, covered in dark spots with green patches on their shoulders and broad, green central lines. However, the bellies are black with bright red or yellow patches which form a unique pattern, rather like human fingerprints. When adults call, they inflate their throats and show off their bright colours.

Marsh frog (*Rana ridibunda*): Females 7.5–14cm (3–5.5in); males 6.5–10cm (2.5–4in)
The marsh frog lives on the plains and rivers of eastern Europe. It also occurs in western Europe, originally introduced by humans. Its loud croaking can be heard from pools during the day and night. When calling, special sacs are inflated and bulge out on either side of the head. The frogs make these strange and loud calls to attract mates throughout May and June. It is the largest European frog and usually remains in the water for most of the year.

Natterjack toad (*Bufo calamita*): Females 5–8cm (2–3.25in); males 4–7cm (1.5–3in)
The natterjack toad is found throughout western and central Europe and is the smallest of all European toads. It has dark, warty skin like the common toad and a yellow line all the way from the head to the end of the spine. It tends to spawn in shallow fresh water. During the breeding season, the males develop purple-violet throats. The females' throats remain white. Natterjack toads are thought to be Europe's noisiest toads because the male's croaking can travel for up to 3km (2 miles).

Bushveld rain frog

Breviceps adspersus

The Bushveld rain frog is a rather rotund burrowing frog with a short head and blunt snout. It spends most of its life underground, only coming up to the surface to feed and breed after rains. Its globular shape makes burrowing through soft sandy soil easier, but it also makes mating difficult. To help the male stay on top of the female, he secretes a sticky substance from glands around his rear. This acts like a glue and binds him to his mate.

The fertilized eggs are laid in an underground chamber. When mating and egg-laying is over, the glue either breaks down or the female sheds her skin to release the male. The tadpoles are unable to feed and have to develop into froglets before they have their first meal.

The males attract females by giving short, blurred whistles, which are emitted in a continuous series of single calls. Two or more may call together in a chorus.

The Bushveld rain frog is brown with rows of light yellow or orange patches along its spine and sides. It also has a broad black stripe from each eye to its armpit and a speckled throat, which may be entirely black in males.

Distribution: South Africa and Swaziland, Mozambique, Botswana and Namibia.
Habitat: Hot, dry foothills. Dry bushveld in northern part of South African range. Breeds in open and closed woodland with sandy soils.
Food: Insects.
Size: 3–6cm (1.25–2.5in).
Maturity: Not known.
Breeding: After rains.
Life span: Not known.
Status: Common.

Foam-nesting frog

Chiromantis xerampelina

Foam-nesting frogs are found in tropical and subtropical parts of Africa, where they inhabit trees and shrubs of the savannah. When mating, pairs of foam-nesting frogs produce large amounts of foam in which the eggs are laid. The foam masses are attached to branches, overhanging temporary pools of water. The foam stops the eggs from drying out in the hot climate where the frogs live, and females occasionally remoisten it with water.

The tadpoles hatch after two days and survive in the foam as it dries out. After about a week, when the nests become very crowded, the tadpoles drop from the foam into the water below. In most matings, two or three males will be involved with each female. All the males help in beating mucus to produce the foam nests. Male foam-nesting frogs have large testicles to produce copious amounts of sperm. This increases their chances of success in fertilizing the eggs.

Foam-nesting frogs live in areas that reach high temperatures, and they can be found sitting in direct sunlight. They lose very little water from their bodies and have a special skin that turns white in the sunshine. This stops them from heating up and losing water through evaporation. To avoid overheating, they also produce a watery mucus from glands in their waterproof skins.

The foam-nesting frog is a light-coloured, grainy, pale green frog with light brown lines on its legs and irregular spots across its body. Many individuals are darker with brown areas.

Distribution: Tropical and southern subtropical parts of Africa, in the south and west of these areas.
Habitat: Bushes and trees in African grassland.
Food: Large insects.
Size: 6cm (2.5in).
Maturity: Not known.
Breeding: During the rainy season.
Life span: 2.5 years.
Status: Common.

Midwife toad

Alytes obstetricans

Distribution: West and south-west Europe.
Habitat: Quarries, scree slopes and uncultivated land. Sand dunes and gardens are inhabited in France.
Food: Small insects.
Size: 5cm (2in).
Maturity: 2 years.
Breeding: Female lays several batches of 20–60 eggs in strings between April and June, which are carried on the male's back legs. Tadpoles released into water between 2 and 6 weeks later.
Life span: Not known.
Status: Locally common.

The midwife toad looks very similar to the common toad. However, it has vertical pupils instead of horizontal ones, a more pointed snout, and does not have the protective glands behind the head. Midwife toads are night-active and spend the day hidden in crevices in rocks, under logs or in burrows.

In late spring, the males give out short peeping calls to attract females. Mating occurs on land. As the females produce strings of 20–60 eggs, the males catch them with their legs. They then position the strings of spawn between their thighs and waists. The females play no part in looking after the eggs. The eggs remain embedded in a whitish-yellow mass of mucus that keeps them moist.

The male secretes an antibiotic solution over the eggs to protect them from fungal or bacterial attack. After two to six weeks, the eggs develop into fully formed tadpoles. The males travel to ponds where the young release themselves into the water. Some males attract two or more females, and therefore look after a larger number of eggs.

The midwife toad is dull grey, olive or brown in colour, occasionally with green spots and often with darker markings. The belly is whitish with grey blotches. Females sometimes have red spots running down their flanks. This toad is particularly proficient at leaping.

Red-legged pan frog (*Kassina maculata*): 6.5cm (2.5in)
The red-legged pan frog is grey with black oval spots, outlined with thin, light-coloured lines. The parts of the legs that are less visible, such as the rear and armpits, are bright red with black spots. This species is active at night in the lowlands of eastern Africa. Males congregate to call while floating in the water.

Trilling reed frog (*Hyperolius parkeri*): 2.5cm (1in)
This African tree frog is pale lime green in colour with broad, whitish bands on the sides of its body, running from its snout to its tail. It lives in low-lying grasslands in East Africa, where it is active at night. Males send out high-pitched bird-like trills to attract females. The frogs live in trees, reeds and grasses and breed by ponds, where the females lay their 70–110 eggs on vegetation, usually grasses growing over the water. After hatching, the tadpoles drop into the water to complete their development. This is the only African tree frog where the male is larger than the female.

Common squeaker (*Arthroleptis stenodactylus*): 4.25cm (1.75in)
These frogs live in undisturbed forested areas of the Democratic Republic of the Congo, Kenya and southern Africa. The males call during and shortly after rainfall and are commonly heard throughout the forest floor and on steep slopes. Females are thought to lay their eggs and bury them in moist earth, where they develop and hatch into small froglets. The tadpole stage seems to be missed out completely.

Greater leaf-folding frog

Afrixalus fornasinii

Greater leaf-folding frogs inhabit savannah country in eastern and southern Africa. The female lays her eggs on grass overhanging water. She folds the edges over, gluing them together with secretions from a gland on her rear. These leaf nests protect the eggs from predators and from drying out in the sun.

The eggs are pale in colour, lacking pigment. This is common with frogs and toads that lay their eggs in burrows or fold them in leaves. As they are not exposed, the eggs do not need to be coloured or have disruption patterns to camouflage them and help them blend into the surroundings. When the tadpoles have developed, their leaf nests break up and they fall into water, where they continue their development.

Distribution: Eastern and southern Africa.
Habitat: Grasslands, particularly with large bushes and trees. Also found in coastal lowlands and up to 1,300m (4,300ft) above sea level in Malawi.
Food: Eggs and developing larvae of other frogs that breed earlier.
Size: 3–4cm (1.25–1.5in); weight not known.
Maturity: Not known.
Breeding: 80 pale eggs laid on a grass leaf.
Life span: Not known.
Status: Not known.

Greater leaf-folding frogs have a dark reddish-brown body colour. They have black warts on their backs and broad silver bands running along their sides from their snouts to their rear. These frogs feed on the spawn and tadpoles of other frogs that breed earlier than they do.

Banded rubber frog

Phrynomerus bifasciatus

The banded rubber frog is pear-shaped, with shiny smooth skin. It is nocturnal and breeds early in the season in floodwaters. The males issue melodious trills, lasting several seconds, from the banks or on floating vegetation. The eggs are laid in large masses on the water's surface or attached to aquatic plants.

The frog has a bright black and red skin, signalling to predators that it is poisonous. The skin, which becomes paler in bright light, contains toxins that can harm any animal that attempts to eat it. During the dry season the banded rubber frog seeks cover in tree hollows and burrows, away from the heat and dryness. This species is also known as the African snake-necked frog, because it is able to bend its neck much more than typical frogs.

The banded rubber frog is a shiny black frog with red spots on its legs and thick red bands running from its eyes, right along the sides of its body.

Distribution: South-eastern Africa.
Habitat: Not known.
Food: Insects.
Size: 7.25cm (3in); weight not known.
Maturity: Not known.
Breeding: Spawn laid in water.
Life span: Not known.
Status: Not known.

TURTLES AND TORTOISES

Tortoises, terrapins and turtles appeared on Earth around 200 million years ago. Tortoises are the land form of the three and have dome-shaped shells. Terrapins tend to live in fresh water while turtles live in sea water, although this is not always the case, and both are often grouped as turtles. Terrapins and turtles have flatter shells than tortoises; they also have webbed feet or flippers and are usually carnivores.

European pond turtle

Emys orbicularis

European pond turtles used to be common in Britain when the weather warmed after the last Ice Age, but they disappeared around 5,000 years ago when temperatures fell once more. Today the species is found across the rest of Europe, including northern France. Although the adult turtle can survive the British climate, it is too cool for the eggs to hatch successfully. During warm weather, European pond turtles can be found basking on exposed rocks. They can be quite shy and if disturbed will quickly dive back into the water where their webbed feet allow them to move around rapidly.

Males can mate with females throughout a seven-month period from March to October, although most activity is seen during March and April. Two or three months after mating the females lay 3–16 eggs in burrows. The young turtles hatch in August and September before the onset of autumn and winter.

The European pond turtle has a smooth, oval shell. Younger individuals have lighter, sometimes yellowish, spots and streaks on their shells, necks and heads. Older individuals are entirely dark. They hibernate in winter, burying themselves in mud.

Distribution: Europe, North Africa and western Asia.
Habitat: Ponds, lakes and slow-moving streams.
Food: Fish, amphibians, insects, molluscs, young snakes and small mammals.
Size: 18–35cm (7–14in); 5–10kg (11–22lb). Female larger.
Maturity: Females 15 years; males 12 years.
Breeding: Females lay eggs in soil during June.
Life span: Up to 120 years.
Status: Common.

Leatherback turtle

Dermochelys coriacea

The leatherback turtle is the world's largest marine turtle. Its shell has a leathery texture and is semi-rigid; it is made from thousands of individual tiny bony plates connected together. Each can move a little, making the shell more flexible than if it were completely solid. The turtles have long front flippers that enable them to swim up to 30km (20 miles) per day.

Leatherback turtles are very unusual reptiles because they are able to generate body heat through the movement of their muscles. The heat is maintained by the turtle's huge size, layers of fat under the skin and also by a long oesophagus, which coils back before reaching the stomach, helping to heat up swallowed food.

The turtles also have special blood vessels that stop heat being lost to cold water. Heat is transferred from arteries entering the flippers to veins carrying blood away from the flippers, keeping the limbs colder than the rest of the body. Mating takes place at sea and the females nest on tropical beaches, where they lay eggs in pits dug into sand.

Distribution: Atlantic, Pacific and Indian Oceans.
Habitat: Marine water.
Food: Jellyfish.
Size: 2–3m (6.5–10ft); up to 900kg (1,980lb).
Maturity: 30–50 years.
Breeding: 80–100 eggs laid on beaches every other year, hatching after 60 days.
Life span: Over 50 years.
Status: Critically endangered.

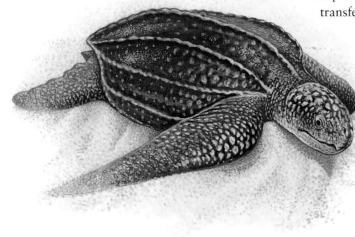

The leatherback turtle has a dark grey or black upper surface with additional spotting. Ridges run from the front end of the shell down to the tail. The span of the flippers is equal to the length of the animal.

Leopard tortoise

Geochelone pardalis

The leopard tortoise is a very distinctive tortoise, with obvious black and yellowish markings on its shell. The shell patterns are extremely variable; indeed each pattern is unique, like human fingerprints. Leopard tortoises from Ethiopia are a pale race, while those from South Africa are exceptionally large.

A musk gland near the tail emits a powerful and distinctive smell, which is used by the tortoises to attract partners for mating or to drive away predators.

When it becomes very hot, the leopard tortoise digs a hole in the soil and remains underground to avoid overheating or dehydrating. It stays in the burrow until the temperatures fall and the rains come again. If food becomes hard to find, the tortoises travel long distances to seek more. To continue growing healthy shells and ensure their bones remain strong, they eat old bones found when they forage.

The leopard tortoise is straw-coloured, with black blotches evenly spread over the shell. Shell markings are reminiscent of the pelt of a leopard cat, hence the tortoise's name.

Distribution: South and east Africa, south of the Sahara.
Habitat: Semi-arid, thorny and dry grassland habitats.
Food: Grasses, fruit of the prickly pear, thistles and other plants.
Size: 40–65cm (16–26in); 10–40kg (22–88lb).
Maturity: 6–10 years.
Breeding: Eggs laid in autumn.
Life span: 50–150 years.
Status: Vulnerable.

Radiated tortoise (*Geochelone radiata*): 40cm (16in)
The radiated tortoise is a very colourful tortoise with streaks radiating out from each section of its shell. It lives on the island of Madagascar and is less common than it used to be because the Chinese prize it as a purported aphrodisiac. The vegetation where it lives is disappearing, including a type of spiny cactus, which provides important cover for the tortoise. Males and females encounter each other during late afternoon sorties, but they only mate if it is dry.

Atlantic or **Kemp's ridley turtle** (*Lepidochelys kempii*): 50–70cm (20–28in)
The Atlantic ridley turtle is the smallest marine turtle and the most endangered. The turtles live in sheltered areas such as large estuaries, bays and lagoons where they feed on crabs, jellyfish, squid, snails, starfish and a variety of other marine invertebrates, as well as some seaweeds. They have distinctive heart-shaped shells that may be black, grey-brown or olive in colour.

East African side-necked turtle (*Pelusios subniger*): 20cm (8in)
The East African side-necked turtle lives in shallow ponds and streams with muddy bottoms. When the pools dry out or it gets too hot or cold, the turtle burrows into the mud and remains protected until the rains come. When threatened, this species pulls its neck to one side rather than bringing it back into the shell like typical tortoises and turtles. They have dark – often black – domed shells with yellow undersides. They are found in East Africa, below the Sahara Desert and throughout Madagascar.

Pancake tortoise

Malacochersus tornieri

The pancake tortoise is very rare and suffered from illegal pet trade in the 1960s and 70s. Its tiny size meant it could be smuggled out of Kenya and Tanzania in very large numbers. The tortoise lives in rocky cliffs, hidden in crevices during the day. Grasses are very important for feeding and breeding. These grassy areas around the cliffs are disappearing through human activity, which prevents the species from increasing its population.

The pancake tortoise has a lightweight shell, which helps it scurry along and escape from predators more quickly. The bony plates that make up the shell are reduced in this species, leaving spaces where the bones would be, making it less heavy and more flexible. The shell is also flattened, which helps the tortoise to rest or escape under very low rocks. The tortoise can wedge itself into crevices by inflating its lungs with air and pushing down with its legs. If the tortoise falls and lands on its back, it can right itself quite easily.

The pancake tortoise has a brown shell, marked with pale yellow and black. It has a more pronounced hook to its beak than other species. The males have longer, thicker tails than the females.

Distribution: Kenya and Tanzania.
Habitat: Small rocky cliffs called "kopjes", over 1,000m (3,280ft) above sea level.
Food: Dry grasses and vegetation.
Size: 15cm (6in).
Maturity: Not known.
Breeding: Single eggs laid 3 or 4 times a year.
Life span: 25 years.
Status: Endangered.

LIZARDS

Of all the reptiles in the world, 80 per cent are lizards and snakes. Lizards are able to move their upper jaws as well as their lower jaws, helping them to tackle large prey and swallow them more easily. Many also possess the ability to lose their tails if attacked by predators; special bones in the tail are pulled apart by muscles and the tail is released from the body. This is called autotomy.

Panther chameleon

Furcifer pardalis

Throughout the range of the panther chameleon, males and females vary in colour. There are at least 25 different forms, with each one occurring in a different region. Males from north-west Madagascar are bright turquoise and green, with red and gold colours radiating from their eyes and heads. Another type of male from a different region has up to six different body colours with white streaks around its eyes. Breeding females become brighter too, developing black and red-orange colouring. Their black markings vary in pattern. The panther chameleon is able to change colour very quickly when it moves into different vegetation – as camouflage – or when being approached by other chameleons – as communication. They can be very aggressive with one another, and changing colour can warn other individuals to keep away.

Males have white stripes along their bodies and can display a variety of colours. Females are grey or brown, but turn red-orange when breeding.

Distribution: North and east Madagascar. Introduced to Reunion and Mauritius and neighbouring islands.
Habitat: Lowland coastal areas.
Food: Small insects.
Size: Females 18–23cm (7–9in); males: 30–45cm (12–18in). Weight not known.
Maturity: Females 5 months; males 12 months.
Breeding: 4–6 clutches of 12–30 eggs are laid per year.
Life span: Not known.
Status: Vulnerable.

Armadillo lizard

Cordylus cataphractus

The armadillo lizard lives in groups of up to 30 animals. Small groups, with nine lizards or fewer, are usually all females with just one adult male. Larger groups contain more males. They are active during the day, searching for insects in the dry desert areas in which they live. Their sandy colour keeps them hidden from birds and other reptiles, and their spines act as a protective armour.

If they are out in the open, away from cover, and are threatened by a predator, armadillo lizards will roll themselves into balls like armadillos, keeping a tight hold of their tails with their mouths. This exposes their tough, horny skin and spines, making it difficult for a predator to eat the lizard. If the lizard has enough time, or is close to cover, it will squeeze into a small crevice in nearby rocks. Because it has a flattened body, few predators are able to follow it into its hideaway.

Armadillo lizards have flattened bodies and broad heads. The body is sandy yellow or brown and covered with spiny scales. They have either yellow or violet throats, embellished with brown blotches. When threatened, these lizards roll into a tight ball, creating a spiny ring.

Distribution: Southern tip of Africa.
Habitat: Dry, desert areas with plants able to withstand drought and high temperatures.
Food: Insects, spiders and other invertebrates.
Size: 7.5–16.5cm (3–6.5in); 400–800g (0.9–1.75lb).
Maturity: Not known.
Breeding: Females give birth to 1 or 2 young lizards towards the end of summer.
Life span: Not known.
Status: Uncommon.

Sand lizard (*Lacerta agilis*): 18–19cm (7–7.5in)
The sand lizard is a colourful species found throughout most of Europe and central Asia. During courtship, fighting may occur between males for the biggest and most fertile females. Females lay 4–12 eggs in dry, sandy soil close to vegetation. Males are bright green, while females are generally brown with darker patterning along their bodies.

African plated lizard (*Gerrhosaurus validus*): 69cm (27in)
Plated lizards live on the rocky hills in southern Africa and use the crevices between rocks to hide. During midsummer, four large, oval eggs are laid between rocks and covered with soil. Plated lizards are dark brown or black, with yellow spots and shields on their heads. Their throats are whitish and their bellies are light brown. Males develop a pinkish-purple hue on their throats, chins and the sides of their heads during the breeding season.

Fat-tailed gecko (*Hemitheconyx caudicinctus*): Females 20cm (8in); males 25cm (10in)
Fat-tailed geckos are very striking in appearance, with alternating thick bands of colour. These are dark brown combined with lighter brown, orange-brown or pinkish-brown. Their bellies are pale pink or white. They live in dry grassland and woodland in western Africa, appearing at night to feed on small insects. If the lizard regrows its tail following an attack, the tail will be much shorter and fatter than before, resembling its head. This is a defence mechanism, designed to fool predators into attacking the wrong end.

Slow worm

Anguis fragilis

The slow worm has a long, smooth body and lacks legs. Although it is often mistaken for a snake, it is a legless lizard. Unlike snakes, it has moveable eyelids so that it can blink. It also has a broader, flatter tongue with a notch at the tip rather than a deep fork.

Slow worms hibernate between October and March. The males appear before the females, and when they come out in the spring, they warm themselves up by resting under rocks and logs. Slow worms are secretive creatures and spend most of their time underground. If they are picked up, they will shed their tails, which continue to wriggle for about 15 minutes. This distracts a predator while the slow worm escapes.

Distribution: Europe, South-west Asia and western Siberia.
Habitat: Rough grassland, hedgerows, heathland, woodland edges, downs and moorland. Also found in gardens and along railway or motorway embankments.
Food: Molluscs and earthworms, and also insects and spiders.
Size: 30–50cm (12–20in).
Maturity: Females 4–5 years; males 3–4 years.
Breeding: Mate in summer; eggs incubated inside body.
Life span: 10–15 years.
Status: Common.

Females are brown with coppery or reddish-coloured backs. Dark stripes run down each side of the body. Males are brown and lack the dark stripes. Both sexes have whitish or reddish bellies and throats, with copper-red eyes.

Savannah monitor

Varanus albigularis

The savannah monitor lizard is a large lizard with a sandy coloured skin, patterned with lines of small black spots. The amount of black can vary and may be quite extensive. The head is darker on top and the tail has black bands. These lizards inhabit dry savannah or rocky terrain, and feed mostly on invertebrates.

The savannah monitor lives in very hot, grassy habitats, feeding on small mammals and insects. During the breeding season, males will search for females. In the Namib Desert, they have been known to travel up to 6km (3.5 miles) per day looking for females ready to mate. Their territories may be up to 18sq km (7sq miles) in size. Females ready to breed will climb trees to make themselves more obvious to males, and release a pheromone into the air.

During very hot weather, savannah monitors help to keep themselves cool by sitting with their mouths open and vibrating their throats very quickly. This is known as gular fluttering and allows water to evaporate from the throat, thus cooling the blood passing through this area. They are unable to sweat, and their covering of tough, waterproof scales means they can lose little heat through their skin.

Distribution: Eastern and southern Africa.
Habitat: Dry grassland or rocky areas.
Food: Mainly invertebrates plus reptiles, birds, mammals, eggs and carrion.
Size: 1–1.9m (3.25–6.25ft); 6–10kg (13–22lb).
Maturity: 2 years.
Breeding: Up to 50–60 eggs laid in burrows during the spring.
Life span: Not known.
Status: Vulnerable.

Viviparous lizard

Lacerta vivipara

One of the most common European reptiles, the viviparous lizard is found across northern and central Europe and into northern parts of Asia. It is the only reptile found in Ireland. This indicates that it was the fastest reptile to broaden its range back northwards when temperatures increased following the last Ice Age, reaching Ireland before the Irish Sea rose up and engulfed the land-bridge connecting it with mainland Britain and the rest of Europe.

Viviparous means "live birth" – viviparous lizards don't lay eggs, but give birth to fully formed young. These miniatures of their parents are completely independent from birth, receiving no help from their mothers. However, by keeping the eggs within their bodies until they have hatched, the female viviparous lizards have already given their progeny a head-start, since they don't have to lie prone and defenceless as eggs.

The viviparous lizard is a common sight in the UK, for those that look closely enough. Up close they are striking animals, with delicate patterns of coloured scales. However, from a distance they blend easily into the background, making life difficult for kestrels and other predators.

The skin of the viviparous lizard is patterned with a mosaic of brown, dark-green and bronze scales.

Distribution: Northern and central Europe and northern Asia.
Habitat: Wide-ranging habitats including woodland, marshland, heath, sand dunes, hedgerows, bogs and rubbish dumps.
Food: Insects, spiders, snails and earthworms.
Size: 10–16cm (4–6.5in).
Maturity: Not known
Breeding: 3–10 live young born between June and September.
Life span: 8 years
Status: Common.

European glass lizard

Ophisaurus apodus

European glass lizards belong to a family of lizards that have given up the pedestrian way of life, preferring instead to crawl around on their bellies in the manner of snakes. Indeed, having lost their legs almost entirely, glass lizards are often mistaken for snakes. Nevertheless, they can be identified as lizards due to their having ears and eyelids, features which snakes do not possess.

A glass lizard's body also differs from that of a snake by the length of its tail. The tail of a snake – the portion of the body behind the anus and genitals – usually only makes up a small proportion of its body length, whereas two-thirds of a glass lizard's body is made up of tail. The tail also gives rise to the glass lizard's name. Like other lizards, this species is able to shed its tail when threatened – a process called autotomy. However, unlike those of other lizards, the glass lizard's tail then breaks up into lots of small pieces, as though it were shattering like glass. As the actual body of the snake is not much bigger than one of the pieces of tail, people used to believe that these lizards were entirely made from glass.

Distribution: South-east Europe and south-west Asia.
Habitat: Open woodland and fields.
Food: Molluscs, insects and small vertebrates.
Size: Up to 1.2m (4ft).
Maturity: 2–3 years.
Breeding: 8–10 eggs.
Life span: 60 years.
Status: Common.

Not a snake but a lizard with no legs, the European glass lizard has a groove down each side of its body. These legless reptiles are fairly common in fields and highly wooded areas, where they hunt hard-shelled snails and insects.

African fire skink

Lygosoma fernandi

The fire skink really lives up to its name, with its shiny scales of many colours – from black and blue to red and gold, including stripes that look like fire on their sides. These fiercely territorial lizards dart among the dead leaves of the forest floor, looking like living flames.

The African fire skink is a medium-sized member of the varied and widespread skink family. It is also one of the most spectacular-looking members of that group. When not in breeding coloration, the male's sides are bright red, merging into the copper colour on its back. This is very impressive in its own right. However, come the breeding season, the red colours extend up on to the back, becoming suffused with the copper and resulting in a brilliant orange. Meanwhile, both pairs of legs darken to near black, with a few light spots, and pearlescent stripes extend from the throat right down the lizard's body. Even juveniles are brightly coloured, having intense light blue tails, which slowly fade as they grow older.

Adult fire skinks are territorial, defending their burrows in the leaf litter on the forest floor from invaders. Their bright colours make them highly visible to predators, so they really need handy bolt-holes for when trouble appears.

Distribution: West Africa.
Habitat: Tropical forest.
Food: Invertebrates.
Size: 30cm (12in).
Maturity: 1 year.
Breeding: Female fire skinks lay 6 clutches of 4–9 eggs per year.
Life span: 10 years.
Status: Threatened.

Ibiza wall lizard (*Podarcis pityusensis*): 20cm (8in)
Native to the Balearic Islands, this is a slim, agile and very hardy lizard, mainly inhabiting barren, sun-baked rocks, often by the seashore. It can also be found combing neglected gardens, rubbish dumps and wasteground for scraps to complement its usual diet of insects and some plant matter. The colouring of this lizard is variable but there seem to be two predominant forms: those from Formentera have green backs with grey-brown sides, while those from Ibiza have brown backs and reddish sides.

Hierro giant lizard (*Gallotia simonyi*): 60cm (24in)
Once believed to be extinct but rediscovered in 1975, the Hierro giant lizard has at present only a small population of 150 individuals, living on the island of El Hierro in the Canary Islands. It is Europe's most endangered reptile. A herbivorous lizard, it feeds almost exclusively on only two types of plant. It is a stocky lizard with a broad head and pronounced jowls. The giant lizard is very shy, and has not coped well with the expansion of tourism in the Canary Islands.

Hardun (*Laudakia stellio*): 20–30cm (8–12in)
A lizard of many names, the hardun is also known as the starred agama, painted dragon and sling-tailed agama. It is found in Greece, south-west Asia and north-east Africa. Like many agamas, harduns can change colour to express their moods. They bask on stone walls, rocks and buildings, and also on trees. They are usually found in rocky habitats, and are quite shy, being very ready to dive into cracks to hide from potential predators.

Moorish gecko

Tarentola mauritanica

Moorish geckos are Europe's most common geckos. They are also found throughout North Africa. Like many of the world's most successful animals, they have learned to live alongside people and even benefit from their presence. They spend most of their time literally hanging around houses. Geckos are fantastic climbers, even able to climb up panes of glass and hang from ceilings. They are able to do this thanks to their toes, which have many tiny suction pads on their undersides. The pads actually comprise thousands of micro-hairs, which form a temporary molecular bond with the surface being walked over.

Moorish geckos are usually easy to spot, since they tend to congregate at night around wall lights. They do this to wait for their favourite food – moths – to arrive. As the moths are drawn in by the light, they become easy prey for the geckos.

Geckos are the only lizards to possess voiceboxes, which allow them to produce the "gecko" calls from which they get their name. They also produce a "tutting" noise, used between rival males.

The Moorish gecko is also known as the crocodile gecko because of its rough scales.

Distribution: Mediterranean regions.
Habitat: Dry, rocky areas.
Food: Mainly insects.
Size: 15cm (6in).
Maturity: 2 years.
Breeding: Up to 6 clutches of 1–6 eggs per year.
Life span: Not known.
Status: Common, but declining due to collection for the pet trade.

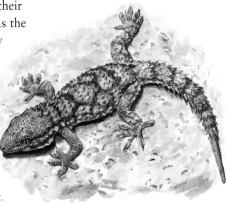

CROCODILES

The last living members of an ancient group known as the archosaurs, crocodiles are little changed from the days of the dinosaurs. The 25 surviving species stand as testament to the success of the crocodilian body design. Thick, scaly skin keeps predators at bay, a special respiratory system allows them to keep hidden underwater for up to five hours at a time, and powerful jaws make them fearsome predators.

Nile crocodile

Crocodylus niloticus

Nile crocodiles were once widespread in eastern and southern Africa, but are now scarcer. With powerful jaws, strong tails, a terrifying turn of speed and stealth belying their enormous size, these crocodiles are efficient killing machines. Nile crocodiles have evolved to be very good at fishing, and during the times of the year when fish migrate along the rivers, they hunt cooperatively. Forming cordons across rivers, they herd the fish into shallow waters, where they can be picked off with ease.

Nile crocodiles are ecologically important as predators. They help to keep the environment in balance by eating catfish, which are predators themselves. By keeping the catfish numbers in check, Nile crocodiles allow the smaller fish, which are eaten by catfish, to thrive, providing food for more than 40 species of bird. In turn, bird droppings fertilize the waters, keeping them rich enough to support a large diversity of life.

The Nile crocodile's powerful body is covered in greyish plate-like scales. The powerful tail is ridged with two keels of scales.

Distribution: Africa (not in the north-west or Sahara region) and Madagascar.
Habitat: Rivers, freshwater marshes, estuaries and mangrove swamps.
Food: Fish, water birds and land mammals.
Size: 3.5–6m (11.5–20ft); up to 225kg (495lb).
Maturity: 10 years.
Breeding: 25–100 eggs laid in nest.
Life span: 45 years.
Status: Common.

Dwarf crocodile

Osteolaemus tetraspis

Distribution: West Africa.
Habitat: Freshwater lakes, swamps and slow-moving rivers.
Food: Fish, birds, crustaceans and occasionally small mammals.
Size: 1.8m (6ft).
Maturity: 6 years.
Breeding: Clutches of up to 20 eggs.
Life span: 40 years.
Status: Vulnerable.

Like other crocodilians, female dwarf crocodiles make very attentive mothers. Laying their eggs in mounds of rotting vegetation on the shore, the females guard them fiercely for the three months it takes for them to incubate. As hatching time arrives, they dig the eggs out of the nests to help the hatchlings escape. They may even roll the eggs gently around in their mouth to break the shells open.

Once out of their eggs, the young face a journey fraught with danger down to the water, but the mothers are there to help again. With surprising gentleness, they pick up their babies in their mouths and flip them into their throat pouches, before carrying them down to the water.

Although adapted to life in water, dwarf crocodiles, like most crocodilians, make shelters on land. These are underground dens dug into the banks of rivers and lakes. They are connected to the outside world by entrances and exit tunnels, both of which can be several metres (tens of feet) long.

Dwarf crocodiles are also known as broad-fronted crocodiles, because of their broad, blunt snouts. People once thought they were cannibals because they carry their young in their mouths.

SNAKES

Snakes are unable to chew their food, so they have to be able to swallow it whole. They are capable of eating large prey items thanks to their perfectly adapted jaws, which they are able to dislocate at will. By detaching their lower jaws from their upper jaws, the snakes are able to open their mouths around animals that are larger than their own heads.

Boomslang

Dispholidus typus

Distribution: Southern Africa.
Habitat: Open woodland.
Food: Reptiles, mammals and birds.
Size: 1.3m–2m (4.25–6.5ft).
Maturity: Not known.
Breeding: 8–13 eggs laid in early summer.
Life span: 18 years.
Status: Common.

Weight for weight, the venom produced by the boomslang is more potent than that of either mambas or cobras. However, the boomslang's shy nature has led to it having less of a fearful reputation than its better-known relatives. Boomslangs also lack the large front fangs of mambas and cobras, having small teeth located at the backs of their mouths. To inject a large amount of poison, boomslangs have to deliver more prolonged bites than front-fanged snakes.

The word boomslang means "tree snake" in Afrikaans – the colonial language of South Africa. This name is very apt, since they are very agile snakes that can slide gracefully through the branches of trees, helped by their strong prehensile tails. Nevertheless, while hunting they will come down to the ground on a fairly regular basis in search of prey.

Most of a boomslang's life is spent coiled and immobile among branches. So effective is their camouflage that birds, which make up a substantial part of the their diet, have been known to actually perch on them.

When immobile in trees, boomslangs are very hard to spot. Their green bodies blend perfectly with the foliage. These highly venomous snakes are members of the colubrid snake family, unlike mambas and cobras.

Common egg-eating snake

Dasypeltis scabra

Very few other snakes share the dietary habits of this fascinating species. Generally most active at night, egg-eating snakes hide out during the day in sheltered areas under rocks or logs. During the night they mainly prey on the eggs of weaverbirds. They are very adept at climbing trees to get to their nests. The snakes test the eggs with their tongues to check whether they have gone off or not. This is important because they cannot spit rotten eggs out once they have swallowed them.

Having found a fresh egg, a snake holds it tightly between its coils and slowly pushes its mouth over and around it. Once the egg is inside the snake's body, it passes farther down the throat until it meets a series of tooth-like structures attached to the vertebrae. These pierce the egg when the snake makes a series of sharp sideways movements of its head. The contents of the egg then drain out of the shell to be digested. Once empty, the egg shell is crushed up and regurgitated from the body. This ability to deal with shells is rare among snakes.

Egg-eating snakes can swallow eggs up to three times the size of their own heads.

Distribution: Southern and central parts of Africa, south of the Sahara Desert.
Habitat: Lowland evergreen forest.
Food: Birds' eggs.
Size: 50–90cm (20–36in).
Maturity: Not known.
Breeding: 6–25 eggs laid each year.
Life span: 14 years.
Status: Common.

Grass snake

Natrix natrix

Grass snakes have dark green bodies with black flecking and whitish-yellow collars around their necks. They inhabit Britain as far as the Scottish border counties.

The grass snake is the most common snake in the Britain. It owes its success to its versatility, being able to hunt both on land and in the water. It prefers to prey on frogs, toads and fish, when it can. To acquire enough heat to be able to function properly, the grass snake has to spend much of its time basking in sunlight. However, this does leave it rather exposed to attack from birds of prey. Foxes, badgers and hedgehogs will also make a meal out of it if they get the chance, but this isn't easy. When threatened, a grass snake has a range of defensive tactics including loud hissing, inflating its body with air, biting, producing a foul-smelling secretion from its anus and playing dead.

Not only is keeping warm a problem for adult grass snakes, it is a problem for the eggs, too. If they are too cold they will take too long to develop, or not hatch at all. Female grass snakes combat this problem by travelling large distances to find suitable places to lay them. Heaps of rotting vegetation, such as compost heaps, are favoured.

Distribution: Europe from Scandinavia south to the Mediterranean, north Africa and central Asia east to Lake Baikal, Russia.
Habitat: Prefer damp grasslands, ditches and river banks.
Food: Amphibians, fish, small mammals and small birds.
Size: 0.7–2m (2.25–6.5ft).
Maturity: Not known.
Breeding: 8–40 eggs laid in June, July or August depending on the latitude, about 8 weeks after mating.
Life span: 20 years.
Status: Common.

Adder

Vipera berus

The majority of members of the viper family are venomous, and the adder – or common viper – is no exception. However, it poses little threat to humans. Adders rarely bite humans, and even when they do, the consequences are usually no more than a painful swelling around the area of the bite. Adders spend most of their day basking in the sunshine, and go out to hunt in the late afternoon. As winter closes in, adders prepare to hibernate, usually burrowing underground to sleep through the cold weather. The duration of hibernation varies with latitude.

The active periods of adders can be divided into three distinct phases. During spring, they come out of hibernation and disperse. This is when the males, having shed their skins, go in search of females, and mating occurs. With the onset of summer, adders migrate along hedgerows and ditches to prime feeding grounds, such as wet meadows. There they stay until summer starts to draw to a close, when they head back to drier areas. The females give birth to their young – they do not lay eggs – which immediately prepare to hibernate too.

Distribution: Throughout Europe and northern and western Asia.
Habitat: Open places such as heaths, meadows and woodland edges.
Food: Lizards, small mammals, nestlings and insects.
Size: 65cm (26in).
Maturity: Not known.
Breeding: 10 young born in late summer.
Life span: 15 years.
Status: Common.

The adder's predominantly grey-brown colour, with zigzag markings down the back, is very different from the coloration of the grass snake, yet people often confuse the two.

Schlegel's blindsnake

Rhinotyphlops schlegelii

Schlegel's blindsnake has very small eyes that are barely capable of vision. The snake's tiny head is covered by large protective scales called scutes. These are often referred to collectively as the "beak".

Schlegel's blindsnake is exceptionally large, being over twice as long as nearly all other blindsnakes. Blindsnakes spend most of their lives underground. This behaviour has earned them their alternative name: wormsnakes. The subterranean environment they occupy has meant that blindsnakes' eyes are mere vestiges of those of their above-ground relatives. However, like Schlegel's blindsnake, few are completely blind. Schlegel's blindsnake is also typical in that it only has teeth in the upper jaw of its small, blunt head. These are all the teeth it needs, because the blindsnake spends most of its time around ant and termite mounds, where it feasts on the soft bodies of the developing insects. The protective beak over the snake's head helps it to tunnel through soft soil without injury. The snake's long, thin body is also covered in smooth, shiny scales that aid in burrowing. Although they are totally harmless, it is unwise to harass blindsnakes. They have well-developed glands near their anuses, packed full of the most noxious-smelling secretions, which they eject upon attack.

Distribution: Southern Africa from Kenya to South Africa.
Habitat: Soft, sandy or loamy soils.
Food: Pupae, eggs and larvae of ants, termites and other subterranean insects.
Size: 1m (3.25ft).
Maturity: Not known.
Breeding: Lays up to 60 eggs underground, which hatch after 4–6 weeks.
Life span: Not known.
Status: Common.

Smooth snake (*Coronella austriaca*): 60cm (24in)
Smooth snakes are Britain's rarest snakes, restricted to just a handful of sites in southern England. They are not venomous at all, killing small rodents and lizards by constriction. Unlike grass snakes and adders, which have keel-shaped scales, smooth snakes have flat, smooth scales; hence their name.

Montpellier snake (*Malpolon monspessulanus*): 2m (6.5ft)
Very fast and shy, Montpellier snakes will flee at the first sign of a disturbance. They prefer open and dry grassland with stones and slopes exposed to sunlight, where they are active only on warm and sunny days. They feed mainly on lizards, which are hunted by sight.

Hooded snake (*Macroprotodon cucullatus*): 60cm (24in)
A unique member of the snake family, the hooded snake is not a very well-known species. Its habitat is always dry and stony. It preys on lizards, which it attacks while they are sleeping, paralyzing them with a mild venom harmless to people. The hooded snake can move quickly and if surprised it will throw its head back to show its underside before fleeing for shelter.

Leopard snake

Elaphe situla

Lacking any venom worth speaking of, leopard snakes are constrictors – they squeeze their prey to death. While the young feed mainly on small lizards, adults prefer to eat rodents. It is this fondness for rats and mice that has made leopard snakes popular pets in some parts of their range. Active mainly by day, leopard snakes are attracted to human settlements by the abundance of rats and mice to be found there. Indeed, in some parts of Greece, far from being feared, people used to actively introduce these snakes into their homes as a way of controlling pests. They are even considered to be good luck charms by superstitious people.

The leopard snake's good reputation, and its ability to live alongside humans, has played highly in its favour, and it is still a common sight throughout much of its range in south-eastern Europe.

The magnificent leopard snake is easily identified by the striking red markings after which it is named.

Distribution: South-eastern Europe.
Habitat: Dry, rocky slopes.
Food: Small mammals and birds.
Size: 1m (3.25ft).
Maturity: Not known.
Breeding: Clutches of 2–5 eggs laid in July or August.
Life span: 15 years.
Status: Common.

Spitting cobra

Naja pallida

Distribution: Eastern and central Africa from southern Egypt to northern Tanzania.
Habitat: Savannah grasslands.
Food: Amphibians, small mammals, birds, eggs and other reptiles.
Size: 0.7–1.5m (2.25–5ft).
Maturity: Not known.
Breeding: Clutches of up to 15 eggs.
Life span: 20 years.
Status: Common.

As its name indicates, this snake has a particularly effective method of defence. When it feels threatened, the spitting cobra rises up in typical cobra fashion, extending its hood, which is quite narrow by cobra standards. Holding its head high off the ground, it then spits large quantities of venom over a distance of more than 2m (6.5ft), aiming for the attacker's eyes.

The venom is very potent, causing blindness if it does reach the eyes, and bites can be fatal to humans. These cobras, however, are very reluctant to bite, preferring a "spit-and-run" tactic, making off while their enemy's eyes are stinging. Of course, cobras do not hold back when they come across prey animals. These are rapidly killed by the powerful venom injected via the snake's fangs.

Adults are predominantly nocturnal, hiding inside termite hills, old logs or piles of leaves during the day. Young cobras are more active during the day, and with good cause: bumping into an adult can have disastrous consequences as spitting cobras are occasionally cannibalistic.

The colour of spitting cobras is very variable. Individuals may be red, yellow, pinkish or steely grey. Cobras (Naja genus) are a sizeable group associated more with Asia.

Black mamba

Dendroaspis polylepis

The black mamba is probably Africa's most feared snake, and justifiably so. It is an aggressive animal, armed with venom capable of killing humans in less than four hours. However, its reputation for unprovoked attacks on humans is unjustified. A black mamba will only attack if it feels threatened. Nonetheless, when it does attack it rarely fails to bite.

Raising its head up off the ground to a height of 1.2m (4ft), black mouth agape, the mamba charges. It can reach a speed of 16kph (10mph), making it one of the fastest snakes in the world.

Clearly the black mamba is a very successful predator. Hunting by day using its excellent eyesight, it usually bites its prey a couple of times and then lets go. The stricken animal may make off but in a very short time it is paralyzed by the snake's toxins, and then swallowed headfirst. Mambas often attack birds, shooting into the air as the birds try to fly away. Adult black mambas are so formidable that they have no natural predators.

Distribution: Southern and central Africa.
Habitat: Tropical forests and savannah.
Food: Mainly small mammals and birds.
Size: 3.5m (11.5ft).
Maturity: Not known.
Breeding: Clutches of 14 eggs laid after a long courtship period.
Life span: 26 years.
Status: Common.

Black mambas are actually grey with white bellies. Their name refers to the colour of the insides of their mouths.

Royal python

Python regius

Royal pythons are Africa's smallest pythons. They are generally active at night, when they hunt using eyes that are well adapted to low light levels. They also have special heat-sensing pits around their mouths to detect prey in the dark. Since these pits pick up heat in the form of infrared radiation, they are well equipped to detect the body heat released by their prey.

Pythons are not venomous; they are constrictors. They grab hold of their prey and throw a number of coils around it, holding so tightly that the animal cannot breathe. Constrictors do not crush their prey; they suffocate them.

During the hot dry season, pythons lie inactive (aestivate) in underground burrows. They emerge when the rains arrive in order to mate. However, royal pythons only mate once every three or four years, so that they reproduce at a low rate. This means that their populations are particularly vulnerable to over-hunting. Royal pythons are endangered in the wild because they are collected for the pet trade, as well as being hunted for their flesh and skins.

Distribution: Central Africa.
Habitat: Grassland.
Food: Small mammals, birds, lizards and other species of snakes.
Size: 1.2m (4ft).
Maturity: 3–5 years.
Breeding: 4–10 unusually large eggs.
Life span: 25 years.
Status: Threatened

Royal pythons are also known as ball pythons because when they are threatened they coil up into tight balls with their heads well protected inside.

Forest cobra (*Naja melanoleuca*): 1.5–3m (5–10ft)
The forest cobra holds the record, along with the anaconda, for being the longest-living snake. It is capable of reaching the ripe old age of 30 years. It is found all over western and southern Africa, inhabiting many different habitats. Forest cobras have a reputation for being ill-tempered and dangerous. Their venom is highly toxic. They chase attackers off with mouths agape and ready to bite.

African house snake (*Lamprophis fuliginosus*): 0.6–1.2m (2–4ft); 200–500g (0.4–1.1lb)
One of the most successful of all the snakes in Africa, the African house snake is found virtually everywhere south and west of the Sahara Desert. It is a species that has learned to live alongside people, who tolerate it because it feeds on rodents.

Rinkhal (*Hemachatus haemachatus*): 1–1.5m (3.25–5ft)
Rinkhals closely resemble cobras in that they have "hoods" that they spread when feeling threatened. Found in southern Africa, they differ from true cobras by having differently shaped scales, and by giving birth to live young (whereas cobras lay eggs). In the wild rinkhals mainly eat toads, but will make meals of any small animals unfortunate enough to come too close.

Malagasy leaf-nosed snake

Langaha madagascariensis

Also known as twig mimic snakes, the habits of these peculiar-looking snakes are not very well known. Lying motionless for hours in the canopy of the tropical forests of Madagascar, leaf-nosed snakes blend into their background incredibly well, becoming extremely difficult to spot. Their camouflage is perfected by the remarkable protrusions from the front of their faces. Males possess long, spiky projections, making them look even more like twigs, whereas the females have leaf-like structures instead.

Leaf-nosed snakes are only active for about one hour in every day, normally waiting until midday, the hottest part of the day, before rousing themselves to go hunting. By remaining inactive, the snakes save a lot of energy, which allows them to have long breaks between foraging trips. A decent meal can keep a leaf-nosed snake going for four days or more, before it feels the need to go hunting again.

Distribution: Madagascar.
Habitat: Tropical rainforests and dry forests.
Food: Tree frogs, small birds and reptiles.
Size: 1m (3.25ft); 50–80g (0.1–0.2lb).
Maturity: Not known.
Breeding: Clutches of around 10 eggs laid in November or December.
Life span: 10 years.
Status: Common.

The leaf-like snout of the Malagasy leaf-nosed snake helps to camouflage it among leaves and twigs.

CATS

Of all the carnivores, the cats have the highest proportion of meat in their diets. Typically, cats hunt alone by night, using their acute senses of hearing, sight and scent to locate and stalk their prey. Once within pouncing distance, they unsheath their curved claws, which are used to grip the prey as the cat delivers fatal neck bites with dagger-shaped teeth.

Lion

Panthera leo

Male lions have thick manes of hair, while the females do not. The manes are symbols of the dominance level in males.

The social behaviour of lions is unique among wild cats. A typical pride contains about ten related females with their cubs and one or two males. Females do most of the hunting. They may work together to isolate and kill large prey such as zebra or buffalo. Males in a pride help themselves to the females' kills and rarely hunt for themselves. They spend much of the night patrolling, marking territory and driving away rival males. A pride male's reign rarely lasts longer than three years before he is usurped. Once adolescent males are evicted from the prides where they were born and reared, they may stay together in hunting groups, or hunt alone before eventually joining other groups.

Distribution: Africa, south of the Sahara, and Gir Forest, India.
Habitat: Open country.
Food: Grazing animals.
Size: 2–2.7m (6.5–9ft); 125–180kg (275–396lb).
Maturity: 3–4 years.
Breeding: 1 litter of 2–5 cubs in alternate years.
Life span: 16 years.
Status: Vulnerable.

Cheetah

Acinonyx jubatus

Distribution: Most of Africa, Middle East to Turkestan.
Habitat: Savannah and open, dry grassland.
Food: Gazelles or antelopes.
Size: 1.6–2.1m (5.25–7ft); 30–45kg (66–99lb).
Maturity: Females 3 years; males 3–4 years.
Breeding: 2–6 kittens every 2–3 years.
Life span: 15–20 years.
Status: Endangered.

Cheetahs differ from typical cats in several ways. Instead of stealth, they use speed to run down their prey, assisted by blunt claws that grip the ground. The dew-claws, however, which are used to grasp the prey, are curved and sharp. A cheetah is built like a racing dog, with a small head and long legs and body, but the teeth and jaws are too small and weak to deliver an effective death bite, so the cheetah is forced to suffocate its prey. After the sustained effort of catching and killing a prey animal, a cheetah may need to rest for half an hour before starting to eat.

The cheetah is well known as the fastest animal on land. Sadly, despite captive breeding programmes, it is now an endangered species. A breeding female requires a hunting range of up to 800sq km (300sq miles) and, apart from some national parks and isolated populations, suitable territories are mainly restricted to Namibia and parts of South Africa.

The cheetah's long, flexible spine helps to lengthen the stride of the animal at full sprint. It is the fastest terrestrial animal, capable of sprinting at 110kph (70mph).

Eurasian lynx

Lynx lynx

Eurasian lynx have three distinct coat patterns: stripes, spots or plain. These markings can be either faint or clearly visible.

This golden, delicately marked cat hunts small game by night in cool mountain forests and woodland. A shortened tail helps to conserve body heat, but it hinders communication between cats to a certain degree. As with other short-tailed cats that live in cold climates, the lynx has developed conspicuous ear-tufts to send visual signals instead.

Lack of a tail also impairs a cat's balance when running and climbing; the lynx hunts mainly by the techniques of stealth or ambush. Its feet are densely furred, even on the pads, giving a good grip as well as warmth on frozen ground.

Most lynxes live in dense forests, but they may also wander into more open country. They build rough beds under rocks and fallen trees, or inside shrubs, resting during the day and hunting at night. While out and about, the lynx climbs trees and fords rivers – swimming if necessary – as it travels far and wide in search of food. It relies on its senses of vision and smell to locate prey, which it then stalks through the trees.

Distribution: Eastern Europe, Pyrenees and northern Eurasia, with distinct races in some regions.
Habitat: Montane forest and woodland.
Food: Rabbits, hares, birds and small deer.
Size: 0.8–1.3m (2.5–4.25ft); 18–21kg (40–46lb).
Maturity: 12–15 months.
Breeding: 2–4 cubs, weaned at 12 weeks, independent at 12 months.
Life span: 10–20 years.
Status: Endangered in south-eastern Europe.

European wildcat (*Felis sylvestris sylvestris*): 35–75cm (14–30in); up to 5kg (11lb)
In parts of its forest range, extending from Scotland to eastern Europe, this subspecies interbreeds with domestic cats, making its pedigree uncertain. The pure wildcat resembles a large, robust dark-grey tabby cat, with short legs and a bushy, blunt-tipped tail. Unlike feral domestic cats, it is entirely solitary apart from a brief association between males and females in the mating season.

African wildcat (*Felis sylvestris lybica*): 30–75cm (12–30in); up to 5kg (11lb)
Whereas the European wildcat avoids people, its sandy-coloured, lightly-striped African counterpart frequently lives around human settlements. The ancient Egyptians, who are credited with domesticating the cat, would have been familiar with this subspecies. These are two reasons for believing it to be the chief ancestor of domestic cats. Genetic fingerprinting also points strongly towards the African wildcat as our modern pet's ancestor.

Caracal

Caracal caracal

The name caracal is Turkish for "black ears". Caracals are also known as desert lynxes because they have short tails and ear-tufts like their northern cousins, an adaptation for cold weather. This has led scientists to conclude that the caracal's ancestors once lived in colder regions.

This adaptation to the cold comes in handy during the night, when caracals generally hunt. It is not unusual for desert temperatures to plunge below 0°C (32°F). Caracals prey on anything they can find and kill, including insects, snakes, lizards, gazelles and even brooding ostriches.

Caracals set up home in the abandoned burrows of porcupines or any other suitable crevices. Like other types of lynx, the caracal hunts at night, stealing up close to its prey before leaping the last few metres in huge bounds. The caracal is the fastest cat of its size. Prey is stalked and then captured after a quick dash or leap. The caracal is easy to tame and has been used as a hunting cat in Iran and India. However, it is also persecuted in this region as a pest.

Distribution: Southern Africa to Senegal and India, excluding the Congo and Arabian Desert.
Habitat: Dry scrubland, but avoids sand areas.
Food: Rodents, hyraxes, hares and small antelopes.
Size: 66–76cm (26–30in); 18kg (40lb).
Maturity: 6 months to 2 years.
Breeding: Litter of 3 young born every year.
Life span: 15 years.
Status: Lower risk (threatened in Asia).

Caracals have narrow, pointed ears with long tufts of hair at their tips. These are used to signal to other cats.

HYENAS

Hyenas are heavily built, long-legged and long-necked carnivores with large, padded feet and short, hairy tails. Their front legs are longer than their back legs and their shaggy coats are either striped or spotted. There are four species, all of which live in Africa. The striped hyena, the widest-ranging species, also lives in Turkey, the Middle East and parts of India.

Spotted hyena

Crocuta crocula

Spotted hyenas are dog-like, with sloping backs and long thick necks. They are the only mammal to disgorge indigestible hair, along with hooves, pieces of horn and bone, and grass.

Spotted hyenas live in female-dominated groups known as clans. The mothers rear all of the cubs together in a communal breeding den that is only big enough for the cubs to enter. The entrance to the den is guarded by one or two adults, helping to reduce the number of young killed by other carnivores or hyenas.

Spotted hyenas have a complicated greeting ceremony, involving a variety of interactions using scents and physical gestures. These are only used by certain individuals in a clan and are uncommon between females and low-ranking males. They help to reduce stress in the group. Females are very aggressive and, to help them dominate their clans, they have developed false genitals to look like males. They will fight other females to win over and mate with favoured males. Hyenas are very vocal and their wails – howling screams and "laughter" – can inform other clan members of a food source from up to 5km (3 miles) away.

Distribution: Most of Africa outside rainforest.
Habitat: Woodlands, savannahs, subdeserts, forest edges and mountains.
Food: Hunt antelope, buffalo and zebra. Scavenge from the kills of other large carnivores.
Size: 1.2–1.8m (4–5.75ft); 60–80kg (132–176lb).
Maturity: Cubs weaned after 18 months.
Breeding: Litter of 1–2 cubs born at any time of the year.
Life span: 12 years, and up to 25 years in captivity.
Status: Declining in all areas.

Aardwolf

Proteles cristatus

The aardwolf is a specialist feeder and mainly consumes harvester termites. These give off a very toxic spray, and few other predators are able to overcome the chemicals emitted. Aardwolfs find the termites by listening for their movements.

Unlike the spotted hyenas which have large crushing teeth, aardwolfs only have small peg-like teeth, ideal for crunching small insects. The aardwolf is mainly nocturnal and lives alone, in pairs or in small family groups. Females often live together in the same den to help increase the chances of survival for their pups. Burrows are either taken over from other species or dug by the aardwolfs themselves.

When feeding, adults may travel up to 10km (6 miles) in one night and in this time they may consume 250,000 termites. When threatened, they raise their long manes and erect their tails but, unusually, they keep their mouths closed – the aardwolf has such tiny teeth that it would appear almost harmless if it opened its mouth.

The aardwolf is slimmer and more agile than the other three species of hyena. When attacked, the aardwolf raises the mane along its back and secretes a foul-smelling odour from its anal glands.

Distribution: Southern Africa and north-east Africa.
Habitat: Heavily grazed and trampled grasslands, and sandy plains and plateaux.
Food: Termites plus other invertebrates including grasshoppers and maggots.
Size: 0.8–1m (2.5–3.25ft); 6–11kg (13–24lb).
Maturity: Weaned after 16 weeks.
Breeding: Litter of 1–4 pups born at any time of the year.
Life span: Not known.
Status: Uncommon.

DOGS

There are several members of the wild dog family, Canidae, *including the African hunting dog, Ethiopian wolf, foxes and jackals. Long legs and muzzles enable these mammals to chase and capture prey. Most have a bushy tail and feet with four toes at the back and five at the front. Small canids are solitary hunters, medium-sized canids hunt alone or in small family groups and large canids hunt in large cooperative groups.*

African hunting dog

Lycaon pictus

Hunting dogs are highly social and live in large packs of around 100 animals. A pack is formed by a group of brothers from one pack meeting with a group of sisters from another. A dominant pair emerges and breeds. Females will fight each other for the top breeding position.

These dogs are truly nomadic carnivores. They are on the move all the time to mark their territories and to avoid conflict with lions. Movement is reduced when there are small pups in the den. Unlike most canids which howl to show their presence, wild dogs use scents that last for months. When packs contain about 20 adults, the older offspring leave to form subgroups and hunt independently.

Individual dogs are capable of killing large prey such as impala antelope, although most hunting is done in packs. Pups typically leave at two to three years of age but sometimes stay to help rear more young. Packs stay together for no more than six years, usually two, when the founder members die. The remaining dogs separate into single-sex groups to find new opposite-sex groups and start all over again.

The African hunting dog has black, white, brown and yellow-brown blotches. It has large, round ears, a broad, black muzzle and a tufted tail, usually with a white tip. It is also the only carnivore except hyenas to have five toes on all four feet.

Distribution: Non-forested, non-desert areas of Africa.
Habitat: Desert plains, open and wooded savannah, and bushed country.
Food: Antelope, eland, buffalo and wildebeest.
Size: 1–1.5m (3.25–5ft); 17–36kg (37–79lb).
Maturity: Pups follow pack after 3 months and join in hunting at 12–14 months.
Breeding: Average of 7–10 pups born in the dry winter months from March–July in the south.
Life span: Not known.
Status: Endangered.

Ethiopian wolf

Canis simensis

Ethiopian wolves' main prey are giant mole rats (*Tachyoryctes macrocephalus*), which make up nearly half of their diet when available. During the day, the wolves lie on the mounds made by the giant mole rats. These make good ambush sites to catch their prey. Ethiopian wolves live in packs with two or more adult females, five closely related males and the current offspring of the dominant pair. The females do not always mate with the males in their pack; indeed three-quarters of matings may be with males from neighbouring packs.

These wolves are extremely vocal, using all types of howls, yelps and screams to mark their territories, which may be 2.4–12sq km (1–4.5sq miles) in size. They forage alone, but the animals will meet in the morning, midday and evening to rest, play, sleep, feed their pups and mark boundaries. This is when they are most vocal.

Ethiopian wolves have reddish-ginger coats, with white throat patches, inner ears, underparts and lower legs, and dark tails. They have long legs, long muzzles and squared-off noses and upper lips.

Distribution: Restricted to the Ethiopian Highlands of Africa.
Habitat: Alpine moorlands.
Food: Naked mole rats and other rodents, hares and antelope calves.
Size: 1.3m (4.25ft); 11–19kg (24–42lb).
Maturity: Not known.
Breeding: 2–6 pups born from August–December.
Life span: Not known.
Status: Critically endangered.

Black-backed jackal

Canis mesomelas

Distribution: Southern Africa and East Africa.
Habitat: Dry savannahs.
Food: Omnivorous diet.
Size: 0.7–1.3m (2.25–4.25ft); 6–12kg (13–26lb).
Maturity: Not known.
Breeding: Usually 3–4 pups born July–October in southern Africa.
Life span: Not known.
Status: Not endangered.

The black-backed jackal is reddish-brown with a white-streaked black band along its back. The thick, hairy tail is also black, particularly at the tip. In parts of South Africa, black-backed jackals used to cause problems by feeding on large numbers of pineapples.

Black-backed jackals live in closely bonded pairs, sometimes with one or two older offspring staying to help rear the pups. The older offspring increase the survival rate of young pups by providing extra food and guarding the den from predators, such as hyenas. When the parents arrive back from hunting, the pups start begging and this encourages the adults to regurgitate food which they have caught and swallowed earlier.

The jackals communicate with screaming yells followed by three or four short yaps. They make these calls more often during the winter when they start mating. In South Africa, where black-backed jackals are the only species of jackal present, howling is common.

Black-backed jackals have very varied diets, feeding on anything from young antelope, rodents and hares through to birds, reptiles, carrion, invertebrates, wild berries and fruit.

Red fox

Vulpes vulpes

The red fox is a very successful and adaptable species. It is mainly active at night but will forage during the day, particularly when there are hungry cubs to feed. It also enjoys curling up and sunbathing in exposed but private spots, often by railway lines or roadsides.

A pair of foxes shares a home range, often with young from the previous breeding season. Mating takes place from December to February and after a few months, females – also known as vixens – give birth to between 3 and 12 cubs. The availability of food determines whether vixens breed and how many cubs they produce. During the mating season, females and occasionally males give out spine-tingling shrieks.

Red foxes mark their territories with a distinctive scent, which lingers and tells when a fox has been in the area. The scent is left with urine or faeces and is produced by special glands at the base of the tail. There are further scent glands between the pads of foxes' feet and around their lips.

Distribution: Europe, Asia and North Africa. Introduced to Australia.
Habitat: Able to colonize almost any habitat available.
Food: Small vertebrates, invertebrates, kitchen scraps, fruit and carrion.
Size: 85–95cm (34–38in); 4–8kg (9–18lb).
Maturity: 10 months.
Breeding: 3–12 pups born in early spring.
Life span: 9 years.
Status: Common.

The red fox is a large fox with a rusty, red-brown coat and a darker bushy tail with a white tip.

Fennec fox

Vulpes zerda

The fennec fox is the world's smallest fox and lives in the hot deserts of North Africa. The animal gets most of its water from solid food. Its body also ensures that the least amount of water is wasted. Fennec foxes are only active at night, when the temperature is much lower.

The fox's very large ears are used to detect the sounds made by prey, such as grasshoppers and other insects, in or on the sand. The large ears also radiate excess body heat. Cream-coloured fur helps keep fennec foxes well camouflaged against the sand when resting during the day. They are able to dig very quickly to catch any fast-moving prey living in the sand.

Fennec foxes are usually seen in pairs. In the breeding season, females are very protective of their pups and will be very aggressive if anything threatens them.

The fennec fox is a small cream-coloured fox with short legs, huge ears, a small pointed muzzle and a black-tipped tail.

Distribution: Sahara Desert through to the Nubian Desert. Also found in North Arabia.
Habitat: Sandy deserts.
Food: Various animal and plant foods, particularly insects.
Size: 42–72cm (17–29in); 1–1.5kg (2.2–3.3lb).
Maturity: Suckled for 2 months and mature by 6 months of age.
Breeding: Mating between January and February. Give birth to 1–5 pups.
Life span: Not known
Status: Common.

Sand or **pale fox** (*Vulpes pallida*): 61–74cm (24–30in); 2–3.6kg (4.4–8lb)
Found across the Sahel belt in northern Africa, the sand fox lives in family parties comprising an adult pair and their offspring. They dig their own burrows to a depth of 2–3m (6.5–10ft) and then extend them for a farther 15m (50ft). They come out at night or early evening to feed on fruit and berries, which provide them with their daily supplement of water. The sand fox feeds on small mammals and insects.

Royal or **hoary fox** (*Vulpes cana*): 40–60cm (16–24in); 2–3kg (4.4–6.6lb)
A shy cat-like fox with very dense, sandy-coloured fur, the royal fox can be found from Pakistan to northern Egypt, living in rock crevices and shelters. It has excellent hearing to find and eat insects. It will also feed on berries. The tail is long with thick fur, which is thought to help the animal evade predators that may try to catch it. If a predator grasps the tail, the royal fox has a chance to run away even if it means the predator being left with a mouthful of fur or even a piece of the tail itself.

Cape fox (*Vulpes chama*): 86–97cm (34–39in); 2.4–4kg (5.25–8.8lb)
The Cape fox is found nowhere else in the world apart from southern Africa – the Cape. It is a small, slim fox with large pointed ears, and lives in open areas where it can feed on a wide range of food, from small rodents and insects to reptiles and birds. Cape foxes live in burrow dens dug out by other mammals, usually hidden among thick vegetation and rocks.

Bat-eared fox

Otocyon megalotis

Bat-eared foxes have very large ears that listen for the movements of harvester termites. Their very thick fur coats protect the foxes from the painful bites of soldier termites that they encounter. They have 46–50 teeth, whereas most mammals have far fewer than this. Their teeth are used to slice up insects that have hard shells and pincers. With the ability to move their lower jaws up and down five times a second, insects are hurriedly chewed and eaten. The bat-eared fox also has very strong claws on its front feet, enabling it to dig very fast.

A pair normally lives together with up to six offspring. They mate for life and have a home range that may be 0.25–3sq km (0.1–1sq miles) in size. Sometimes a second female will join the pair and share the breeding den. Individuals feed by walking long distances over their territories, continually listening for small invertebrates. When they hear something underground, they dig vigorously, catching the prey before it has a chance to get away.

Bat-eared foxes are smaller than most canids. They have huge ears and dark, bushy tails.

Distribution: Southern Africa and East Africa.
Habitat: Open country, including short scrub, grassland, steppes, lightly wooded areas and farmland.
Food: Harvester termites, beetles and other insects.
Size: 75–90cm (30–36in); 3–5kg (6.6–11lb).
Maturity: Not known.
Breeding: 1–6 pups born from September–November.
Life span: Not known.
Status: Common.

SMALL CARNIVORES

Some of the small carnivores, the mustelids, are very fast and efficient hunters. They can tackle prey much larger than themselves. Mustelids tend to be solitary animals, defending their territories from all comers. Their long, lithe bodies, short legs and sharp claws mean that they are often skilful climbers, capable of reaching the most inaccessible of places and leaving their prey few places to hide.

Stoat

Mustela erminea

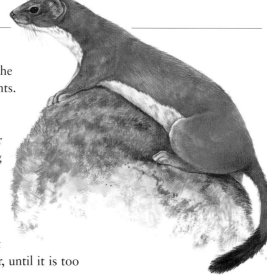

Although rarely seen, stoats are common in the countryside, where they mainly feed on rodents. However, the large males will often prey on rabbits, even though rabbits are considerably larger. Stoats are famed for mesmerizing their prey by dancing around them, before nipping in for the kill. This is not just an old wives' tale. Stoats have been observed leaping around near rabbits in a seemingly deranged fashion. This curious "dance" seems to have the effect of confusing the rabbits, which just watch the stoat draw slowly closer and closer, until it is too late to escape.

As winter approaches, populations of stoats that live in cooler, northern areas change the colour of their coats. In summer, they are a chestnut colour but, by the time the first snows have fallen, the stoats have changed to pure white. White stoats are known as ermines, and their fur was once prized for its pure colour and soft feel.

In mild climates, stoats have chestnut fur all year round. In colder areas, they moult into white fur in winter. Stoats are distinguished from their smaller cousins, the weasels, by having black tips to their tails.

Distribution: Widespread in northern and central Europe extending into Asia and across northern North America. Introduced to New Zealand.
Habitat: Anywhere with enough cover.
Food: Mammals up to the size of rabbits.
Size: 16–31cm (6.5–12.5in); 140–445g (0.3–1lb).
Maturity: 1 year.
Breeding: 1 litter per year of 5–12 young.
Life span: 10 years.
Status: Common.

Zorilla

Ictonyx striatus

Zorillas have an uncanny resemblance to skunks, although they are more closely related to ferrets and polecats. Their alternative name is the striped polecat. Not only do they share black and white markings with their North American relatives, but they also eject a foul-smelling liquid from glands near their anuses if alarmed. When faced with enemies, zorillas puff up their fur in an attempt to look bigger, and then squirt their noxious liquid towards their assailants. If the liquid gets in a predator's eyes, it causes intense irritation, as well as smelling very unpleasant. This strategy is extremely effective, with few predators prepared to risk the stinking spray.

Zorillas are nocturnal animals, resting during the day in burrows or rock crevices. At night they hunt small animals, as well as eating the eggs of ground-nesting birds, which are a particular favourite. Zorillas are predominantly ground-living animals, but they are proficient swimmers and climbers when the need arises.

With their bold black and white markings, zorillas are easily mistaken for skunks.

Distribution: Sudan to South Africa.
Habitat: A wide variety, including temperate forest, tropical forest, savannah and grasslands.
Food: Rodents, large insects, eggs, snakes, birds, frogs and reptiles.
Size: 33–38cm (13–15in); 1kg (2.2lb).
Maturity: 1 year.
Breeding: 1 litter of 1–3 young born each year.
Life span: 13 years.
Status: Common.

Badger

Meles meles

Large members of the mustelid family, badgers have a much more diverse diet than most of the small carnivores. Adept at making a meal out of most situations, badgers will eat anything they find, including berries, fungi and carrion. Worms are a particularly favourite, and on warm, damp nights badgers can regularly be observed patrolling through pastureland, searching them out.

One of the badger's greatest assets is its mouth. The way a badger's skull is structured means that it is physically impossible for the animal to dislocate its jaw, allowing badgers to have one of the most powerful bites in the natural world. This trait makes the badger a fearsome foe for any animal that happens to cross its path. Unlike most other mustelids, badgers are very social animals. They live in large family groups centred on communal dens, or setts.

The badger's black and white face makes it instantly recognizable.

Distribution: Throughout Europe (but not north of Arctic circle) and Asia.
Habitat: Favours a mixture of woodland and pastureland, also moving into urban habitats.
Food: Omnivorous diet.
Size: 65–80cm (26–32in); 8–12kg (17.5–26.5lb).
Maturity: 1–2 years.
Breeding: 1 litter of 1–5 young per year.
Life span: 15 years.
Status: Common.

Sable (*Martes zibellina*): 32–46cm (12–18.5in); 0.9–1.8kg (2–4lb)
Restricted to the northern forests of Siberia, the sable has a long, thick, soft coat which protects it from the cold. Largely solitary, the sable may occupy home ranges of up to 25sq km (8sq miles) of forestland. It needs this amount of land to provide it with enough food in the harsh conditions of its habitat.

Weasel (*Mustela nivalis*): 17–30cm (6.8–12in); 30–70g (0.06–0.15lb)
Similar, but much smaller than their close relatives the stoats, weasels are fierce mini-predators. The weasel's tail lacks the black tip of the stoat's. In Scandinavia these brown mustelids turn white in winter. Females may live up to three years, giving birth to litters of around five kittens in their second and third years. Males have even more fast and furious lives. The onus is on travelling far and wide, looking for mates. This makes them much more vulnerable to predation, and male weasels rarely live long enough to see their first birthday.

Beech marten

Martes foina

Not found in Britain but common in continental Europe, the beech marten was originally an animal of woodland and hilly habitats. However, it has greatly increased its range by exploiting the habitats humans have created. In some regions of France, Germany and Switzerland, beech martens have become very common in towns, frequently occupying the loft spaces of people's homes.

They can actually be quite a nuisance, chewing electrical wiring and making off with roof insulation to use as bedding. Beech martens have also been reported to have developed a liking for cars. The learned behaviour of sleeping under car bonnets, where it's nice and warm, has spread across central Europe. Every day, up to 40 cars in Switzerland are damaged by beech martens chewing through the wires under their bonnets. This compulsive chewing behaviour is a consequence of the marten's dietary flexibility. Youngsters will test anything and everything to see if it is edible or not.

Beech martens have a silky dark-brown coat with a white throat patch. People tolerate them in towns partly because they help to control rodents. Their main enemies are birds of prey and foxes.

Distribution: Throughout Europe.
Habitat: Deciduous woodland, open rocky hillsides and urban habitats.
Food: Rodents, fruit and eggs.
Size: 42–48cm (16–19in); 1.3–2.3kg (2.8–5lb).
Maturity: 1–2 years.
Breeding: 1 litter of 1–8 kittens per year.
Life span: 18 years.
Status: Common.

MONGOOSES AND CAT-LIKE ANIMALS

Mongooses, civets and genets form a group of small carnivores called the viverrids. In general, viverrids have long, slender bodies with short legs and sharp snouts. They can be split into two broad groups. Mongooses have weasel-like bodies and tend to live in large units, or bands, in open country, while genets and civets look more like cats, and mostly live solitary lives in dense forest.

Banded mongoose

Mungos mungo

Distribution: Africa south of the Sahara.
Habitat: Grassland and dry woodland.
Food: Insects and millipedes.
Size: 30–45cm (12–18in); 1.5–2.5kg (3.3–5.5lb).
Maturity: 9–10 months.
Breeding: Litters of 3 or 4, up to 4 times per year.
Life span: Up to 12 years.
Status: Common.

The banded mongoose is one of the most common mongooses in Africa. It lives in open grassland and areas of dry woodland, and is also found in rocky, broken country. It lives in bands of up to 40 individuals, sharing dens inside old termite mounds or abandoned aardvark holes. The dens have central sleeping chambers, which are reached from several holes.

Dens are used for only a few days at a time, with bands regularly moving on to new foraging sites. Banded mongooses feed during the daytime, returning to their dens before sunset. Their diet consists of invertebrates, such as beetles and millipedes.

Banded mongooses have excellent senses of smell, hearing and vision. Their bands are highly social, with members rarely straying far from each other and communicating by making several distinct sounds. All females in a band breed at the same time. The young are raised together, and are suckled by all the adult females in the band.

Banded mongooses have brownish-grey fur with dark brown stripes, or bands, across their backs and tails. Each foot possesses five long claws.

Meerkat

Suricata suricatta

Meerkats are relatives of mongooses, which live in large bands in the arid, semi-desert areas of southern Africa. They are efficient diggers and live in large underground burrows.

Meerkats live in highly organized societies. While feeding, at least one band member keeps a look-out for danger, communicating to the others with an array of sounds. For example, howling warns that a bird of prey is approaching, while double-barking informs the band that a terrestrial predator, has been spotted.

A meerkat band has between 10 and 15 individuals, with two or three pairs of males and females which do all the breeding. The young kits stay close to their dens and are looked after by at least one adult while the rest of their band forages for food.

Meerkats live in dry, open country in southern Africa, especially in the semi-desert regions of Namibia, southern Angola, Botswana and western South Africa.

Distribution: South-western and southern Africa from Angola to South Africa.
Habitat: Semi-desert and scrubland.
Food: Insects, scorpions, small vertebrates and eggs.
Size: 25–35cm (10–14in); 600–975g (1.3–2.1lb).
Maturity: 1 year.
Breeding: Litters of 2–5 kits born once per year in November.
Life span: 10 years.
Status: Common.

Common genet

Genetta genetta

A row of black erectile hairs is usually present along the middle of the back of the common genet. The tail has black and white rings. A genet's claws can be withdrawn inside the paws, just like a cat's.

Common genets, also called small-spotted genets, are related to civets. They are common in Africa, and a few are found in western Europe, although biologists think that these are descended from genets introduced to the area many years ago.

Genets live alone or in pairs, resting by day in sheltered spots or abandoned burrows. They feed at night, hunting for small animals in a range of habitats, from dense forest to open grassland. They climb trees to prey on roosting birds or silently stalk victims on the ground.

Genets mainly communicate by sound and smell, but also use their tails to signal. In warmer parts, genets breed during the wet season, with a few females managing to produce two litters each year.

Distribution: South-western Europe, including France and Spain, and Africa, excluding tropical rainforests and deserts.
Habitat: Forests and grasslands.
Food: Rodents, birds, small reptiles and insects.
Size: Length 42–58cm (16–23in); 1–3kg (2.2–6.6lb).
Maturity: 4 years.
Breeding: 2 litters of 1–4 kittens every year.
Life span: 13 years.
Status: Common.

Aquatic genet (*Osbornictis piscivora*): 45cm (17in); 1.5g (3.3lb)
These are very rare cat-like animals found in the dense tropical forests of the Congo. Their fur is chestnut-red, their tails are black and they have white spots between their eyes. This species is thought to live alone and spend a lot of time in or near water, feeding on fish and frogs. Unlike other genets, aquatic genets do not have hairs on their palms, which may help them feel for prey in muddy water holes.

Cusimanse (*Crossarchus obscurus*): 30–45cm (12–18in); 1.5kg (3.3lb)
Cusimanses are small mongooses that live in patches of swampy forest in West Africa. Their bodies are covered in long brown-grey-yellow hairs. Cusimanses travel in groups and appear to be active both day and night, taking shelter when convenient. They feed on fruit, seeds, insects and small reptiles. Cusimanses also crack open snail shells and eggs by hurling them between their back legs on to hard stones.

African civet (*Civettictis civetta*): 68–89cm (27–35in); 7–20kg (15–44lb)
The African civet lives all over sub-Saharan Africa, being equally at home in open grassland and dense forest. Its coarse hair is black with yellowish spots and stripes. During the day, civets hide in thickets of grass. At night they cross large distances, even swimming across rivers, in search of carrion, small animals, eggs, insects and fruit. African civets live alone and only settle in one place when nursing young. Breeding takes place throughout the year.

Fossa

Cryptoprocta ferox

The fossa is the largest carnivore in Madagascar. Looking very similar to a cat, it hunts by leaping through the trees to prey on lemurs and other small animals, such as birds and frogs. The fossa lives alone, patrolling its forest territory at dawn and dusk and sheltering in caves or inside disused termite mounds by day.

Fossas sometimes attack domestic animals, such as pigs and poultry, and are often killed as pests by people, who also unnecessarily fear that the fossas may attack them. This persecution, combined with the destruction of their forest habitat, means that fossas have become very rare, like much of Madagascar's native wildlife.

Fossas only spend time with other members of their species during the breeding season, which is in September and October. The females give birth three months later, in the height of summer.

Fossas walk in a flat-footed manner on their soles, like bears, rather than on their toes, like cats.

Distribution: Madagascar.
Habitat: Forests.
Food: Rodents, birds, frogs, reptiles and young lemurs.
Size: 61–80cm (24–32in); 7–12kg (15–26.5lb).
Maturity: 4 years.
Breeding: Twins born once per year.
Life span: 17 years.
Status: Endangered.

RODENTS

The Rodentia, *with over 2,000 species distributed all around the globe, is by far the largest order of mammals. All rodents have two upper and two lower chisel-like incisor teeth. These incisors grow continuously throughout their lives, so they can gnaw anything and everything without the possibility of their teeth getting worn down.*

Edible dormouse

Glis glis

When awake, all species of dormouse belie their dozy reputation, being incredibly lithe and agile climbers – the edible dormouse being no exception. These dormice spend virtually their entire lives in the treetops, searching for food, and are very reluctant to leave the safety of the branches. If they cannot leap between trees, they will not cross the open areas on the ground. Roads and tracks cut through woodland can therefore inhibit the movement of dormice.

Dormice are champion sleepers, being one of the few types of mammal to enter a true state of hibernation. Come autumn, dormice descend into the bases of hollow trees, wrap themselves into balls and fall into a state of very deep sleep. They allow their body temperature to drop very low, barely more than the temperature of the air around them. Heart rate and breathing also slow right down. By doing this, they are able to conserve enough energy to last them through the winter. When spring arrives, the dormice's metabolism speeds up again, bringing them out of six or seven months of uninterrupted sleep.

Also known as fat dormice, the Romans kept edible dormice in jars, called gliraria, to fatten them for the table.

Distribution: Throughout central and eastern Europe, extending west through northern Spain. Introduced into England.
Habitat: The canopy of mature deciduous woodland.
Food: Nuts, fruit, fungi, bark, insects and occasionally eggs and nestlings.
Size: 13–19cm (5–7.5in), 70–300g (0.15–0.66lb).
Maturity: 2 years.
Breeding: 1 litter of 2–9 offspring born in summer.
Life span: 7 years.
Status: Common.

Water vole

Arvicola terrestris

Distribution: Widespread across Europe and Asia.
Habitat: Banks of slow-flowing rivers and streams.
Food: Grasses, rushes and sedges.
Size: 14–22cm (5.5–8.8in); 150–300g (0.33–0.66lb).
Maturity: 2 months.
Breeding: 3 or 4 litters of 5 young born throughout spring and summer.
Life span: Up to 3 years.
Status: Common.

Water voles are also known – confusingly – as water rats. Ratty, of *The Wind in the Willows* fame, was really a water vole, and like him, these rodents are found living alongside slow-moving rivers, ditches, dykes and lakes. In areas of central Europe, however, water voles do not live by water, preferring dry habitats instead. In some places they are considered to be a serious agricultural pest.

Water voles excavate extensive burrow systems in the banks of the rivers, with plenty of entrance and exit holes so that they can escape from the various predators they encounter – both in and out of the water. Even so, the average life span of a water vole is a mere five months. Herons, barn owls, brown rats and pike are all known to prey on water voles, but the rodents' most important predators are stoats and mink. Indeed, the introduction of the American mink to Britain has been blamed for the species' recent and rapid decline.

Water voles are often mistaken for rats, but they differ from rats by having blunter snouts, more rounded bodies, smaller ears and shorter, hairy tails.

Siberian lemming

Lemmus sibericus

Contrary to popular belief, lemmings do not commit suicide. During favourable years, the lemmings' ability to reproduce very quickly leads to population explosions of amazing proportions. As the population size goes up, space becomes more and more difficult to find, and young are pushed away from the best habitat, down the mountains and into the valleys.

Lemmings are good swimmers when they have to be, but they don't know their limits. During dispersal, youngsters often try to cross large bodies of water, drowning in the process. It is this behaviour which gave rise to the misconception that they kill themselves.

During the summer, lemmings spend much of their time underground in burrows, but when the ground starts to freeze in autumn, the lemmings cannot dig through the ground and are forced to forage on the surface. The lemmings do not hibernate during the harsh Scandinavian winter, but construct tunnel systems under the snow in search of food. The tunnels keep them out of sight from hungry predators, such as great grey owls, which are heavily reliant on lemmings as a source of food.

Unlike other species of lemming, the Siberian lemming does not change the colour of its coat in winter.

Distribution: Siberia and northern North America.
Habitat: Tundra grassland.
Food: Moss and grass.
Size: 13–18cm (5–7in); 23–34g (0.05–0.07lb).
Maturity: 5–6 weeks.
Breeding: These prolific breeders may produce 8 litters of up to 6 young each throughout the summer.
Life span: Less than 2 years.
Status: Common.

Alpine marmot (*Marmota marmota*): 45–60cm (18–24in); 3–4.5kg (6.5–10lb)
Alpine marmots live in the alpine and subalpine pastures of the Alps. Like many other marmots, alpine marmots live in family groups, consisting of a breeding pair and their offspring from previous years. Older male offspring are known to help keep their younger siblings warm during the cold alpine winters. Litter sizes tend to be small – about two pups. The pups stay with their parents until they are three years old.

Southern birch mouse (*Sicista subtilis*): 5–9cm (2–3.5in); 6–14g (0.015–0.03lb)
These tiny mice inhabit the forests, moors, meadows and steppes of eastern Europe and Asia. They excavate shallow burrows, in which they build oval-shaped nests of dry grass and cut plant stems. They travel over the ground in leaps and bounds. They are also great climbers. Strong outer toes grip twigs, and their prehensile tail curls around other branches for additional support.

Common hamster (*Cricetus cricetus*): 20–27cm (8–11in); 200–500g (0.45–1.1lb)
The stocky common hamster feeds on cereal crops, potatoes and beets, and also on small birds and other rodents when it has the chance. It makes large stockpiles of food within its large burrow system, which is dug in the ground and has an intricate network of tunnels. Food, intended for storage, is carried back home in its cheek pouches. Its range extends from western Europe to central Russia. Females often produce 2 litters of 6–12 young during summer.

House mouse

Mus musculus

The key to the house mouse's phenomenal success as a species is its ability to follow humans around the globe, and the way it is able to make use of whatever food sources people provide. By stowing away on ships and, latterly, aeroplanes, house mice have been able to colonize every continent of the world.

Mice were first domesticated, and in some instances worshipped, by the Romans and ancient Greeks. However, these days house mice are considered to be a major pest. They cause billions of dollars' worth of damage to food stores worldwide every year. They also damage buildings, woodwork, furniture and clothing, and are known to carry various dangerous diseases, including typhus and salmonella.

However, house mice are virtually unrivalled in their capacity to adapt to new surroundings. Their generalist habits, rapid breeding rate and talent for slipping into places unnoticed has enabled mice to become possibly the most numerous mammal in the world today.

A common sight all over the world, the house mouse is capable of making the most of any opportunity.

Distribution: Every continent of the world, including Antarctica.
Habitat: Generally near human habitation.
Food: Virtually anything.
Size: 15–19cm (6–7.5in); 17–25g (0.04–0.05lb).
Maturity: 5–7 weeks.
Breeding: Usually around 5–10 litters of 3–12 offspring during the year.
Life span: 12–18 months.
Status: Abundant.

Cape porcupine

Hystrix africaeaustralis

The Cape porcupine shares its habitat with a whole array of dangerous predators, but its sharp quills can repel even lions and hyenas. A mane of long, white bristles runs down the neck to the back. The rodent has special hollow quills attached to its tail, which can be rattled together as a warning to any unsuspecting animal that gets too close for comfort. Covering the lower back are 40cm (16in) long quills, equipped with tiny barbs. These quills are only loosely held in the skin and will embed themselves easily into any animal attempting to attack. Porcupines have keen hearing and an excellent sense of smell, which they use to locate nutritious bulbs underground. The Cape porcupines, like other rodents, also chew bones from carcasses to obtain calcium, phosphorus and other essential minerals. Chewing bones also helps to keep their incisor teeth sharp. Porcupines will often share burrows, forming clans comprising adult pairs and up to four offspring of varying ages. Members of the clan share common runs, trails and latrines, and also common feeding sites and refuges.

The Cape porcupine has the longest quills of any species of porcupine in the world.

Distribution: Widespread in Africa south of the Sahara Desert.
Habitat: Grassland.
Food: Roots, bark, herbs and fruit.
Size: 0.7–1m (2.25–3.25ft); up to 17kg (37.5lb).
Maturity: 9 months.
Breeding: Mated females produce up to 2 offspring at a time.
Life span: Up to 20 years.
Status: Endangered in some parts of its range, but common elsewhere.

Red squirrel

Sciurus vulgaris

Red squirrels can be quite variable in colour, with some individuals being jet black, while others are strawberry blonde. The bushy tail helps them to balance in the treetops. These arboreal rodents are very acrobatic.

The red squirrel has undergone a well-documented decline in Britain due to its not being able to compete with the larger and more robust grey squirrel, which was introduced from North America. The two species actually hardly ever come to blows, and it is thought that the main problem may be that the grey squirrels harbour a viral infection that decimates red squirrels whilst leaving the greys unaffected.

Red squirrels tend to be most active during early mornings and late afternoons. They rest in the middle of the day. As winter sets in, the squirrels rapidly put on weight, and settle down for a long period of inactivity. Squirrels do not truly hibernate. They never let their body temperatures drop, and they regularly wake up to stretch their legs, drink and feed from food caches made in the autumn.

Red squirrels are mainly solitary animals, and apart from when there is a large concentration of food, the only time they get together in any numbers is when the females become ready to breed. Males fight over them at this time.

Distribution: Europe and Asia.
Habitat: Primarily coniferous forests.
Food: Seeds and nuts when available, and also fungi, eggs, flowers and tree sap.
Size: 25–35cm (10–14in); up to 350g (0.75lb).
Maturity: 9–10 months.
Breeding: 2 litters of 5–7 young per year.
Life span: 4–6 years.
Status: Rare in the UK, common elsewhere.

Naked mole rat

Heterocephalus glaber

Naked mole rats live in societies which are more like social insects' colonies than those of other mammals. They live an entirely underground existence, and colonies can occupy 4km (2.5 miles) of tunnels, which are dug out by the rodents' claws and incisors. Some of these tunnels run just beneath the surface of the ground; others descend up to a 2m (80in) depth.

Like colonies of bees and ants, naked mole rat colonies are governed by queens, which give birth to the young. The queens are the largest individuals in the colonies, which usually comprise around 70 animals, but can number 300. The other individuals – the workers and drones – are separated into castes depending on their size. The members of each different caste have their own particular jobs, for example foraging, tunnel maintenance, caring for the young or nest defence.

Naked mole rats are the only mammals that have lost the ability to produce their own body heat. Instead, they bask in shallow tunnels warmed by the sun, or huddle together to keep warm.

As their name suggests, naked mole rats are almost hairless, with the pinkish skin showing through. They use their strong incisors and large claws for digging tunnels. These rodents are virtually blind.

Distribution: Kenya, Ethiopia and Somalia.
Habitat: Underground in arid savannah and grassland.
Food: Underground parts of plants, particularly the succulent tubers.
Size: 6–10cm (2.4–4in); 25–70g (0.05–0.15lb).
Maturity: 1 year.
Breeding: Usually about 12 young per litter, with 8 litters per year.
Life span: Over 20 years.
Status: Common.

Lord Derby's flying squirrel (*Anomalurus derbianus*): 27–38cm (11–15in); 0.5–1kg (1.1–2.2lb)
Belonging to an unusual group of rodents from central Africa known as scaly-tailed squirrels, these creatures glide from tree to tree. They leap into the air with their arms, legs and tails extended, stretching out membranes of skin that allow them to glide, but not fly, up to 250m (830ft). The scales on their tails are used as anchor-brakes, preventing them from skidding when they land on the trunks of trees.

North African gundi (*Ctenodactylus gundi*): 16–20cm (6.5–8in); 175–195g (0.3–0.4lb)
Found in the arid areas of northern Africa, gundis are small diurnal rodents that have very short legs, flat ears, big eyes and long whiskers. To warm up in the morning, they sit crouched on sunny rocks. When the wind is blowing through their fur, they have been said to resemble face-powder puffs.

Great cane rat (*Thryonomys swinderianus*): 35–61cm (14–24in); 3.5–4.5kg (7.5–10lb)
Great cane rats are large rodents that live in groups comprising one male, several females and the young from previous litters. They are nocturnal, and create trails through grass and reeds that lead from shelter to feeding and watering sites. They pound down tall grasses to make nests and also make shallow burrows for shelter. They are good swimmers and divers. If great cane rats become afraid, they either stomp their hind feet and grunt, or quickly run towards water.

Springhare

Pedetes capensis

Hopping is a very efficient way to travel, and it allows springhares to bound rapidly around the African savannah at night. Usually they do not move too far from their burrows, but during times of drought they have been known to travel up to 40km (25 miles) in search of water.

Springhares have incredibly keen senses. As well as having fantastic sight, scent and hearing, they use their huge back feet to pick up vibrations from the earth.

Springhares need all their senses to be able to avoid the long list of predators that would happily make meals of them. They are small enough to be manageable for wild cats, jackals, ratels and large owls, but big enough to interest larger predators, such as lions and leopards, should they get close enough to be able to catch them.

Rather like a small kangaroo, the bizarre springhare is in a family all of its own.

Distribution: Southern and eastern Africa.
Habitat: Grasslands with sandy soil.
Food: Vegetation, mainly bulbs and grasses.
Size: 35–45cm (14–18in); 4kg (8.8lb).
Maturity: 1 year.
Breeding: Around 3 or 4 young per litter, with litters born about every 100 days.
Life span: 10 years.
Status: Common and widespread.

BATS

With nearly 1,000 species, bats form one of the largest groups among the mammals, living in almost all temperate and tropical parts of the world. They are the only mammals to have truly mastered flight, and more than half of the species are known to use echolocation for navigating and capturing prey at night. Different bats are specialized for eating insects, fruit, flowers, blood, fish and small animals.

Greater mastiff bat

Mops condylurus

This species is also known as the Angolan free-tailed bat, reflecting the disagreement in its classification. Some scientists place the greater mastiff bat in the same group as the free-tailed bats, while others place it in a separate group.

The greater mastiff bat roosts in caves, mines, hollow trees and can even be found under thatched roofs and in attics. The bats form groups of several hundred individuals. At sundown they fly out of their roosts to hunt insects. A colony of 500 individuals can consume a tonne of insects per year, and ecologists are thinking of using these bats to control insect pests in Africa, such as mosquitoes that carry malaria. Scientists have started designing artificial roosts or bat "hotels" to encourage the bats to feed in areas where insect pests breed. While designing the artificial roosts, researchers discovered that the bats are capable of tolerating up to 45°C (113°F) during the heat of tropical midday.

This bat is characterized by having wrinkly lips and a band of skin joining the ears, over the top of its head.

Distribution: Africa south of the Sahara Desert, including Madagascar.
Habitat: Forest, savannah and dry brushland.
Food: Insects.
Size: 5–6cm (2–2.5in); 7–64g (0.015–0.15lb).
Maturity: 3 months.
Breeding: 2 breeding seasons per year, with a single young produced per season.
Life span: Not known.
Status: Not included in IUCN Red List.

Hammer-headed fruit bat

Hypsignathus monstrosus

This is the largest bat in Africa, and is remarkable in having the greatest difference between males and females (sexual dimorphism) of any bat species. Males are nearly twice as heavy as females and, unlike females, they have an unusually large square-shaped head, giving the species its name. The male head-shape is one of several adaptations for calling, which include a greatly enlarged voice box, allowing males to produce a continuous and very loud croaking and quacking, probably to attract females.

Twice a year, male hammer-headed fruit bats congregate into groups of up to 130 individuals, in order to compete for mates. The males attract attention by croaking as loudly as possible and flapping their wings. The females are very selective, and most opt to mate with just a few of the noisiest males. When the bats are not breeding, they roost quietly during the day in small groups high up in the treetops. At night, hammer-headed bats fly up to 10km (6 miles) from their roost sites to find trees with ripened fruit to eat.

The male's head is large and square, and the muzzle is hammer-shaped. The males also have large lips and warty snouts. Females have thinner, fox-like muzzles.

Distribution: Central and western Africa.
Habitat: Forests, swamps, mangroves and river margins.
Food: Fruit, and also reported to have killed and eaten tethered chickens.
Size: Up to 0.9m (36in); up to 0.5kg (1.1lb).
Maturity: Females 6 months; males 18 months.
Breeding: Give birth to single young, or sometimes twins, once or twice per year.
Life span: Not known.
Status: Common.

Little flying cow (*Nanonycteris veldkampi*): 5–7.5cm (2–3in); 19–33g (0.04–0.07lb)
This small flower-feeding bat can be found in parts of western and central Africa. It gets its curious name from the apparently calf-like appearance of its head. This species migrates from forests to savannahs during the rainy season.

Butterfly bat (*Glauconycteris variegata*): 35–65mm (1.5–2.5in); 6–14g (0.01–0.03lb)
This African bat gets its name from its beautifully patterned wings and butterfly-like flight, and can be found roosting in small groups under palm fronds or banana leaves. Butterfly bats feed on small insects, sometimes foraging in broad daylight.

Long-tailed bat (*Rhinopoma microphyllum*): 5–9cm (2–3.5in); 6–14g (0.01–0.03lb)
This species has a tail nearly as long as its body, and lives in dry, treeless regions in northern and western Africa, parts of the Middle East and southern India. Long-tailed bats can often be found roosting in houses, and in Egypt they are believed to have roosted in the great pyramids for thousands of years.

Noctule bat

Nyctalus noctula

The noctule bat is one of the largest and most common European bats. In winter, noctules roost in hollow trees or old woodpecker holes, and occasionally in buildings. In some parts of Europe, groups of 1,000 individuals may roost together.

Noctules hunt insects in flight, and are capable of flying at speeds of 50kph (30mph) or more. Usually they forage at dusk, catching insects over woodland or close to water, and sometimes they are seen hunting insects that gather around street lamps in towns.

Although noctules are capable of surviving in cold conditions without food for up to four months, they also migrate to warmer areas where there is more food. Noctules have been known to migrate as far as 2,347km (1,455 miles). In late summer, solitary male noctules set up breeding roosts in tree holes, attracting up to 20 females with mating calls and pheromones. In early summer, pregnant females form groups of related individuals, then they help one another nurse their young.

Distribution: Europe to Japan.
Habitat: Forests.
Food: Insects, especially beetles, and also midges and moths.
Size: 32–40cm (12–16in); 15–40g (0.03–0.08lb).
Maturity: Females 3 months; males 1 year.
Breeding: Single litter of 1, 2 or occasionally 3 young born per year.
Life span: 12 years.
Status: Declining in some parts of its range.

The colour of the noctule bat ranges from a golden brown to a dark brown on the back, usually with paler brown coloration on the belly.

Pipistrelle bat

Pipistrellus pipistrellus

These small bats are common throughout most of Europe, but have declined in some countries due to the loss of natural roosting sites in trees. The reduction is also due to toxic chemicals that have been used to treat wood in the buildings where many pipistrelles roost during winter time. In some parts of Europe, pipistrelles hibernate in winter, either individually or in groups, hidden in crevices in buildings and trees. However, very cold weather may force wintering pipistrelles to move to warmer areas.

Mating usually takes place in autumn, when the bats congregate at traditional breeding roosts. Females give birth to their young in summer, when they come together in large maternity colonies to suckle and care for them.

Pipistrelles leave their roosts early in the evening to feed, chasing after insects in a characteristic fast and jerky pursuit flight, using echolocation. A single pipistrelle can eat as many as 3,000 insects in one night. Usually the high-pitched squeaks that pipistrelles make for echolocation are inaudible to humans, but some people can hear the lower-frequency parts of their calls.

There are two subspecies of pipistrelle bat, distinguished by the pitch of their calls. One is known as the tenor, while the other is the soprano. The largest colonies may number many thousands.

Distribution: Europe, North Africa, south-western and central Asia, and possibly Korea and Japan.
Habitat: Forests, farmland, wetlands and urban habitats, nesting in lofts.
Food: Insects.
Size: Wingspan 19–25cm (7.5–10in); 3–8g (0.006–0.017lb).
Maturity: Females 6 months; males 1 year.
Breeding: 1 young or occasionally twins produced per year.
Life span: 16 years.
Status: Common.

AARDVARK AND PANGOLIN

Recent scientific work has shown that, although the aardvark and pangolin share some superficial resemblance and behaviour, they do not have common ancestry. Indeed, they are now placed in separate groups. It is perhaps not surprising that specialist ant-eating mammals evolved independently several times, given the abundance of ants and termites found in almost all habitats around the world.

Aardvark

Orycteropus afer

Distribution: Sub-Saharan Africa.
Habitat: Woodland, savannah, grassland and shrubland.
Food: Ants, termites, other insects, small mammals and vegetable material.
Size: 1–1.5m (3.25–5ft); 40–70kg (88–154lb).
Maturity: 2 years.
Breeding: 1 or occasionally 2 young per year.
Life span: 20 years.
Status: Common.

These animals are often found foraging out in the open at night, systematically covering the ground in search of ants or termites. Aardvarks travel long distances in looking for food, often travelling 10km (6 miles) in a single night. Not surprisingly, given their long tubular ears and snout, they have acute hearing and a good sense of smell with which to detect their prey. They use their powerful front claws to dig open ant and termite nests, and their long sticky tongues to collect the insects. These animals have very thick skin, and seem to be immune to insect bites.

The aardvark's skin is so tough that it also saves it from bites by predators. Aardvarks are very well adapted for digging. When alarmed, they will either run away or start digging a burrow. A single aardvark can dig a hole faster than several people using shovels. Temporary aardvark burrows are less than 3m (10ft) deep, with end chambers large enough for the animals to turn in. More permanent burrows can be 13m (42ft) long with several chambers and entrances.

The word aardvark means "earth-pig" in Afrikaans, reflecting both the burrowing habits and pig-like features of this unusual animal. It has long ears, an elongated snout, a shaggy body and powerful tail. It folds its ears back while making its burrows.

Cape pangolin

Manis temmincki

There are four species of pangolin, also known as scaly anteaters, living in Africa. Two of them are tree-living animals with long prehensile tails, which they use when climbing. The other two species, which include the endangered Cape pangolin, live in burrows and forage on the ground.

Pangolins feed solely on ants and termites. They have several adaptations, such as having no teeth, which help them in this regard. Like other ant-eating mammals, they have sticky tongues up to 25cm (10in) long for collecting their prey, and strong claws to tear open termite nests. Unlike any other mammals, however, pangolins have scales rather than hairs, giving them a reptilian appearance. When a pangolin is threatened, it rolls up into a tight ball, protecting its soft underparts and presenting a formidable, scaly barrier to predators. The Cape pangolin has declined in numbers because, like its Asian cousins, it is in demand for its scales, which are used in local medicines.

Pangolins usually walk on their knuckles to save wear and tear on their claws, which they use for opening ant and termite nests. Sometimes they walk on their back legs, using the trailing tail to keep balance.

Distribution: Chad and Sudan to Namibia and South Africa.
Habitat: Savannah and shrubland.
Food: Ants, termites and occasionally other insects.
Size: 40–50cm (16–20in); 15–18kg (33–40lb).
Maturity: 2 years.
Breeding: 1 or occasionally 2 young.
Life span: Not known.
Status: Threatened.

ELEPHANTS AND RELATIVES

There are only two living species of elephant: African and Indian. Extinct species include the woolly mammoth and pygmy elephant. Although there is some disagreement among scientists, the closest relatives of the elephants are thought to be sea cows and hyraxes, neither of which bear much resemblance to elephants. However, similarities in their DNA codes reveal their shared ancestry.

African elephant

Loxodonta africana

There are two races of African elephants: the savannah elephant, which is the world's largest living land animal, and the smaller forest elephant that lives in the rainforests of central and western Africa. The savannah elephants are social animals and, like Indian elephants, they form groups consisting of related female elephants and their young.

The leaders of elephant groups are always the eldest and largest females. Male elephants leave their groups at puberty, driven away by older females, to go and join groups of other young males. Males compete to mate, and usually these contests are settled by pushing and aggressive displays, but sometimes fighting leads to fatal injuries.

Forest elephants do not form large groups, but are able to maintain contact with other elephants in the dense jungle by producing deep, rumbling calls.

One of the most distinctive features of an elephant is its trunk. It is a very adaptable tool, and can be used for picking up anything from peanuts to trees. It is used for feeding, drinking, fighting and communication.

Distribution: Sub-Saharan Africa.
Habitat: Forest, savannah, marshland and semi-desert.
Food: Grass, leaves, shrubs, bark, twigs, roots and fruit.
Size: 6–7.5m (20ft–25ft); up to 7.5 tonnes (16,500lb).
Maturity: 10–20 years.
Breeding: Single calf born every few years.
Life span: 50–70 years.
Status: Endangered.

Rock hyrax

Procavia capensis

These small rodent-like animals live in groups in rocky areas, where there are plenty of nooks and crannies in which to hide. Hyraxes are surprisingly agile, and can run up even the steepest, smooth rock surfaces with ease, gripping the rocks with the rubber-like soles of their feet. Hyraxes have many enemies, which include leopards, eagles and pythons, so they have to be quick and watchful. In fact, the dominant male of a family group, which typically consists of several females and young, and sometimes a subordinate male as well, usually stands guard while the rest of the group feeds or basks in the sun. If the sentry animal spots danger, he will warn the rest of the group with an alarm call, signalling them to scamper off and hide in their burrows or between rocks.

Rock hyraxes don't like cold or wet weather, and will stay in their burrows if it is raining. When it is cold, groups of up to 25 animals will huddle together in a shelter to keep warm. On warm days, they come out to feed or bask in the sun. Hyraxes only come out at night if the weather is warm and there is plenty of moonlight, otherwise they stay in their burrows until daytime.

Rock hyraxes will eat almost any type of vegetation, even plant species poisonous to other mammals.

Distribution: Most of Africa, excluding the north-western regions.
Habitat: Rocky scrubland.
Food: Grass, leaves and shrubs.
Size: 30–58cm (12–23in); 4kg (9lb).
Maturity: 16–17 months.
Breeding: Litter of 1–6 young.
Life span: 11 years.
Status: Common.

HOOFED ANIMALS

This large group of plant-eating mammals is divided into two main groups, depending on whether they have an odd or even numbers of toes. They range in size from the tiny mouse deer, weighing less than 1kg (2lb) to the massive rhinoceroses and hippopotamuses that can weigh several tonnes. Hoofed animals are important for humans, having been domesticated as work animals and to provide food and clothing.

Dromedary camel

Camelus dromedarius

Distribution: North Africa to western India.
Habitat: Deserts and scrubland.
Food: Vegetation and carrion.
Size: 2.2–3.5m (7.25–11.5ft); 300–690kg (660–1500lb).
Maturity: 3 years.
Breeding: Single young or twins every 2 years.
Life span: 50 years.
Status: Common.

These tough animals have been domesticated in and around the Arabian peninsula for more than 4,000 years, and are prized for their endurance in hot, dry conditions. The dromedary, or one-humped camel, can carry loads of more than 200kg (440lb) for several days.

Camels can survive for long periods without drinking water. However, when water is available they can drink up to 57 litres (12 gallons) at a time to restore normal levels of body fluids. Camels have almost no sweat glands, so they lose water much more slowly than other mammals. Contrary to popular belief, the camel's hump contains fat, not water, and serves as an energy reserve – although the blubber does hold some water. During the breeding season, dominant males defend groups of up to 30 adult females from other males. Younger males form groups of bachelor males.

As well as its characteristic hump, camels have other adaptations to the harsh conditions of the desert, including broad feet for walking on loose sand, long eyelashes, hairy ears, and nostrils that can be closed to keep out sand and dust.

Common zebra

Equus burchelli

The common or Burchell's zebra has the broadest stripes of the three zebra species, and its stripes usually join at the belly.

There are three different species of zebra, all found in Africa and each with its own distinctive pattern of black and white stripes. The stripes make these hoofed mammals blend into the natural patterns of light and shade in their habitat, making it more difficult for a predator to keep track of its quarry during a chase, especially when the zebras are running in a herd formation.

Zebras usually live in small family groups headed by dominant stallions, which lead groups of one to six mares with their young. When young male zebras reach maturity, they leave their family groups and form groups of bachelor males, while females stay behind. Males fight amongst each other for access to females, circling and trying to kick or bite one another. Within a group, zebras can be affectionate, and may spend a lot of time grooming one another.

Distribution: Ethiopia to southern Africa.
Habitat: Grassland and open woodland.
Food: Grass, herbs and leaves.
Size: 2.2–2.5m (7.25–8.25ft); 290–340g (640–750lb).
Maturity: 3 years.
Breeding: Single foal born every 1–2 years.
Life span: Up to 40 years in captivity.
Status: Declining, but unlike other zebras, not present on the IUCN Red List.

Giraffe

Giraffa camelopardalis

Giraffes are the world's tallest living land mammals, with some exceeding 5m (16.5ft) from top to toe. The giraffe's long neck has the same number of vertebrae as other mammals, but each one is greatly elongated. The giraffe's great height is an adaptation for feeding on young leaves in the upper branches of trees, which other browsing mammals cannot reach.

Giraffes have excellent sight, and because of their height they have the greatest range of vision of any terrestrial animal. If a giraffe spots danger, it will run away at speeds of up to 56kph (34mph). Occasionally, a giraffe will face its attacker, striking out with its front hooves or swinging its head like a club.

In order to reach fresh grass or drinking water, giraffes must splay their front legs apart, so that they can get their heads down to ground level. Giraffes settle on to their withdrawn legs to rest, and lie down when sleeping, resting their heads back on their hindquarters.

In times gone by, giraffes could be found in parts of North Africa, but due to a combination of over-hunting and the effects of climate change on vegetation, they are now only thinly distributed south of the Sahara Desert.

Distribution: Sub-Saharan Africa.
Habitat: Open woodland and savannah.
Food: Leaves, grass and grains.
Size: 5.9m (19.5ft); 550–1,930kg (1,200–4,200lb).
Maturity: Females 3.5 years; males 4.5 years.
Breeding: Usually 1 young born every 2 years.
Life span: Up to 26 years recorded in the wild, and 36 years recorded in captivity.
Status: Conservation-dependent.

Giraffes have prehensile lips and long tongues to help them gather leaves. They also have short horn-like ossicones on their heads – a feature they share with okapis.

Donkey (*Equus asinus*): 2m (6.5ft); 250kg (550lb)
This species was originally found wild in North Africa and the Middle East, but now occurs around the world as a domestic animal. Although much slower than horses, donkeys are very strong and they are capable of enduring harsh conditions.

Ibex (*Capra ibex*): 1.1–1.7m (3.5–5.5ft); 35–150kg (77–330lb)
A relative of the domestic goat, the ibex lives in Alpine regions of Europe, parts of the Middle East, north-eastern Africa, and some mountainous regions of Asia. The ibex has massive, curved horns that can be over half the length of the animal's body in males. The coat is grey-brown. Older males have a small beard and a "mane" of longer hairs on the back of the neck. It is threatened with extinction in some parts of its range.

Okapi

Okapia johnstoni

The okapi is a close relative of the giraffe. Although okapis are nowhere near as tall as giraffes, they do have relatively long necks and legs. Females are usually larger than males. Okapis have a deep red-brown coloration with distinctive horizontal black and white stripes along their rumps and legs. Despite their large size and unique appearance, they were not known to science until 1900.

Male okapis have small, hair-covered, horn-like ossicones. They also have very long tongues, capable of reaching their eyes.

Okapis spend most of their time alone, and they are very wary, running into dense cover if they detect danger. Sometimes okapis form small family groups and communicate with vocalizations and mutual grooming.

It is thought that there are between 10,000 and 20,000 okapis in the wild, but their dense forest habitat makes it very difficult for scientists to estimate their true population status.

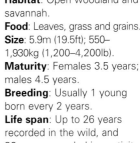

Distribution: Congo Region.
Habitat: Dense tropical forest.
Food: Leaves, twigs and fruit.
Size: 1.9–2.1m (6–7ft); 200–300kg (440–660lb).
Maturity: Females reach sexual maturity at 1.5 years; males probably do not have the opportunity to mate until older.
Breeding: Single offspring born after a gestation of 421–427 days.
Life span: 30 years.
Status: Threatened.

Black rhinoceros

Diceros bicornis

The black rhino can be distinguished from Africa's second rhino species, the white rhino, by its pointed, prehensile upper lip, as compared to the white rhino's squared, non-prehensile upper lip. Despite the names, there is no colour difference between them.

The black rhinoceros is the smaller and more abundant of the two species of rhino found in Africa, but it is still critically endangered. These animals form clans that sometimes come together at wallowing sites, where they have mud baths. The baths help to keep the skin healthy and free of parasites. Rhinos within a clan are usually tolerant of each other, though occasionally serious fights may occur between bulls that are courting the same female.

Black rhinoceroses can be quite dangerous. They have very bad eyesight and may charge at anything large enough to be a threat, including vehicles, tents and campfires. However, they usually run away when they detect the scent of humans. Indeed, rhinos have good reason to fear humans. Hunting has destroyed the populations of both of the African species. People have hunted the rhino for sport, for its tough hide, but mostly for its horn. A rhino's horn is made from the same material as hair, and can be carved into ornamental objects or ground into medicinal or aphrodisiac powders. Many countries have banned trade in rhino products, but illegal trading still occurs.

Distribution: Eastern and southern Africa from southern Chad and Sudan to South Africa.
Habitat: Scrubland and woody savannah.
Food: Twigs and leaves.
Size: 3–3.75m (10–12.25ft); 800–1,400kg (1,760–3,080lb).
Maturity: Females 4–6 years; males 7–9 years.
Breeding: Single calf born every 2–5 years.
Life span: Can exceed 45 years in captivity.
Status: Critically endangered.

Hippopotamus

Hippopotamus amphibius

These enormous animals spend much of their time in water, where they keep cool out of the hot sun and take the weight off their legs. Hippopotamuses lie in the water with only their nostrils, eyes and ears above the surface, and they can also submerge for up to 30 minutes, while walking on the bottom of the river or lake. At night they leave their watery refuge in search of grass, sometimes travelling more than 3km (2 miles) from water.

Large males set up territories along riverbanks, which they defend against other males. Although neighbouring territory-holders are usually peaceful, confrontations sometimes occur. When this happens, the males challenge each other with displays, including lunging, splashing, scattering dung with their short tails and displaying their tusks with great yawns of their mouths. If neither male backs off, fighting occurs, and sometimes they attack each other with their tusks – which can lead to fatal injuries. Males are usually aggressive towards any intruders into their territories, including young hippos. Females are aggressive when they have young, and many consider hippos to be among the most dangerous of African mammals.

Distribution: Most of Sub-Saharan Africa.
Habitat: Deep water near reeds or grassland.
Food: Grass.
Size: 2–5m (6.5–16.5ft); 1–4.5 tonnes (2,200–9,900lb).
Maturity: 6–14 years.
Breeding: Usually a single young born during rainy season, with 2 years between births.
Life span: 40 years.
Status: Common.

The hippo's tusks – actually its canine teeth – can weigh up to 3kg (6.5lb) each, and are used in fighting. There have been some reports of hippos overturning small boats and biting the occupants to death.

Warthog

Phacochoerus africanus

This species gets its name from the warty protuberances located on the sides of the head and in front of the eyes, found only in the males. These powerful animals have large heads in proportion to the rest of their bodies, and both males and females have sharp tusks.

Unlike most species of wild pig, warthogs are active during the day, except in areas where they are likely to be attacked by humans. There they change to a nocturnal lifestyle in order to avoid human contact. When sleeping or rearing young, warthogs take refuge in holes – often those made by aardvarks.

If attacked by predators such as hyenas or lions, warthogs flee to the nearest available hole, backing into it so that they can face their attackers with their vicious tusks. Warthogs sometimes come together in groups called sounders, usually numbering 4–16 individuals. Although they are fairly abundant throughout their range, people hunt warthogs for their meat and to stop them eating crops. This poses a threat to warthog populations.

In male warthogs, the upper tusks can exceed 60cm (24in) in length. However, it is the smaller and sharper lower tusks that are the warthog's main weapon. Curiously, warthogs kneel down to feed on grass and roots.

Distribution: Throughout Africa from Mauritania to Ethiopia, and southward to Namibia and eastern South Africa.
Habitat: Savannah and open woodland.
Food: Grass, roots, berries, and sometimes carrion.
Size: 0.9–1.5m (3–5ft); 50–150kg (110–330lb).
Maturity: 18–20 months.
Breeding: 1–8 young.
Life span: Can exceed 18 years in captivity.
Status: Abundant, but the subspecies *P. a. aeliani* is classified as endangered.

Pygmy hippopotamus
(*Hexaprotodon liberiensis*): 1.5–1.7m (5–5.5ft); 160–270kg (350–600lb)
This animal is found in hot lowland jungles in parts of West Africa, and although it looks like a miniature version of the hippopotamus, there are a number of notable differences. These include a more rounded head and eyes on the side, rather than the top of the head.

Giant forest hog (*Hylochoerus meinertzhageni*): 1.3–2.1m (4.25–7ft); 130–275kg (280–600lb)
These large wild pigs travel about their tropical forest habitats in groups, or sounders, of up to 20 individuals, led by old males. Males are aggressive, will charge intruding males, and have also been known to charge humans.

Bush pig (*Potamochoerus porcus*): 1–1.5m (3.25–5ft); 46–130kg (100–285lb)
These pigs have long pointed ears, long white whiskers, and white crests along their backs. They live in the jungles of West Africa, where they forage for a wide range of food types at night. Their numbers have increased, probably as a result of the reduction of leopard populations.

Wild boar

Sus scrofa

Although domestic pigs usually look quite different from wild boar, they are in fact the same species, and can readily interbreed. Wild boar live in groups called sounders, consisting of females and their young. The males live alone, but join sounders in the mating season, when they compete for access to females.

Male wild boar can be very aggressive. In Doñana National Park in Spain, they have been known to chase adult lynxes away from carrion. Wild boars sometimes construct shelters from cut grass, and female wild boars are the only hoofed animals that give birth and look after their young inside a crude nest.

These animals have an excellent sense of smell, and are able to sniff out nutritious tubers and roots underground, while they snuffle through the leaf litter. Foraging wild boars often leave telltale signs, frequently ploughing up large patches of soil. In some countries, where wild boar have been introduced, they have had a negative impact on local animals and plants, either by feeding on them directly, or by disturbing their habitats.

Only male wild boar have tusks, which are extended upper and lower canine teeth. Piglets have striped patterns, which they lose as they get older.

Distribution: Europe, North Africa and Asia.
Habitat: Forest and shrublands.
Food: Leaves, roots, fungi, small mammals and reptiles, eggs, carrion and manure.
Size: 0.9–1.8m (3–5.75ft); 40–350kg (88–770lb).
Maturity: 8–10 months.
Breeding: 1 litter of 1–12 young born annually.
Life span: 10 years.
Status: Common.

Dibatag (*Ammodorcas clarkei*):
1.5–1.7m (5–5.5ft); 22–35kg (50–77lb)
Dibatags are beautiful antelopes which live in savannah habitats in Ethiopia and Somalia. They have very long, slender necks that are used to reach leaves on high branches. This species is now under threat of extinction due to poaching.

Roe deer (*Capreolus capreolus*):
0.9–1.5m (3–5ft); 15–50kg (33–110lb)
This graceful deer is found over large parts of Europe, including Britain, where it lives in forests and on farmland. The smallest European deer, it lives alone or in small groups. Roe deer have adapted well to habitat changes, and have actually increased in number.

Mouse deer (*Hyemoschus aquaticus*):
60–85cm (24–34in); 7–15kg (15–33lb)
This species is found in lowland forests in central and western Africa. Neither males nor females have antlers, but the males have enlarged canines, similar to those of musk deer.

Red deer (*Cervus elaphus*): 1.6–2.6m (5.25–8.5ft); 75–340kg (160–750lb)
This species is found throughout Europe, temperate Asia, north-west Africa and North America. Adult males possess antlers that can span up to 1.7m (5.5ft) across, and are used as weapons during the rutting season.

Fallow deer

Dama dama

Fallow deer are easily distinguishable from other species of deer by their somewhat flattened antlers and spotted summer coats. In some places fallow deer live alone, while in others they come together to form small herds of up to 30 individuals.

Breeding behaviour is variable, and may depend on the distribution of food. In some places males come together and attempt to attract females with dance-like rituals and bellowing – a rut. In other places, males attempt to monopolize females by defending good feeding areas from other males. Fallow deer have been introduced to many new places, but their populations are falling because of hunting and climate change.

Distribution: Originally found around the Mediterranean and parts of the Middle East, but since introduced to other countries, including Britain and New Zealand.
Habitat: Wide variety of habitats, including open woodland, grassland and shrubland.
Food: Mostly grass, but also leaves and twigs.
Size: 1.3–1.7m (4.25–5.5ft); 40–100kg (88–220lb).
Maturity: Females around 16 months; males around 17 months.
Breeding: A single fawn born annually.
Life span: 20 years or more in captivity.
Status: Common, but is disappearing from its original range.

Only the males sport antlers, which can span 80cm (32in) from tip to tip. Adults shed and regrow their antlers every year.

Reindeer

Rangifer tarandus

The reindeer, also known as the caribou in North America, is the only deer species in which both males and females possess antlers. Herds are organized into hierarchies based on the size of the deers' bodies and antlers. Most herds make seasonal migrations, moving to where food is available. Northern populations often travel more than 5,000km (3,000 miles). During the migration, reindeer groups congregate into great herds of up to half a million individuals.

Reindeer have been domesticated for 3,000 years, and there are huge numbers in northern Siberia.

The antlers of males can exceed 1m (3.25ft). Reindeer hooves are broad and flat – an adaptation for walking on soft ground and deep snow.

Distribution: Greenland, Scandinavia, Siberia, Mongolia, north-eastern China, Alaska, Canada, and northern USA.
Habitat: Arctic tundra, boreal forests and mountainous habitats.
Food: Plant material (especially new growth in spring), leaves, twigs and lichens.
Size: 1.2–2.2m (4–7.25ft); 60–318kg (130–700lb).
Maturity: 1.5–3.5 years.
Breeding: 1 fawn produced annually.
Life span: 15 years.
Status: Common.

Royal antelope (*Neotragus pygmaeus*): 50cm (20in); 2kg (4.4lb)
This is one of the smallest hoofed animals in the world, and is often found in forest clearings in parts of West Africa. It is well camouflaged, but will make enormous bounds if spotted by predators, reportedly achieving leaps of up to 2.8 m (9ft).

Thomson's gazelle (*Gazella thomsoni*): 0.8–1.7m (2.5–5.5ft); 12–85kg (26–187lb)
These attractive gazelles are found in the dry habitats of Sudan, Kenya and Tanzania. Like several other antelopes, they have a behaviour called stotting. When they spot predators stalking them, they make a series of curious jumps, thought to act as signals. This behaviour probably signals to the predators that they have been spotted and should not bother trying to chase the obviously agile gazelles.

Bongo (*Tragelaphus eurycerus*): 1.7–2.5m (5.5–8.25ft); 150–220kg (330–484lb)
This forest-dwelling animal has a chocolate-brown coat with creamy vertical stripes down its flanks. It has large ears, an erect mane running from its shoulders to its rump, and twisted horns. The bongo population is in decline because of hunting and habitat loss.

Blue gnu
Connochaetes taurinus

The blue gnu, also known as the wildebeest, is one of the most abundant large mammals in Africa. There are thought to be 1.5 million migratory individuals in the Serengeti alone, forming the greatest concentration of wild grazing animals on Earth. Some herds stay in the same place; others are nomadic, constantly searching for new sources of food.

The males leave their herds when they are over a year old, forming groups of bachelors. At about three or four years old, males set up small territories which they defend from other males, and attempt to mate with females entering their areas. Mating activity is seasonal, and is usually timed so that the majority of calves are born close to the beginning of the rainy season, when new grass is plentiful.

Although populations have increased in the Serengeti, numbers have declined in other areas, such as south-west Botswana. There, competition with livestock and destruction of crops has prompted farmers to kill gnus and set up long fences to prevent them from migrating to wetlands when there are seasonal droughts.

Distribution: Southern Kenya and southern Angola to northern South Africa.
Habitat: Savannah.
Food: Grass and succulent plants.
Size: 1.5m (5ft); 118–275kg (260–600lb).
Maturity: Females 2–3 years; males 3–4 years.
Breeding: Usually a single calf born each year.
Life span: Up to 21 years in captivity.
Status: Abundant, but continuing survival is dependent on conservation efforts.

Gnus are named after the calls made by competing males – "genu". There are two species; this one is blue-grey, while the other is dark brown and black.

Impala
Aepyceros melampus

Like many other antelopes, impalas have pointed, spiralling horns. Both sexes are similarly coloured, with a white belly, chin and tail, and black-tipped ears.

Impalas are one of a number of antelopes that live on the African savannah. They are very quick and agile, and are capable of jumping high in the air, often clearing heights greater than 3m (10ft).

When conditions are harsh in the dry season, impalas come together in mixed herds, which may number in the hundreds, to search for food. During the more plentiful wet season, males and females separate into different groups, with males competing for territories. Successful males mark their territories with urine and faeces and then lure females into them with tongue-flashing displays. This signal has the effect of making the females group together as they pass through the displaying males. Non-resident males run away or flash their own tongues in defiance.

Distribution: Kenya and southern Angola to northern South Africa.
Habitat: Savannah and open woodland.
Food: Grass, and leaves from bushes and trees.
Size: 1.1–1.5m (3.5–5ft); females 40–45kg (88–99lb); males 60–65kg (132–143lb).
Maturity: 1 year.
Breeding: Single fawn born at a time.
Life span: 13 years.
Status: Common.

Arabian oryx

Oryx leucoryx

The Arabian oryx is the only oryx found outside Africa. It is adapted to survive in very arid country. By the early 1970s the Arabian oryx was thought to be extinct in the wild, due to excessive hunting throughout the early 20th century. At this time, the only herds existed in zoos around the world. However, a captive-breeding programme was started in the 1960s, and oryx have been reintroduced into the wild in Oman, Jordan and Saudi Arabia. Wild populations now number around 500 individuals.

Since dry habitats contain relatively little nourishing plant material, oryx must range over vast areas to obtain enough food. Oryx are surprisingly good at detecting rainfall from a great distance, and will move towards areas where rain is falling so that they can eat fresh plant growth and drink water.

When water is not available, they eat succulent foods, such as melons or bulbs, to get the moisture they need. Oryx live in groups of around ten individuals, either consisting of a dominant male and females, or of a group of young males. Although the oryx's exceptionally long and sharp horns are formidable weapons, most contests between males are settled by ritualized sparring.

Distribution: Originally in much of the Middle East, now only a few reserves in Oman, Jordan and Saudi Arabia.
Habitat: Dry habitats, including arid scrubland and deserts.
Food: Grass, shrubs, succulent fruit and bulbs.
Size: 1.5–2.3m (5–7.5ft); 100–210kg (220–462lb).
Maturity: 1–2 years.
Breeding: Single calf born.
Life span: 20 years.
Status: Endangered.

Oryx have striking black or brown markings on their heads and lower bodies, and very long, straight horns, up to 1.5m (5ft) in length.

Chamois

Rupicapra pyrenaica

Distribution: North-western Spain, Pyrenees and central Italy. *R. rupicapra* is more widespread from Europe to the Middle East.
Habitat: Alpine meadows.
Food: Herbs, flowers, lichen, moss and pine shoots.
Size: 0.9–1.3m (3–4.25ft); 24–50kg (53–110lb).
Maturity: 8–9 years.
Breeding: 1–3 young born in spring.
Life span: 22 years.
Status: Endangered.

There are two distinct species of chamois, both found in mountainous areas of Europe. They are both quite similar in appearance and behaviour, but this species – *Rupicapra pyrenaica* – has a more restricted distribution, is rarer than the other, and is now dependent on conservation efforts for its survival.

One of the reasons that chamois are rare is because they were hunted excessively for their meat – considered a delicacy in some regions – and for their hides, which was once made into high-quality leather for polishing glass and cars. Chamois are well adapted to living in mountainous habitats, and are very agile. When they are alarmed, they can bound up steep rocky slopes, and can leap almost 2m (6.5ft) straight up to get to inaccessible rocks.

Chamois live in small herds, usually consisting of females and their young. In autumn, males join the herds to compete for females, fighting each other with their sharp horns. Female herd members will often help one another. If a mother dies, other females will look after the young, and the animals are generally thought to take it in turns to stand guard while the rest of the herd feeds.

Chamois have long, thick fur to keep them warm in alpine conditions. Both males and females possess the distinctively slender, sharp horns, which are shaped like upside-down "J"s.

European bison

Bison bonasus

These large animals are now very rare, but like their close relatives the American bison, they used to be very abundant. European bison disappeared from western Europe by the late Middle Ages, and became extinct in eastern Germany by the 18th century. The main reason for this decline was the loss of their habitat and an increase in hunting as human populations rose across northern Europe. By the early 20th century, European bison could only be found in Poland, and by 1925 both populations were extinct. Since then, new populations have been established in these places from captive European bison in zoos.

In former times, European bison formed groups of hundreds of animals during migrations or in good feeding grounds. Nowadays groups are much smaller, consisting of a few related females and their young. During the mating season there is fierce competition over females, and males charge and clash heads.

European bison have slightly less shaggy manes than those of American bison, but they have more powerfully built hindquarters. Both males and females have horns.

Distribution: Originally found over large parts of Europe including England, but now restricted to eastern Europe.
Habitat: Forest and grasslands.
Food: Leaves, twigs, bark and grass.
Size: 2.1–3.5m (7–11.5ft); 350–1,000kg (770–2,200lb).
Maturity: 2–4 years.
Breeding: Single calf born every 1–2 years.
Life span: Up to around 20 years in the wild, and 40 years in captivity.
Status: Endangered.

African buffalo (*Syncerus caffer*): 2.1–3.4m (7–11.25ft); 300–900kg (660–1,980lb)
These formidable animals can be very aggressive, and have been known to inflict fatal injuries on lions. Accordingly, lions tend to be reluctant to tackle these large buffalo unless they are very hungry. African buffalo form herds of 50–500 individuals.

Addax (*Addax nasomaculatus*): 1.5–1.7m (5–5.5ft); 60–125kg (132–275lb)
This antelope is found in the Sahara Desert, and is well adapted to dry, hot conditions. It rarely drinks, and can obtain most of its moisture from the plants that it eats. It moves great distances in search of vegetation. This species is now endangered as a result of overhunting.

Sitatunga (*Tragelaphus spekei*): 1.1–1.7m (3.5–5.5ft); 50–125kg (110–275lb)
This African species of antelope is related to the kudu, but is unusual in its semiaquatic habits. It spends much of its time wading around in dense reed beds in swampy ground, and is a good swimmer. If threatened, it may hide underwater with only its nostrils above the surface.

Common eland

Taurotragus oryx

This is one of two species of eland, both of which occupy similar types of open savannah habitat. The eland is the largest of a number of related species, characterized by spiralling horns and vertical cream-coloured stripes along the flanks and haunches.

Elands occupy large home ranges, using different habitats at different times of the year, and can cover in excess of 220sq km (86sq miles) per year. Approximately 14,000 eland live in the Serengeti National Park in East Africa, where they form small herds, usually consisting of less than 25 animals.

Like many hoofed animals, eland males fight for dominance and the opportunity to mate with females. Competing males shove each other with locked horns, until one gives up and retreats. Elands are easily tamed and, due to their highly nutritious milk, tender meat and good-quality hides, people are trying to domesticate them on farms in Africa and Russia.

Male elands tend to be larger than females, but both sexes carry characteristic spiralling horns, which may be up to 1m (3.25ft) long.

Distribution: Southern and eastern Africa.
Habitat: Savannah and open woodland.
Food: Leaves and fruit.
Size: 1.8–3.4m (5.75–11.25ft); 400–1,000kg (880–2,200lb).
Maturity: Males 4 years; females 3 years.
Breeding: Single calf born.
Life span: 23 years.
Status: Conservation-dependent.

APES

There are four species of great ape: the orang-utan of South-east Asia and the chimpanzee, bonobo and gorilla of Africa. There are three races of gorilla, though it is not certain whether they are separate subspecies. The great apes are human being's closest animal relatives. Humans share 98 per cent of their genetic code with the great apes. Our common ancestor – Kenyapithecus – lived in Africa 15 million years ago.

Chimpanzee

Pan troglodytes

Distribution: Gambia to Uganda.
Habitat: Tropical forest and woody savannah.
Food: Fruit, leaves, flowers, bark, insects and animals.
Size: 1–1.7m (3.25–5.5ft); 26–70kg (57–154lb).
Maturity: Females 13 years; males 15 years.
Breeding: Single young born every 3–6 years.
Life span: Around 60 years.
Status: Endangered.

These intelligent, social animals are very closely related to human beings, and give us some indication of the kind of animal from which we evolved. Indeed, chimps have a number of characteristics that were once thought to be exclusively human. For example, they are able to construct and use simple tools – tasks that few other animals, except humans and orang-utans, are capable of. One tool commonly used by chimps is a probe, made of a thin twig stripped of leaves, which is inserted into termite nests to extract these insects, which are then eaten.

Chimps live in groups comprising 15–80 animals, which have complex social structures. The dominant males are not necessarily the biggest or strongest individuals, but the ones best able to recruit the most allies. Chimps are territorial, and neighbouring groups are often aggressive towards one another. Indeed, chimps share an unpleasant characteristic with humans: they go to war, and sometimes individuals of one group will hunt and kill members of a neighbouring group.

Chimpanzees are tool-users, and they are also skilled at communication, which they do with vocalizations and facial expressions.

Western-lowland gorilla

Gorilla gorilla gorilla

Currently, three different races of gorilla are recognized: the western-lowland gorilla, the eastern-lowland gorilla and the mountain gorilla. The western-lowland gorillas are separated from the nearest population of eastern-lowland gorillas by at least 1,000km (625 miles).

Western-lowland gorillas live in relatively small groups of only about six animals, lead by dominant males, or silverbacks – so-called because of the grey-white fur only found on the backs of older males. Although gorillas are large and extremely powerful, they are gentler than chimpanzees.

Gorilla groups tend to avoid one another although, on occasion, groups will meet amicably for a short time. Sometimes meetings are not peaceful, and a dominant silverback may respond to intruders by standing up, hooting and beating his chest with cupped hands, followed by a display of strength by breaking branches. This display may lead to an all-out attack.

The armspan of a gorilla is greater than its height – up to a huge 2.75m (9ft). This illustration shows a female with her young.

Distribution: South-eastern Nigeria, west-central and southern Cameroon, south-western Central African Republic, Guinea, Gabon and the Congo.
Habitat: Lowland tropical forests.
Food: Leaves and shoots.
Size: 1.25–1.75m (4–5.5ft); females 70–140kg (150–300lb); males 135–275kg (300–600lb).
Maturity: Females 7 years; males 15 years.
Breeding: Single young, or occasionally twins.
Life span: 50 years.
Status: Endangered.

Mountain gorilla

Gorilla gorilla beringei

Although there is doubt as to whether mountain gorillas constitute a separate subspecies, genetic analysis has shown that they are more closely related to the eastern-lowland gorillas than the western-lowland gorillas. Mountain gorillas tend to be larger, and have much longer and silkier fur, especially on their arms, than their lowland cousins. They also occupy a very different habitat, and are found almost exclusively in cold mountain rainforests of bamboo, at altitudes over 2,000m (6,666ft).

Scientists George Schaller and Dian Fossey, who spent many years living in close contact with mountain gorillas, studied these enigmatic animals in detail. They found that they live in relatively large groups of up to 30 individuals, and that they communicate with a wide range of calls.

Gorillas travel up to 1km (0.6 miles) in search of food each day, and build crude nests out of leafy branches, usually on the ground, where they sleep at night. Mountain gorillas are only found in the region of the Virunga volcanoes (two of which are active) and Bwindi Forest in Uganda. They number little more than 600 animals in the wild. Mountain gorillas have suffered heavily from poaching and accidental trapping.

The long, silky fur of the mountain gorilla helps to protect it from the freezing conditions sometimes found in its mountain habitat. This illustration shows a male silverback foraging for leaves.

Distribution: The Virunga volcanoes lying between Congo, Rwanda and Uganda.
Habitat: Montane forest and bamboo forest.
Food: Leaves and shoots.
Size: 1.5–1.8m (5–6ft); females 110–140kg (240–300lb); males 200–275kg (440–605lb).
Maturity: Females 7 years; males 15 years.
Breeding: Single young, or occasionally twins, born after 9 months' gestation. Females usually give birth to only 2–3 surviving young in a lifetime.
Life span: 50 years.
Status: Critically endangered.

Bonobo

Pan paniscus

Although commonly known as the pygmy chimpanzee, this species is often the same size as its close relative – *Pan troglodytes* – and is also very similar in appearance, though less powerfully built. Unlike chimpanzees, bonobos have never been observed to use tools in the wild, though in captivity they have been seen to use leaves to clean themselves, and sticks to pole-vault over water.

Bonobos are very social animals, and live in groups of 40–120 individuals. These groups move about by day searching for fruiting trees. When a food source is located, individuals make loud calls, probably to alert other members of their group and warn off members of other groups. Like chimps, bonobos construct temporary nests made from leafy branches, to sleep in at night.

Bonobo societies are much less aggressive than groups of chimps. Serious fighting is rare, and they never make deliberate lethal raids on neighbouring groups. Unlike chimp societies, females have equal ranking with males in bonobo groups, and form the cores of bonobo societies. A curious characteristic of bonobo behaviour is the use of sexual contact to settle arguments or to calm down aggressive situations.

Unlike in chimpanzee societies, it is frequently the females that adopt the leadership roles in bonobo groups.

Distribution: Central Congo.
Habitat: Lowland forests.
Food: Mostly fruit, occasionally leaves and seeds, rarely invertebrates and small vertebrates.
Size: 70–83cm (30–35in); 27–61kg (60–135lb).
Maturity: 9 years.
Breeding: Single young, or occasionally twins, born every 3–6 years after a gestation of 227–232 days.
Life span: Probably similar to that of the closely related chimpanzee.
Status: Endangered.

MONKEYS

There are nearly a hundred species of monkey found in the Old World (Africa and Eurasia). Old World monkeys belong to the family Cercopithecidae. Most species of monkey are well adapted for life in trees and can move with great agility, jumping from branch to branch. Most monkeys live in tropical regions, where leaf and fruit production is year-round, providing these active animals with continuous food.

Hamadryas baboon

Papio hamadryas

There are five species of baboon living in Africa, although some are known to be able to interbreed, leading some scientists to suggest that they are just different varieties or subspecies. If suitable resting sites are rare, hamadryas baboons can be found congregating in large groups, called troops, consisting of 100 or more individuals.

When baboons start looking for food in the morning, they split up into bands, each consisting of several groups of four or five females and young, led by a dominant male. When a female is ready to mate, the dominant male prevents other males from approaching, striking out when an intruder gets close. Sometimes young male baboons form temporary partnerships to defeat dominant males and get access to females. One of the pair distracts a dominant male by starting a fight with him, while the other mates. At a later time, the individuals in the partnership swap roles, and the one who had to fight last time will have the opportunity to mate.

Male hamadryas baboons have bright red faces and wild silvery hair. Females are smaller, sometimes only half the size of males, and have paler faces with brown hair.

Distribution: North-eastern Africa and western Arabian peninsula.
Habitat: Open woodland, savannah and rocky hill country.
Food: A wide range of plants and small animals.
Size: 61–76cm (24–30in); 14–41kg (30–90lb).
Maturity: Females 5 years; males 7 years.
Breeding: Single young.
Life span: 30 years.
Status: Threatened.

Mandrill

Mandrillus sphinx

This is the largest monkey in the world, with males weighing up to 54kg (120lb). The adult males are particularly colourful, with bright blue and purple nose ridges, scarlet noses and lilac buttock pads. There is a strong hierarchy among male mandrills, and it has been shown that the males with the most prominent facial coloration and the biggest rumps have the most success in attracting females and fathering young.

A male mandrill's face is very brightly coloured, especially when he becomes excited. Females have duller, blue faces and are less heavily built than males.

Mandrills move about in groups of up to ten adult females – with or without infants – around ten juveniles, and single dominant males.

Foraging mandrills cover around 8km (5 miles) per day. Usually the male stays close to the back of the group, but when there is danger he moves to the front to defend the group. Although mandrills are famous for their formidable appearance and ferocity, captive individuals are usually quite gentle.

Distribution: Southern Cameroon, Equatorial Guinea, Gabon and Congo.
Habitat: Dense lowland rainforest.
Food: Mostly fruit, nuts and other vegetable material, and also invertebrates and occasionally small mammals.
Size: 61–76cm (24–30in); 30–54kg (66–120lb).
Maturity: Females 3.5 years; males probably much older.
Breeding: Single young born each year.
Life span: 45 years.
Status: Threatened.

Vervet

Cercopithecus aethiops

Male vervets posses bright blue scrotums, which are used in signals of dominance over other males in a group.

Like many monkey species, vervets are very social, forming communicative groups of up to 50 individuals. These monkeys have a broad repertoire of calls, and are able to express alarm, excitement, rage and even sadness. Vervets forage in trees and occasionally on the ground. If predators are spotted, particular alarm calls are given, depending on the type of predator approaching. When vervets hear their snake alarm call, they all stand upright, scanning the surrounding grass for pythons. If they hear their leopard alarm call, they run into the trees, keeping their eyes on the leopard, and if they hear their eagle alarm call, they hide deep in the tree canopy.

Female vervets tend to remain in the groups into which they they were born, whereas males are forced to leave when they become sexually mature, moving into new groups. Vervets have adapted well to living alongside people. They are common in even the suburbs of big cities. Many people welcome their presence, but others treat them as pests because they can damage property and crops.

Distribution: Eastern and southern Africa.
Habitat: Riverine woodland, wooded savannah, open forests and agricultural land.
Food: Fruit and vegetable material, insects, crustaceans, birds' eggs and vertebrates.
Size: 35–66cm (14–27in); 2.5–9kg (5.5–20lb).
Maturity: Females 3 years; males 5 years.
Breeding: Usually a single young born each year.
Life span: 30 years.
Status: Common.

Barbary ape (*Macaca sylvanus*): 76cm (30in); 18kg (40lb)
Despite its name, this species is not actually an ape, but a macaque monkey. This is the only species of macaque living in Africa, and is also found on the Rock of Gibraltar, where it was introduced by the Romans. It is the only species of monkey living in the wild in Europe.

Gelada (*Theropithecus gelada*): 50–72cm (20–28in); females 14kg (30lb); males 20kg (44lb)
Geladas have long side whiskers, a mane of hairs on the neck, and three bare red patches of skin on the chest and throat. This is the only species of grazing monkey, and is found in very large groups in a small area in the mountains of central Ethiopia. It lives in rocky gorges where it can find sleeping sites and refuge from predators.

Guereza colobus monkey (*Colobus guereza*): 45–72cm (18–29in); 5–15kg (11–33lb)
There are five species of colobus monkey, and this one has a distinctive white beard and a face framed by white fur, a long white mantle, and a white tuft on the end of the tail, contrasting with the rest of its fur, which is black. Colobus monkeys have no thumbs.

Red-capped mangabey

Cercocebus torquatus

These monkeys are large and very vocal. Their calls can be heard from over 1km (0.6 miles) away. Groups of red-capped mangabeys consist of about 30 individuals, and unlike many species of monkey, their groups may include more than one adult male. All mangabeys have pale upper eyelids, which they flutter to attract attention and signal sexual intentions and status.

Although mangabeys spend a lot of time in the treetops searching for fruit, they will also forage on the ground, searching the leaf litter for mushrooms and small animal prey.

Mangabeys are territorial when food is relatively scarce in the dry season, and their loud calls help neighbouring groups maintain their distance from one another. At other times of the year, mangabey troops come together without conflict.

Mangabeys are threatened by the loss of their forests to logging. However, the red-capped mangabey seems to be quite adaptable to new habitats, hopefully making this species less susceptible.

Distribution: Senegal to Congo.
Habitat: Mostly tropical rainforest, but also mangroves, degraded forest, swamps and agricultural land.
Food: Mostly fruit, but other vegetable matter and insects and small animals are also taken.
Size: 38–89cm (15–35in); 7–14kg (15–30lb).
Maturity: Females 4 years; males 5–7 years.
Breeding: Single young, or occasionally twins, born at an average 16-month interval.
Life span: Probably around 30 years.
Status: Endangered.

The fur on the top of this species' head is a dark maroon-red. The white hair on the sides of the head extends around the neck like a collar, giving rise to the other common name of this species: the collared mangabey.

PRIMITIVE PRIMATES

This group includes some of the most specialized mammals in the world. They are referred to as primitive because they usually have much simpler social structures than other primates, and are more closely related to the insectivorous mammals from which all primates evolved. Also known as prosimians, primitive primates can be found in tropical regions of Africa, Asia and Madagascar.

Ruffed lemur

Varecia variegata

Distribution: Eastern Madagascar.
Habitat: Tropical forest.
Food: Fruit.
Size: 51–56cm (20–22in); 3.2–4.5kg (7–10lb).
Maturity: 2–3.5 years.
Breeding: 1–6 young, most commonly twins.
Life span: 33 years.
Status: Endangered.

This is the largest of all the lemurs. Lemurs are prosimians that are found exclusively on Madagascar and some surrounding islands. Ruffed lemurs live in trees, and although they are good climbers, they are not as agile as some other species of lemur.

Ruffed lemurs are most active at dusk, and at this time it is possible to hear their mournful territorial calls. Sometimes just a pair of ruffed lemurs occupies a territory, but more often groups of about 15 individuals will live together, sharing the same home range.

As well as calls, ruffed lemurs use scent-marking to signal their territorial boundaries. The males mark branches and other objects with a secretion from glands found on their necks. Scent-marking males are seen rubbing their chests, necks and chins on to trees or on the ground. Sadly, like many lemurs, these beautiful animals are in danger of extinction due to the overexploitation of their habitat and also overhunting of the animals themselves for their meat and fur, and for commercial exportation.

There are two subspecies of ruffed lemur. One has mostly black fur with white markings; the other has mostly red fur with white markings.

Indri

Indri indri

The indri is the largest of all the living prosimians, and like the lemurs, it is found only in Madagascar. Indris are arboreal and move about by jumping between tree trunks and stems. Sometimes indris come down to the ground, where they stand upright, moving in series of ungainly leaps.

They are mostly active by day and spend a lot of time feeding on leaves and fruit. Indris live in small family groups of up to five members, and occupy large home ranges. The central part of a home range is defended from others by the adult male, which uses scent markings and calls to signal the limits of the territory.

Sometimes several members of a group will make loud tuneful songs that can be heard up to 2km (1.25 miles) away. These songs are thought to signal occupancy of a territory to other groups, but also to unite groups and broadcast willingness to mate.

Indris have thick silky fur, which may be particularly useful for living in cold mountain forests, as high as 1800m (6000ft) above sea level. There is considerable variation in fur colour, which ranges from black through browns and greys to white.

Distribution: North-eastern Madagascar.
Habitat: Tropical rainforest.
Food: Leaves, flowers and fruit.
Size: 61–90cm (24–36in); 6–10kg (13–22lb).
Maturity: 7–9 years.
Breeding: Single young born every 2–3 years.
Life span: Not known.
Status: Endangered.

Aye aye

Daubentonia madagascariensis

This remarkable species is another prosimian found only in Madagascar. Aye ayes live alone. They are exclusively nocturnal and search for food high up in the trees, moving up to 4km (2.5 miles) a night within a small home range of around 5ha (12 acres). During the day, aye ayes sleep in spherical nests, made from branches and interwoven leaves. The nests are hidden in dense foliage in the forks of trees, and there may be several nests within a single home range.

Aye ayes have a most unusual way of finding food. Using a specially adapted finger, which is very long and thin like a probe, they tap the surface of decaying wood in search of tunnels made by insect larvae or ants and termites. Using a combination of a good sense of touch and a sort of echolocation with their sensitive ears – able to pinpoint a hollow sound from tapping – aye ayes locate the tunnels occupied by their prey. They then use their strong incisor teeth to make small holes in the wood, into which they insert their probe-like finger to extract their insect prey with a hooked claw. Unfortunately, these fascinating creatures are suffering from the loss of Malagasy forest. Local people also persecute them because they are seen as bad omens.

The aye aye not only uses its specialized third finger for locating and catching insects in decaying wood, but also for determining the milk content of coconuts and extracting coconut pulp.

Distribution: Northern, eastern and west-central Madagascar.
Habitat: Tropical forests, but seems adaptable to secondary forest, mangroves and even coconut groves:
Food: Fruit, seeds, nectar, other vegetable matter and insect larvae.
Size: 36–44cm (14–17in); 2–3kg (4.4–6.6lb).
Maturity: 3 years.
Breeding: Single young born every 2–3 years.
Life span: 20 years.
Status: Endangered.

Ring-tailed lemur (*Lemur catta*): 38–45cm (15–18in); 2.3–3.5kg (5–8lb)
These lemurs, named after their striking tail markings, spend quite long periods of time on the ground, searching for fallen fruit and other plant material. Although fairly common throughout their range in southern Madagascar, they are declining in number.

Bushbaby (*Galago senegalensis*): 8–21cm (3–8.5in); 95–300g (0.2–0.6lb)
There are three species of bushbaby, or galago, all of which live in Africa. This species is found in open woodland and savannah habitat, from Senegal to Tanzania. It has wide eyes and a long, bushy tail, and is largely nocturnal and tree-dwelling.

Golden potto (*Arctocebus calabarensis*): 23–30cm (9–12in); 266–465g (0.6–1lb)
This little prosimian has long, thick, woolly fur with a golden sheen, and is found in tropical forests from south-eastern Nigeria to southern Congo. This slow-moving solitary animal feeds mostly on insects, and occasionally catches moths in flight.

Potto

Perodicticus potto

These animals forage high up in the treetops at night, climbing slowly through the branches, using their wide, sensitive eyes to locate fruit in the moonlight, and a good sense of smell to find ants and other insects. Pottos also sleep high up in trees during the day.

Females occupy large ranges, big enough to provide food for themselves and their young. Males occupy larger ranges, which cover as many female ranges as possible. Pottos are fairly solitary creatures, but males and females in overlapping ranges make contact throughout the year, communicating with vocal calls and scent marks.

In the first few days of life, baby pottos cling to their mothers' bellies, but later the mothers leave their young hidden near their nests when out foraging. The young are collected at the end of the night. After a few months, the young pottos begin to follow their mothers around as they search for food. The mothers may carry their young on their backs. Young male pottos leave their maternal territories when they are only six months old, but young females stay with their mothers for much longer.

Distribution: Guinea to western Kenya and central Congo.
Habitat: Tropical forest.
Food: Fruit, insects and small vertebrates.
Size: 30–90cm (12–36in); 0.85–1.6kg (1.8–3.5lb).
Maturity: 18 months.
Breeding: Single young, or occasionally twins.
Life span: 25 years.
Status: Common.

When threatened, pottos lower their heads between their forelegs, so that they are protected by their shoulderblades.

RABBITS

There are 54 species of rabbit and hare, all of which belong to the same family, the Leporidae. They are found in many parts of the world, and some species have been introduced to areas well outside of their original range. Strictly speaking, "hare" is the name given to members of the genus Lepus, while all other species in the family are referred to as rabbits.

Brown hare

Lepus europaeus

Unlike rabbits, hares do not live in burrows. They spend most of the time alone, although a few may be seen together at good feeding sites. Hares are mostly active by night. During the day they crouch in small hollows in the grass called forms, sometimes leaving their backs just visible over the vegetation. In Europe, the main breeding season is in spring, and at this time hares can often be seen during the day, with males fighting one another and pursuing females. Hares fight by kicking with their back legs and boxing with their forelegs.

A number of predators target hares, and in Europe these include foxes and eagles. If a predator detects a hare, the hare flees, running at speeds of up to 60kph (37mph) and making sharp, evasive turns. Injured or captured hares are known to make high-pitched screams.

In order to reduce the risk of losing all of their young leverets to predators, females hide them in different locations in specially dug forms, and visit them one by one to nurse them. Although brown hares are common, changing farming practices have caused a decline in hare numbers in some countries, such as Britain.

Brown hares are easily distinguishable from European rabbits by their larger size and longer ears and limbs.

Distribution: Southern Scandinavia, northern Spain and Britain to Siberia and north-western Iran.
Habitat: Grasslands and agricultural land.
Food: Grass, herbs, crop plants and occasionally twigs and bark.
Size: 60–70cm (24–28in); 3–5kg (6.6–11lb).
Maturity: 1 year.
Breeding: Litter of 1–8 young; 2 or more litters per year.
Life span: 7 years.
Status: Common.

European rabbit

Oryctolagus cuniculus

The rabbit has had a long association with humans, who have prized it for its soft fur and tasty meat. This species was probably introduced to the Mediterranean from its original home in the Iberian Peninsula more than 3,000 years ago. Rabbits often live in large colonies, inhabiting complex labyrinths of burrows, or warrens, that may have hundreds of entrances. Although rabbits live in close proximity to one another, there is a strong dominance hierarchy within a warren. Each male defends a territory, especially during the breeding season.

Rabbits are famed for their rate of reproduction, and a single female has the potential to produce 30 young per year. Rabbits have been introduced to some areas, such as Australia, where there are no predators capable of controlling their numbers. In these places they have created huge problems, crowding out local species and destroying crops. Ironically, rabbit populations in the species' original range in Spain are too small to support their rare predators such as the Iberian lynx and the imperial eagle.

There are as many as 66 domestic breeds of rabbit, and they vary considerably in size, shape and coloration. In Australia, rabbits occurred in such high numbers that they left little food for local marsupials, and even threatened the sheep industry. Two diseases – myxomatosis and viral hemorrhagic – have been successfully introduced into rabbit populations to control them.

Distribution: Originally Iberian Peninsula and southern France. Introduced to most of Europe, north-west Africa, Australia and many other countries.
Habitat: Farmland, grassland and dry shrubland.
Food: Grass, herbaceous plants, bark and twigs.
Size: 35–45cm (14–18in); 1.3–2.3kg (2.8–5lb).
Maturity: 1 year.
Breeding: 1–9 young per litter; up to 7 litters per year.
Life span: 9 years.
Status: Common.

INSECTIVORES

The insectivores are a wide-ranging group of small mammals, all with sensitive and highly mobile noses, small eyes and relatively small brains. They are generally solitary and nocturnal animals, the majority of which eat insects, earthworms and other invertebrates. Their teeth are well designed for eating insects, with long incisors for seizing their prey and sharp molars for dealing with their tough bodies.

Hedgehog

Erinaceus europaeus

Few members of the insectivore family have been able to grow much larger than moles because the food they eat – insects – are so small that they would need to eat a very large quantity. Hedgehogs, however, are more eclectic in their tastes, with a diet that includes earthworms, birds' eggs, frogs, lizards and even snakes. Eating these larger foods has allowed hedgehogs to grow much bigger than is the norm for the group.

Nonetheless, being larger can have its disadvantages, not least being more conspicuous to predators. This is where the hedgehog's most famous asset comes in handy. All over its back the hedgehog has rows of thickened hairs, which narrow at their tips into sharp, prickly points. Using muscles located around the base of the coat, which act like drawstrings, the hedgehog can roll into a ball, becoming an impregnable mass of prickles, which is very effective at deterring the advances of predators.

Distribution: Western Europe and Northern Russia.
Habitat: Woodland, grassland and gardens.
Food: Invertebrates.
Size: 22–28cm (8.8–11in); 0.4–1.2kg (0.9–2.6lb).
Maturity: 2–3 years.
Breeding: 2–6 young born in summer.
Life span: 3–4 years.
Status: Common, but declining in the UK.

The hedgehog's Latin name Erinaceus *is derived from the word ericius, meaning a spiked barrier. Hedgehogs are mostly solitary, but when they do come together, they follow a pecking order.*

Golden mole

Eremitalpa granti

Distribution: South-western Africa.
Habitat: Coastal sand dunes.
Food: Insects, and also small lizards.
Size: 76–87mm (3–3.5in); 120–150g (0.25–0.33lb).
Maturity: Not known.
Breeding: 1 litter of 1–2 young born every year.
Life span: Not known.
Status: Rare.

There are no species of true mole in Africa. Their niche is filled by another group of insectivores called the golden moles. Found mainly in dry sandy areas, golden moles lead entirely subterranean lives, feeding mainly on insects. Their underground existence means that they have little need for vision, and consequently they have lost the power of sight.

Since it is impossible to construct burrows in the dry sands of their desert habitats, golden moles constantly have to plough their way through the sand. Their small but powerful forelimbs are well designed to help them "swim" through sand.

Golden moles may not be able to see, but they do have incredibly acute hearing, being able to pick up the tiny noises made by their insect prey as they move on the surface. By orienting themselves towards these sounds, golden moles can pinpoint the precise location of their prey and emerge from below to snatch their meals.

Skin grows over the golden mole's useless eyes, giving them a bizarre appearance.

Russian desman

Desmana moschata

Distribution: South-western Russia and eastern Europe.
Habitat: Slow rivers and oxbow lakes.
Food: Aquatic invertebrates, including insects, amphibians, crustaceans and molluscs, and also fish and plant roots.
Size: 18–22cm (7–9in); 100–220g (0.2–0.5lb).
Maturity: 1 year.
Breeding: Litters of 1–5 young.
Life span: 2–3 years.
Status: Vulnerable.

Looking somewhat like a cross between a shrew and a mole, there are only two species of desman alive in the world today. The Pyrenean desman lives in northern Spain and Portugal, and its relative the Russian desman inhabits areas in Russia and eastern Europe.

Desmans have webbed feet and broad tails fringed with stiff hairs. These adaptations help them swim, and it is underwater that desmans do most of their hunting, feeling around with their long whiskers for prey items such as dragonfly larvae and tadpoles.

Desmans do not just swim; they also burrow, looking for worms. They tunnel into riverbanks, making networks of burrows which can extend for many metres. The entrances to the systems of tunnels are always located below the waterline, so that the desmans can come and go as they please, without having to worry about any predators that may be watching from above. There are many predators that will feed on desmans, including hawks, kestrels, foxes and weasels.

Like their close relatives the shrews, desmans must feed almost constantly to keep up their energy reserves.

Pygmy white-toothed shrew (*Suncus etruscus*): 3.5–5.2cm (1.5–2in); 1.5–2.5g (0.003–0.005lb)
One of the world's smallest mammals, pygmy white-toothed shrews are found across southern Europe. These shrews have scent glands on their sides, which secrete a pungent odour. The glands are especially well developed in the males during the breeding season, when they are trying to intimidate their rivals and impress females.

Alpine shrew (*Sorex alpinus*): 6–7.5cm (2.5–3in); 5.5–11.5g (0.01–0.025lb)
Inhabiting alpine grasslands up to an altitude of 3,400m (11,333ft) above sea level, alpine shrews are often found in rocky habitats. They are especially common on stony banks and beds of mountain streams, seeking out invertebrate prey. Unlike most shrew species, alpine shrews are adept climbers.

Blind mole (*Talpa caeca*): 9.5–14cm (3.5–5.5in); 65–120g (0.14–0.25lb)
Unlike the common European mole, the blind mole of southern Europe is physically unable to open its eyes. It has membranous coverings over them, which it cannot pull back. However, the membranes do allow some light through, and it is said that blind moles are not totally insensitive to the visual world, being able to react to changes in light and dark.

Rock elephant shrew

Elephantulus myurus

It's not easy being a small diurnal insectivore in the African bush. There is a whole host of other animals that are intent on making them their next meal, from hawks and eagles to small cats, mongooses and a multitude of snakes.

Elephant shrews are well aware of the danger that surrounds them, and they are always on the run from it. They carefully maintain tracks throughout their home ranges, linking feeding areas to bolt holes. These tracks are kept meticulously tidy, and for good reason. The elephant shrews sprint along them at breakneck speed, relying on being simply too fast for their predators to catch them.

Home ranges may be up to 1sq km (0.4sq miles) in size. This is a large area for an animal only 10cm (4in) long to maintain, but where food is scarce, it needs to search a large area to remain well fed. In places where food is much easier to come by, the home ranges tend to be considerable smaller. Young elephant shrews are born very well developed, and after just two days they are able to sprint nimbly around with their mothers.

Elephant shrews get their name from their elongated, mobile snouts.

Distribution: South-eastern Africa.
Habitat: Savannah grassland.
Food: Insects.
Size: 10–14cm (4–5.5in); 40–55g (0.09–0.12lb).
Maturity: 2 months.
Breeding: 1 young per litter.
Life span: 1–3 years.
Status: Common.

SEA MAMMALS

Having conquered the land, some mammals have returned to the seas. Some, such as seals and sea lions, lead predominantly aquatic lives, but must come on to land to give birth. Others have completely dispensed with the terrestrial way of life. The most highly adapted group of sea mammals, comprising whales, porpoises and dolphins, is known as cetaceans. They are highly intelligent.

Mediterranean monk seal

Monachus monachus

This is the darkest seal of the region, uniformly dark brown except for a white patch on the belly.

Distribution: Less than 20 sites around the Mediterranean and Black Sea and Atlantic coast of Mauritania.
Habitat: Subtropical coastline.
Food: Fish and cephalopods.
Size: 2.3–2.8m (7.5–9.25ft); 250–300kg (550–660lb).
Maturity: 3 years.
Breeding: 1 pup born every other year.
Life span: 24 years.
Status: Critically endangered.

The Mediterranean monk seal is possibly Europe's most endangered mammal, with only about 500 animals remaining in small, scattered groups around the Mediterranean and Black Sea. There is also a small isolated population off the Atlantic coast of Mauritania, in West Africa.

Monk seals are very intolerant of disturbance. If a pregnant female is distressed, she will abort her foetus, and mothers may desert their young. The increasing development of the Mediterranean and Black Sea coastlines has meant that there are fewer and fewer secluded spots left for these peaceful animals. They also suffer from hunting pressure and from becoming entangled in fishing nets. Being mammals, all seals have to breathe air; if they get caught in fishing nets and held underwater, they drown before too long.

Females give birth to their young in grottoes and sea caves. Those with underwater entrances are particularly favoured. Youngsters stay with their mothers for about three years, learning how to fish and interact with other seals before seeking their own territories.

Harp seal

Pagophilus groenlandicus

Harp seals are very social animals, congregating in huge numbers to give birth on ice floes in areas along the Arctic coastline. However, their sociality has led ultimately to their decline. The pups have very soft, thick fur, which is much sought after in some parts of the world. When the pups are gathered in large numbers, they are easy for hunters to find and club to death. Extensive hunting by humans reduced the total harp seal population from around ten million individuals to just two million by the early 1980s. However, once their plight was realized, hunting pressure was reduced and the population is now slowly recovering.

It will take a long time for harp seal numbers to reach their previous levels because the seals have a low rate of reproduction. Producing just one pup a year means that the population does not grow very quickly. When hunting, adult seals may dive to depths of 200m (666ft) in search of herring and cod, which make up the bulk of their diet.

Distribution: Arctic Ocean.
Habitat: Open sea for most of the year.
Food: Pelagic crustaceans and fish.
Size: 1.7–1.9m (5.5–6ft); 120–130kg (260–285lb).
Maturity: 5 years.
Breeding: 1 pup born every year.
Life span: 16–30 years.
Status: Vulnerable.

The luxuriant fur of harp seal pups keeps them warm as they grow up on the Arctic icepack.

Narwhal

Monodon monoceros

Some people believe that the bizarre appearance of the narwhal first gave rise to the legend of the unicorn. The function of the male's long tusk is not properly known, but it may function as a hunting implement, or as a tool to break up ice and allow access to the air, so that the animals can breathe. However, the most favoured explanation is that the males joust with each other, fighting over access to females during the breeding season.

The narwhal's swollen forehead is known as its melon, a feature shared with other toothed whales, such as dolphins. The melon serves to focus the ultrasonic clicks that narwhals use, like other small cetaceans, to navigate and find their food. As in a sophisticated sonar system, narwhals listen as the high-frequency sounds they make rebound off objects nearby. So sensitive is this method of orientation that narwhals are able not only to tell what is food and what is not, but also how big, how distant and how quickly a potential prey item is moving.

Distribution: Parts of the Arctic Ocean near Greenland and the Barents Sea. Their range is patchy.
Habitat: Coastal Arctic waters.
Food: Cuttlefish, fish, crustaceans and squid.
Size: 4–5.5m (13–18ft); 800–1,600kg (1,760–3,520lb).
Maturity: Females 5–8 years; males 11–13 years.
Breeding: Single calf born every 2–3 years.
Life span: 50 years.
Status: Common.

The male narwhal's tusk is in fact an elongated front tooth that spirals as it grows from a hole in its lips. Females may possess a short tusk, too. Their name means "corpse whale" in Old Norse, perhaps referring to their bluish-grey skin with white blotches.

Atlantic humpback dolphin

Sousa teuszii

The humpback dolphin gets its name from its distinctive method of surfacing and its slightly bulbous dorsal fin.

Atlantic humpbacks are shy dolphins and rarely approach boats, making them a difficult species for scientists to observe and study. Political instability in many West African countries along the coasts of which this dolphin lives has also compounded the problems of studying these animals.

They inhabit tropical coastal waters, preferring to stay in water no deeper than 20m (65ft) and with shallow banks. They also like river channels and muddied waters. Typical school sizes range from between three and seven individuals, but groups of up to 25 have been observed. As these dolphins get older, they become more and more solitary by nature, and eventually hardly ever associate with other individuals.

The humpback dolphin has a unique way of surfacing: the beak and often the entire head break the surface of the water before the body arches tightly, making the hump and dorsal fin more prominent. Orcas (killer whales) are a major threat to this species. They locate the dolphins by listening in to their echolocation calls. By staying close to land, the dolphins are able to disrupt their calls and thwart these aggressors.

Distribution: Eastern Atlantic Ocean off West Africa.
Habitat: Tropical coastal waters, usually less than 20m (65ft) deep, and tidal zones of rivers.
Food: Fish.
Size: 1.2–2.5m (4–8.25ft); 75–150kg (165–330lb).
Maturity: Between 4 and 8 years.
Breeding: Single calf born every 1–2 years.
Life span: Not known.
Status: Declining because of habitat loss and entanglement in fishing nets.

White-beaked dolphin

Lagenorhynchus albirostris

Distribution: Ranges widely through the North Atlantic and Arctic Oceans.
Habitat: Coastal waters.
Food: Medium-sized fish, squid and crustaceans form the bulk of the diet.
Size: 2.3–2.8m (7.5–9.25ft); 180kg (396lb).
Maturity: Not known.
Breeding: 1 calf born every year.
Life span: Not known.
Status: Common.

Dolphins are notoriously difficult animals to study because they are relatively small, and also very wide-ranging. Consequently, not much is known about the habits of this remarkable group compared to most land-living mammals.

Like most cetaceans, white-beaked dolphins live in groups known as schools, which have very complex social structures. Schools are usually made up of 2–20 individuals, but occasionally lots of schools will come together to form large aggregations containing more than 1,000 individuals.

Dolphins are famed for a behaviour known as breaching, when they leap clear of the water, somersault and splash back down through the waves. Dolphins have also been observed playing games underwater, such as "chase the seaweed". White-beaked dolphins undertake annual migrations, moving between temperate and subpolar waters, tracking their favoured prey of mackerel and herring.

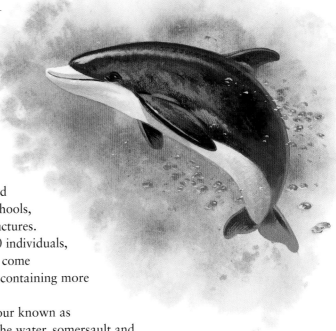

The white-beaked dolphin's counter-shaded coloration, with a darker upperside and pale belly, helps to camouflage it from both above and below.

Harbour porpoise (*Phocoena phocoena*): 1.3–1.9m (4.25–6ft); 35–90kg (77–198lb)
Generally found in small groups in shallow coastal waters and river estuaries, harbour porpoises are relatively common in European waters. These social, highly vocal cetaceans live in groups of up to 15 members. Porpoises generally are distinguished from dolphins by having blunt faces that lack "beaks".

False killer whale (*Pseudorca crassidens*): 3.7–5.5m (12.25–18ft); 1.2–2 tonnes (2,640–4,400lb)
Like its namesake the killer whale, the false killer whale is actually a member of the dolphin family. This is a wide-ranging species, which travels throughout the world's oceans. The false killer whale is able to reach speeds of up to 30 knots (30 nautical mph or 55kph) and is often encountered racing ships.

Common seal

Phoca vitulina

One of the two seal species found commonly in British waters, the common seal has a dog-like face. Its snout is much more rounded than the Roman-style nose which typifies the grey seal, Britain's other common seal.

It is difficult to get a good estimate of the common seal's population size because it lives in small, widely distributed groups, and is highly mobile.

Common seals have large, sensitive eyes with specialized retinas, which allow them to see well underwater. However, sometimes the water is too murky for seals to be able to hunt by sight. At these times common seals switch to another sense – touch. Their long whiskers are highly sensitive and allow the seals to feel for prey in the gloom.

Distribution: North Atlantic, Pacific and Arctic coastlines.
Habitat: Sheltered coastal waters.
Food: Fish, cephalopods and crustaceans.
Size: 1.2–2m (4–6.5ft); 45–130kg (99–285lb).
Maturity: Females 2 years; males 5 years.
Breeding: Single pup produced every year.
Life span: 26–32 years.
Status: Common.

From a distance, a seal's head poking above the waves can closely resemble that of a human. They are sometimes mistaken for swimmers in trouble. The common seal is also known as the harbour seal.

ANIMALS OF ASIA, AUSTRALIA AND NEW ZEALAND

Asia is the world's largest continent, stretching halfway around the globe, while Australia, an island between the Indian Ocean and the Pacific, is the smallest continent. Being an island, Australia's wildlife has been isolated for many millions of years and today the animals that live there are very different from those found in Asia and beyond. While Asia is home to mammals such as elephants, orang-utans, wild horses and camels, Australia is populated by kangaroos, wombats and possums. Most of Australia's mammals carry their young in pouches, and a few even lay eggs like reptiles. The reptiles and amphibians of Australia are more similar to those found in Asia, but they are by no means ordinary. Perhaps the most unusual reptile of all, the tuatara, lives in New Zealand, a group of islands in the South Pacific. These ancient reptiles have no living relatives anywhere else in the world.

Above from left: Carpet python, pretty face wallaby, koala.

SALAMANDERS AND RELATIVES

Salamanders can be found in both aquatic and terrestrial habitats, although they need water for survival during the early stages of their lives. Young salamanders breathe through external gills. Once they reach adulthood, salamanders develop lungs and start to breathe air, but they can also absorb oxygen through their skins, which allows them to spend long periods underwater.

Ceylon caecilian

Ichthyophis glutinosus

Distribution: Sri Lanka.
Habitat: Underground in damp forest soils.
Food: Insect larvae, termites and earthworms.
Size: 30–50cm (12–20in).
Maturity: Not known.
Breeding: 7–20 live young born after gestation of 9–11 months.
Life span: 6–7 years.
Status: Common.

Caecilians look like snakes or worms, but they are neither. In fact they are amphibians, being closely related to frogs, toads and salamanders. Unlike most amphibians, which have few or no teeth, caecilians have two sets of backward-pointing teeth on their upper and lower jaws.

While being relatively common in their forest habitats, Ceylon caecilians are difficult animals to find. This is because they spend virtually their entire lives under the thick leaf litter of tropical forests, away from the sharp eyes of the many birds, mammals and reptiles that would eat them.

Being blind, caecilians find food and mates using smell. They have small tentacle-like appendages that protrude from just behind their nostrils. These tentacles smell the environment immediately around them, detecting their prey – insects and earthworms – and mates. Females produce strong odours when they are fertile.

With eyes covered by skin and bone, caecilians are totally blind. Their slender body shape makes them perfectly adapted for a subterranean, burrowing lifestyle. The family holds over 90 species in all.

Japanese giant salamander

Andrias japonicus

This salamander is one of Japan's most impressive inhabitants, and one of the world's largest salamanders. It belongs to a small group of salamanders called *Cryptobranchidae*, to which American hellbenders also belong. Weighing over 20kg (44lb) and reaching sizes well in excess of 1m (3.25ft), the Japan giant salamander is found only in cold, fast-flowing mountain streams. It spends the daytime hiding under rocks and branches, coming out at night to feed on its prey, which it catches using a sticky tongue and powerful jaws.

This creature actually has three names in Japanese; they are "Osanshouuo", "Hanzaki", and "Hajikamiio". These names are derived from the fact that the salamanders secrete mucus from their skins that smells like the Japanese peppers called "sansho" and "hajikami". Until recently the Japanese giant salamander was a highly prized source of food for people living in the mountainous regions of Japan. However, the pressures of over-hunting and water pollution have caused the population to drop very sharply, and now the giant salamander is strictly protected by law.

Distribution: Japan.
Habitat: Cold, fast-flowing mountain streams with rocky bottoms.
Food: Mainly worms and insects, and also crabs, fish, frogs, snakes and mice.
Size: 40–70cm (16–28in), up to 140cm (56in); over 20kg (44lb).
Maturity: 5–10 years.
Breeding: 500–600 eggs laid in autumn, hatching after 40–50 days.
Life span: 70 years.
Status: Vulnerable.

This huge salamander is dark brown with black spots. It has characteristically warty skin on its head. Its pepper-like smell is caused by mucus from glands in the skin.

Western Chinese mountain salamander

Batrachuperus pinchonii

This sturdy salamander inhabits the fast-flowing streams of the mountainous Sichuan province of China. These streams are too cold for a lot of animals, especially fish, which tend to be a major predator of salamander larvae. Therefore, the young salamanders grow up in relatively predator-free environments; they just have to contend with the cold.

This species' tail is relatively short for a salamander, and is flattened from side to side – laterally – into a paddle. This helps the salamander swim against the fast currents. Eggs are laid under stones so that they do not get washed away. In the very cold conditions, the salamanders have low metabolic rates and do not move very quickly, appearing a bit slow and ponderous. They take many years to reach maturity in their chilly habitat.

The Western Chinese mountain salamander is a robust amphibian with a mainly glossy, brown or green skin, generally with spots. Its diet consists mainly of insects.

Distribution: Sichuan Province, China.
Habitat: Fast-flowing mountain streams.
Food: Mainly insects.
Size: 15–20cm (6–8in).
Maturity: Not known.
Breeding: 7–12 eggs laid per year.
Life span: Not known.
Status: Locally common.

Paddletail newt (*Pachytriton labiatus*): 12–15cm (4.8–6in)
Found only in southern China, the paddletail newt is aptly named. It has a very broad, flat tail, which helps it to swim rapidly through the slow-flowing rivers in which it lives. It has very smooth, shiny skin which is dark brown along its back, but bright red with black patterning on its belly. It is a very secretive animal, spending most of its time hiding away under rocks and in crevices, only coming out at night to feed.

Afghan salamander (*Batrachuperus mustersi*): 12–17cm (4.8–6.8in)
Found only in the Paghman Mountains of Afghanistan, this salamander inhabits cool highland streams fed by glaciers. Indeed, it seems that it cannot survive in streams that are warmer than 14°C (57°F). The Afghan salamander is entirely aquatic and has a dark olive-brown coloration, with little in the way of markings. The restricted range of this animal means that it is highly endangered, and it is feared that it may have been badly affected by the recent conflicts in Afghanistan.

Chinese fire belly newt (*Cynops orientalis*): 10cm (4in)
Found throughout most of China, fire belly newts are striking little animals. Although they are dark grey or brown on top, when they are turned over it is easy to see how they got their name. Their bellies are coloured bright red, with small black spots. Chinese fire belly newts spend most of their time in water, but come on to land occasionally in search of the small invertebrates that make up their diet. In the breeding season, females lay single eggs on the leaves of water weeds and then fold the leaves over to hide the eggs.

Crocodile newt

Tylototriton verrucosus

The crocodile newt is named after the raised spots that line its back, reminiscent of the raised scutes of crocodiles. However, the newt's bumps are bright orange as a warning to predators that they secrete foul-tasting toxins. Crocodile newts leave the water at the onset of winter, when they bury themselves into soft soils to hibernate. During their active period – in spring, summer and autumn – the newts only come on land when water has become too scarce.

Like most newts, crocodile newts have a very acute sense of smell, being able to find food even in total darkness. They are mainly nocturnal and often forage in muddy pools. These newts can locate prey by smell alone when the density of mud makes their sense of sight useless. They also use smell to attract their mates. The males release a sex-smell which attracts the females to them. Males then perform courtship dances to induce the females into picking up their packages of sperm, known as spermatophores, which they deposit as they dance in circular patterns.

The crocodile newt has black skin, an orange head and limbs, and raised orange spots down its spine and back.

Distribution: Mountains of south-east and southern Asia.
Habitat: Aquatic habitats, mainly shallow temporary pools.
Food: Worms and insects.
Size: 12–22cm (4.8–8.8in).
Maturity: 1 year.
Breeding: 30–150 eggs laid, which take about 2 weeks to hatch.
Life span: 12 years.
Status: Endangered.

FROGS AND TOADS

Frogs and toads, collectively known as anurans, are by far the best known of the three groups of amphibian. Adult anurans are characterized by their lack of a tail, which is lost in the metamorphosis from tadpole to adult. Tadpoles tend to feed mainly on algae and plant matter, whereas adults tend to eat insects and other animals. Adult frogs are also characterized by their strong rear legs, used for jumping.

Oriental fire-bellied toad

Bombina orientalis

Oriental fire-bellied toads have green backs with black blotches. Their bellies are orange-red with black mottling.

Despite the remarkably vivid colouring of its underbelly, the fire-bellied toad merges perfectly with its surroundings; its dull brown to bright green back renders it almost invisible against the muddy margins of the pools and ponds where it lives. The back is also usually dotted with glossy black spots, which further help to camouflage it. Its skin gives off a milky secretion which irritates the mouth and eyes of would-be pedators.

When the fire-bellied toad feels threatened, it has a surprising trick, known as the unkenreflex. The toad flips over on to its back and arches its body, revealing the bright warning colours on its belly. These colours warn potential predators that the toad can secrete poisonous chemicals from its skin. When a predator has tasted these secretions once it will rarely try and attack a fire-bellied toad again. However, some snakes and birds do appear to be able to eat the toads with no ill-effects.

Distribution: Korea.
Habitat: Warm, humid forest areas, usually near water.
Food: Invertebrates, including worms, molluscs and insects.
Size: 4–5cm (1.6–2in).
Maturity: 2 years.
Breeding: 40–250 eggs laid in batches of 3–50 eggs throughout the summer. Hatch in June–July.
Life span: 30 years.
Status: Common.

Asian horned frog

Megophrys montana

Distribution: Thailand, Malaysia, Indonesia and the Philippines.
Habitat: Rainforest.
Food: Insects.
Size: 10–13cm (4–5.2in).
Maturity: Not known.
Breeding: Not known.
Life span: Unknown.
Status: Common, but declining due to habitat loss.

The Asian horned frog inhabits the dense rainforests of South-east Asia. It is a master of disguise, and might easily be mistaken for a leaf. A long snout, large eyelids and skin the colour of dried leaves all help the animal to stay hidden on the forest floor. By doing this it can remain motionless, in relative safety from predators, while waiting for its next meal to walk past.

The tadpole of the Asian horned frog has evolved a curious specialization that concerns its mouth. The tadpole gets most of its food from the surface of the pool or stream that it is living in. Most tadpoles have downward-pointing mouths, but this would make it difficult for this particular species to reach food, so it has evolved a mouth that points upwards instead. The tadpole is therefore able to cruise just beneath the surface of the water and pick off the tiny plants on the surface.

The points of skin above the eyes constitute the "horns" of the Asian horned frog. These and its leaf-like coloration help it to camouflage itself among fallen leaves on the forest floor.

Southern gastric brooding frog

Rheobatrachus silus

There are two species of gastric brooding frog, both now feared to be extinct in the wild. They are the only species in the world to share a particularly bizarre method of looking after their young. Immediately after laying her eggs, the adult female frog, somewhat surprisingly, swallows them. However, she has the extraordinary ability to switch off the production of digestive juices, and she turns her belly into a nursery for six or seven weeks, during which time she is unable to eat. The eggs hatch, and the tadpoles develop to near-maturity within the safety of their mother's stomach, before being "born again" through her mouth.

Southern gastric brooding frogs were only discovered in 1973, at which time they were thought to be relatively common. However, during the following few decades a combination of habitat destruction, increased pollution levels and over-collection for the pet trade have seen this incredible species driven into extinction in the wild. The species now only survives in captivity.

This small, dull-coloured frog with large bulging eyes has a special method for looking after its young. They develop within the mother's stomach before emerging out of her mouth.

Distribution: Queensland, Australia.
Habitat: Rocky creek beds and rainforest rock pools.
Food: Small insects.
Size: 3–5.5cm (1.2–2.2in).
Maturity: 1 year.
Breeding: 18–30 eggs are brooded for 6–7 weeks within the stomach of the adult female.
Life span: 3 years.
Status: Extinct in the wild, but survives in captivity.

Stonemason toadlet (*Uperoleia lithomoda*): 1.5–3cm (0.6–1.2in)
This tiny frog is found only in the northernmost areas of Australia. Emerging from its underground burrow only when the infrequent rains arrive, the stonemason toadlet has to find a mate rapidly and produce young before conditions again become too dry. The male produces a strange click-like courtship call which sounds like two stones being knocked together. It is this call which gave the stonemason toadlet its name.

Asian painted frog (*Kaloula pulchra*): 5–7cm (2–2.8in)
After a heavy bout of rain, the deep, booming bellows of this frog can be heard from most drains, culverts, lakes and ponds throughout much of South-east Asia. This chubby little frog lives up to its name, being coloured with browns, blacks and beige. When threatened, it puffs itself up with air, and contorts its face as a warning to any would-be predator.

Brown-striped frog (*Limnodynastes peronii*): 3–6.5cm (1.2–2.5in)
Also known as the Australian grass frog, this long-limbed amphibian with dark stripes running down its body lives in and around swamps in eastern Australia. This amphibian is nocturnal in its habits, feeding at night on insects and other invertebrates. During the winter and dry periods, it buries itself underground. During mating, pairs make floating foam nests into which 700–1,000 eggs are laid. The eggs hatch quickly and the tadpoles develop very rapidly, too.

Giant tree frog

Litoria infrafrenata

Found in forests and gardens, the giant tree frog is Australia's largest native species of frog, and one of the largest tree frogs in the world. As its name suggests, this frog spends most of its life in the branches of tall trees, feeding on insects at night. During the day, when it is more visible to predators such as birds of prey, it stays well out of sight in foliage. Its green coloration helps to camouflage it as it hides away.

Following spring storms, males gather in trees around swamps, lakes and ponds and produce bizarre calls in an attempt to attract females to mate. The mating calls resemble the deep-throated barks of large dogs, but it isn't just dogs that the frogs can sound like. When distressed, giant tree frogs may make loud meowing sounds, just like the distress calls of cats.

Once the eggs have been laid they develop quickly, hatching within 28 hours. Hatching so quickly means that the young only spend a short period of time lying motionless and prone to predation within their eggs.

Usually an olive or emerald-green shade, the giant tree frog has the ability to change colour depending on temperature and the surrounding vegetation.

Distribution: Northern Australia to Indonesia.
Habitat: Occurs in a variety of habitats, ranging from tropical forest to cultivated areas.
Food: Insects.
Size: 14cm (5.6in).
Maturity: Not known.
Breeding: Between 200 and 300 eggs laid in spring and summer.
Life span: Not known.
Status: Common.

Cane toad

Bufo marinus

Distribution: Originally from the Amazon Basin, now introduced into Australia, the United States, the West Indies, Puerto Rico, Taiwan, Hawaii, the Philippines and many other islands.
Habitat: Wide-ranging and adaptable to many different habitats.
Food: Insects and small vertebrates.
Size: 24 cm (10in); 1.8kg (4lb).
Maturity: 1 year.
Breeding: 2 clutches of between 8,000 and 35,000 eggs produced each year. Eggs hatch into free-swimming tadpoles that become adult in 45–55 days.
Life span: 40 years.
Status: Common.

The cane toad, or marine toad, is now most famous for being a serious pest. Originally native to the Amazon Basin, it was deliberately released into Australia in the 1930s in the hope that it would control the grey-backed beetle, a pest of sugar cane. Unfortunately the cane toad preyed on almost everything except the grey-backed beetle, which stayed out of reach high up the stems of cane crops. Now a number of Australian species, including other frogs and toads, are in danger of dying out after being extensively preyed upon by these toads.

The cane toad's success in both its native habitat and in new areas where it has spread is helped by the fact that it has two glands just above its shoulder blades, which produce large quantities of highly toxic venom. This venom is so potent that snakes, which have tried to eat the toads, have been found dead with the toads still lodged in their mouths.

Snakes are not the only animals affected. Native marsupial predators such as quolls, along with introduced cats and dogs, are all at risk if they try to eat the toads. Cane toads also push native tree frogs out of the best breeding grounds, further establishing their reputation as a serious problem for Australia's native wildlife.

The large, brown cane toad has become a common sight in eastern Australia in recent years. The amphibian has a large, wide head with bony ridges on the top and sides, large protruding eyes, and a stout, powerful body. The glands on its shoulder blades produce a venom that is capable of killing goannas, crocodiles, snakes, dingoes, quolls, cats, dogs and humans within the space of 15 minutes. Cane toads eat almost anything, including pet food, carrion and household scraps, as well as their main diet of insects and small vertebrates.

Holy cross frog

Notaden bennetti

The holy cross frog is also known as the catholic frog or crucifix frog. A native of Australia, it is a yellow or greenish amphibian, and its name is derived from the dark cross-like pattern on its back. It is a desert-dwelling frog, surviving the heat by burrowing underground.

Summer in the Australian desert is not a hospitable season. The sun bakes the ground with great ferocity and there is virtually no water to be found anywhere. However, despite these harsh conditions, the holy cross frog is able to survive. It is active for only a few weeks every year, just after the rains, when it emerges from its burrow and busily sets about the business of finding a mate, reproducing and preparing to sit out another summer.

When it rains, holy cross frogs are able to absorb water through glands in their skins. They can absorb as much as half of their body weight, and become as round as balls. Then, when the rains stop, they burrow 30cm (12in) or more under the desert floor, where they stay until the next rainfall. During this time they virtually shut down completely, with all of their vital life processes running at the lowest possible level to make sure that they do not use any more water than they need to. This survival mechanism is called aestivation.

Distribution: Australia.
Habitat: Widespread throughout arid regions.
Food: Small black ants form the main element of the diet.
Size: 4cm (1.6in).
Maturity: 1 year.
Breeding: Occurs after heavy rains in summer.
Life span: Not known.
Status: Common.

Hochstetter's frog

Leiopelma hochstetteri

The Hochstetter's frog is believed to be one of the world's most primitive frogs. It is one of the few species of frog that shares some specific physical characteristics with fish, which are relatives of the amphibians. For example, it has no external ear openings, and no vocal sac. Also, the frog does not croak, and can only manage a quiet squeak at the best of times. Additionally, it has two tail-wagging muscles, but no tail.

Hochstetter's frog lives mainly under rocks and boulders near mountain streams and other wet places in New Zealand. In fact, it is one of only three species of frog native to this region. It is still relatively common in some localized areas of the North Island, whereas the other two species are exceedingly rare, confined to just a few offshore islands.

The tadpoles of this species are unusual in that they don't feed until they change into adult frogs. When a female lays her eggs, she does so into a large, water-filled capsule. After hatching, the tadpoles stay within this capsule until they mature.

Distribution: North Island, New Zealand.
Habitat: Under stones or vegetation alongside creeks.
Food: Insects, spiders, worms and slugs.
Size: 5cm (2in).
Maturity: 1 year.
Breeding: Egg clusters laid in damp, shady places.
Life span: Not known.
Status: Threatened.

This small brown frog is believed to be one of the most primitive of all frog species.

Corroboree frog

Pseudophryne corroboree

The strikingly beautiful corroboree frog is thought to be Australia's – and possibly one of the world's – most endangered species of frog. Less than 200 individuals are still alive, isolated from each other in small groups numbering no more than 25. It is believed that corroboree populations have been decimated by a disease known as chytrid (pronounced kit-rid).

The frogs are particularly at risk due to their slightly peculiar lifestyle. Corroboree frogs have much slower breeding cycles than other frogs. While tadpoles are fully formed just four weeks after the female has laid her eggs, they don't actually hatch out of the eggs for another six months. Having finally broken out of their eggs, the tadpoles then take a long time to reach maturity and become adult frogs.

This slow lifestyle means that it takes corroboree frog numbers longer to recover from a population crash than it would other frogs. The population is at a very low ebb today, and is in great danger of dying out entirely.

The corroboree frog is a spectacularly colourful species, with well-defined black and yellow markings.

Distribution: Kosciuszko National Park in New South Wales, Australia.
Habitat: Bogs and surrounding woodland.
Food: Insects.
Size: 2.5–3cm (1–1.2in).
Maturity: 2 years.
Breeding: 16–38 eggs laid in summer, hatching 7 months later.
Life span: Not known.
Status: Critically endangered.

Solomon Islands horned frog (*Ceratobatrachus guentheri*): 5–8cm (2–3.2in)
Unusually for a frog, this species has tooth-like projections growing from its lower jaw. It uses these to keep hold of its prey, such as worms and insects. The projections may also play some role in competition between males for mates, because they are larger in the males than they are in females. After mating, the females lay batches of eggs which develop directly into miniature adult frogs, with the tadpole stage occurring within the eggs.

Fijian ground frog (*Platymantis vitiensis*): 3.5–5cm (1.4–2in)
Confined to the forests of Fiji, little is known about the habits of this small orange-brown frog. It has very prominent eyes and large eardrums, as well as large pads on its toes, which help it to climb around. The female lays a small number of large eggs directly on to the ground. The young develop directly into young adults, the tadpole stage being completed within the eggs. Fijian ground frogs are highly endangered due to their limited original habitats being deforested.

Ornate narrow-mouthed frog (*Microhyla ornata*): 2–3cm (0.8–1.2in)
The ornate narrow-mouthed frog inhabits the rainforests and paddy fields of South-east Asia, where it feeds on insects and other invertebrates. This small frog has a plump, smooth-skinned body, with short front legs, and long back legs. It is mainly coloured yellow, with dark stripes along the back and a darker marbled pattern on its back.

Asian blue-web flying frog

Rhacophorus reinwardtii

Flying frogs don't fly as such – they glide downwards from tree to tree using the webbing between their toes. When feeling threatened, these frogs will leap from their current branch into the air. They spread their toes, expanding the flaps of blue skin between them, and use these as parachutes. This technique allows the frogs to glide more than 12m (40ft) between trees, giving them a useful technique for escaping predators.

This species of flying frog has an interesting breeding method. The females create foam nests in which they lay their eggs. These nests are positioned above pools of water that collect in leaves high up in the forest canopy. The foam prevents the eggs from drying out while the tadpoles are developing within. Once sufficiently mature, the tadpoles then break out of their foam nests and drop into the water below, where they complete their development into adult frogs. The generally green coloration provides camouflage in the forest canopy.

Well camouflaged by their green skins amongst the leaves, the blue webbing between the flying frog's toes provides a startling contrast when they jump.

Distribution: Indonesia, Malaysia and South-east Asia.
Habitat: Rainforest.
Food: Insects.
Size: 4–7cm (1.6–2.8in).
Maturity: Not known.
Breeding: Clutches of up to 800 eggs in a foam nest placed above a pool of water.
Life span: 5 years.
Status: Common.

Indonesian floating frog (*Occidozyga lima*): 10–12cm (4–4.8in)
The Indonesian floating frog spends most of its time simply bobbing about in the ponds and lakes in which it lives. It holds on to a piece of weed with one or more feet, looking like a fallen leaf resting on the surface of the water. When insect prey come close enough, they are gobbled up with quick lunges.

Black-spined toad (*Bufo melanostictus*): 10cm (4in)
One of Asia's most successful amphibians, the range of the black-spined toad stretches from India in the west to Hong Kong in the east and Indonesia in the south. It has been able to colonize cultivated and urban areas, making use of drainage ditches, ponds and paddy fields. These toads have numerous warts on their backs, and it is these that have given them their name. Black-spined toads produce venomous secretions from their warts, which also have the effect of staining their skin black.

Crab-eating frog (*Ratia cancrivora*): 8–10cm (3.2–4in)
The crab-eating frog is one of the few species of amphibian that can tolerate living in salty, brackish water. Inhabiting brackish waters brings the frog into contact with prey that frogs would not usually encounter, crabs being a good example. As their name suggests, crab-eating frogs will often feast on crabs when they get the chance, but they are not fussy, and will eat pretty much any prey that is small enough for them to swallow.

White's tree frog

Litoria caerulea

It may look as though the blue-green skin of White's tree frog is ill-fitting, but it is this skin which is the frog's key to success. During very wet conditions, the amphibian is able to absorb large amounts of water and store it under the loose folds of skin. The water can then be used in times of drought. However, water-storing is not the only talent possessed by this frog's skin. It also produces various anti-bacterial compounds, and a chemical which has been shown to be useful for treating high blood pressure in humans.

During the mating season, males often cling to the backs of females for days on end, waiting for them to lay eggs, which are then laid in an unusual fashion. Instead of carefully placing their eggs into water, like many frogs, female White's tree frogs squirt their eggs out underwater with such great force that they may travel for more than 2m (6ft) before coming to a stop. White's tree frogs are able to produce some very loud sounds. When alarmed, the frogs will emit ear-piercingly loud screams – enough to put off many predators.

Distribution: Australia and southern New Guinea.
Habitat: Moist, forested environments are preferred, but can live in drier areas.
Food: Moths, locusts, cockroaches and other insects.
Size: 7–11.5cm (2.8–4.6in).
Maturity: 2 years.
Breeding: 1,500–3,000 eggs hatch within 2 or 3 days of being laid.
Life span: 21 years.
Status: Common.

The White's tree frog has a waxy, blue-green colour and rolling skin folds of fatty material that have earned it the nickname of "dumpy tree frog".

Giant frog

Cyclorana australis

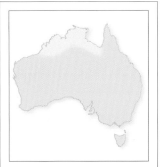

Distribution: Northern Australia.
Habitat: Grassland and open woodland. Can survive in more arid areas than most species.
Food: Insects.
Size: 7–11cm (2.8–4.4in).
Maturity: 2 years.
Breeding: Occurs after the summer rainy season. 7,000 eggs laid in temporary ponds. Tadpoles mature quickly before pools dry up.
Life span: Not known.
Status: Common.

The giant frog is a species of frog that is able to live in much drier areas than most frogs. It survives the long, dry days of an Australian winter by cocooning itself in a mixture of shed skin, mucus and damp earth. It can also retain large amounts of water beneath its skin and in its bladder and body cavity – an adaptation which helps it to sit out long dry spells in the safety of its cocoon.

The ability to hold large amounts of water has made the giant frog, and its relative the water-holding frog, a valuable animal for Aboriginal people, who dig them up and squeeze the pure water out of the frogs to gain a drink. The frogs are released lacking water supplies but otherwise unharmed.

Once the summer rains arrive, the frogs leap into action, feasting on the large numbers of insects and preparing to mate. The males gather around the edges of temporary pools and call to females, which come down and lay up to 7,000 eggs. The young have to hatch and develop into adult frogs within the space of a few short weeks, before their pools of water dry up in the hot sun.

The giant frog's large eyes give it excellent vision, which it uses to spot insects such as beetles, grasshoppers and termites. It is a nocturnal, burrowing frog, and is usually only seen above ground after rain. These amphibians of dry terrain in Australia are much prized by the local Aboriginal people, who use them to gain moisture when water is scarce.

Asian tree toad

Pedostibes hosii

The Asian tree toad, also known as the brown tree toad, is a large and stocky toad that lives in lowland tropical forest below 660m (2,165ft) above sea level. It is distributed throughout Borneo and is also known in Sumatra, Peninsular Malaysia and southern Thailand. The tadpoles develop in quiet pools of water and at the bottoms of streams, amongst dead leaves. When they become adults, the toads develop arboreal skills and spend some of their time in trees, hence their name.

This toad is unusual among toads in its extraordinary ability to climb. While most toads lead purely terrestrial lives, the Asian tree toad has sucker-like pads on its toes, which enable it to climb with ease. It spends its days hidden away in crevices in trees and in foliage, only becoming active when the sun sets.

Throughout the night, the tree toad comes down to the forest floor along rivers and streams and feeds mainly on ants, which it picks up with its long, sticky tongue. The animal calls to other toads by making a grating, slurred squawk that rises slightly in pitch from beginning to end.

The female lays her eggs in strings in rivers. These rivers need to be fairly fast-flowing because the eggs need to be kept in conditions where the concentration of oxygen in the water is relatively high. Once they hatch, however, the tadpoles have to battle against the fast water currents to prevent themselves from being washed away. They have large sucker-like mouths with which they cling to rocks, anchoring themselves against the flow.

Distribution: South-east Asia.
Habitat: Lowland tropical forest.
Food: Insects, mainly ants.
Size: 5–11cm (2–4.4in).
Maturity: 2 years.
Breeding: Many small eggs laid in a string in rivers.
Life span: 16 years.
Status: Common.

The Asian tree toad varies in colour from greenish-brown to black, with a dense pattern of yellow spots. Some females are dark purple. Unlike most toads, this South-east Asian species is a skilled climber, shinning up trees with the aid of the sticky pads on its toes.

TURTLES

Among the oldest surviving groups of reptiles, turtles first evolved about 200 million years ago. They have changed very little since then, a fact that bears testament to their successful body design and lifestyle. Turtles live both on land and in water, with the land-living species being more commonly referred to as tortoises. All species of turtle lay their eggs on land.

Common snake-necked turtle

Chelodina longicollis

The neck of the common snake-necked turtle is very long. When extended, the neck is longer than half the length of the shell.

With their long, flexible neck, good eyesight and strong jaws, snake-necked turtles are formidable predators in their aquatic habitats. They are cosmopolitan animals, feeding on any creatures they can catch, including frogs, tadpoles and fish. Breeding occurs in September and October – the spring months in Australia – and in November the females lay clutches of eggs in holes in the banks of swamps or ponds. They then cover the holes over and leave the eggs to develop on their own. After three to five months the young turtles hatch and dig themselves out of the holes, scurrying down to the comparative safety of the water.

Most snake-necked turtles live close to streams, rivers, swamps and lagoons in eastern Australia. From time to time, they migrate over land in groups to search out new habitats. It is not unusual for these turtles to colonize artificial ponds.

Distribution: South-eastern and eastern Australia.
Habitat: Swamps, lakes, slow-moving waterways, creeks and billabongs.
Food: Frogs, tadpoles, small fish and crustaceans.
Size: 30cm (12in); 1.2kg (2.6lb).
Maturity: 4–5 years.
Breeding: Clutches of 8–24 eggs hatch after 3–5 months.
Life span: 50 years.
Status: Common.

Chinese soft-shelled turtle

Pelodiscus sinensis

Distribution: China, Korea and Japan.
Habitat: Rivers, lakes, ponds and reservoirs.
Food: Snails, molluscs, crabs, fish, shrimp, insects, frogs and earthworms.
Size: 20–35cm (8–14in).
Maturity: Not known.
Breeding: Eggs hatch 28 days after laying.
Life span: Not known.
Status: Endangered.

The Chinese soft-shelled turtle inhabits slow-flowing rivers and ponds with sandy or muddy bottoms. Occasionally it can be found out of water, basking on stones, but it is quick to disappear underwater when it feels threatened. The Chinese soft-shelled turtle is a predominantly nocturnal animal, foraging on the riverbed at night for prey. This turtle is extremely cosmopolitan in its tastes, eating most animals that it can get its powerful jaws around. Crayfish, snails, insects, fish and amphibians are all on the menu during a night's foraging.

The soft-shelled turtle's jaws are also useful for defence. Unlike most types of turtles, this species cannot fully retract its head under its shell. It also lacks the hardened, bony plates on the shell which protect other turtles. Instead it has a vicious bite, enough to protect it from most would-be predators. The turtle's long snout acts as a snorkel, allowing it to stay completely submerged in shallow water and yet still breathe.

The Chinese soft-shelled turtle has a flat, soft and rubbery shell and a long snout which acts as a snorkel.

Indian starred tortoise (*Geochelone elegans*): 24–27cm (9.6–10.8in)
One of the world's most distinctive species of tortoise, the Indian starred tortoise is found only on the Indian subcontinent. It has a bizarrely shaped and beautifully marked shell. Each section of the shell, known as a scute, rises to a domed point. These tortoises are mainly active in the monsoon season, when there is plenty of moisture around. During the driest season, they are active only in the mornings and evenings.

Pig-nosed river turtle (*Carettochelys insculpta*): 70–75cm (28–30in)
Found only in the far north of Australia, the pig-nosed river turtle is unlike most freshwater turtles in that it has broad flipper-like limbs, more reminiscent of sea-living turtles. Its name refers to its pig-like snout, which is used for breathing while the rest of the body remains underwater.

Chinese box turtle (*Cuora flavomarginata*): 10–12cm (4–4.8in)
The Chinese box turtle has a hinged line along its plastron (the underside of its shell). This allows it to close up entirely when it feels in danger. Found only in a small area of eastern Asia, this endangered species spends most of its time in paddy fields feeding on fish, crustaceans, worms and fruit.

Asian leaf turtle

Cyclemys dentata

The early part of an Asian leaf turtle's life is spent almost entirely in water. The young are virtually exclusively aquatic. However, as they grow older the turtles spend increasing amounts of time on land. This species of turtle is omnivorous in habits, feeding on both plant and animal matter. It will quite happily switch from eating leaves to picking off passing snails or crickets.

The lower half of a turtle's shell is called the plastron, and in most turtles this features a series of radiating lines. In the Asian leaf turtle the plastron is hinged along the length of the animal in such a way that, when threatened, the turtle can pull its head and legs fully into its shell, and then pull the lower part of the shell up to close off the holes. This forms a near-impenetrable barrier, behind which the turtle can take cover.

The Asian leaf turtle has a flatter shell than most turtles. It is usually dark brown in colour, but can be lighter.

Distribution: South-east Asia.
Habitat: Streams.
Food: Invertebrates, tadpoles and some plant material.
Size: 15–24cm (6–9.6in).
Maturity: Not known.
Breeding: 5 clutches of 2–4 eggs laid each year.
Life span: Not known.
Status: Not known.

TUATARA

While looking like a typical lizard, the tuatara is actually a member of a completely separate group of reptiles known as the Rhynchocephalia, *of which it is the sole remaining example.*

Tuatara

Sphenodon punctatus

Tuataras are often described as living fossils. They are the only surviving members of a group of reptiles that otherwise died out long ago.

The *Rhynchocephalia* flourished about 200 million years ago, living alongside the dinosaurs. However, most of the species suffered the same fate as the dinosaurs: extinction. The only members to survive were the tuataras. There are only two species still living, both found in New Zealand.

Unlike lizards, tuataras have a third eye. This is a light-sensitive organ lying just under the skin on the top of the head. When they are young, the third eye absorbs ultraviolet rays, helping the youngsters produce vitamin D – essential for bone growth. Nearly everything about the lifestyles of tuataras is slow. Eggs develop within the female's body for about ten months before they are laid. It then takes another year for the baby tuataras to hatch. They do not become sexually mature until the age of 20 years. Tuataras have very slow metabolic rates, and breathe on average only once every seven seconds. However, they can hold their breath for over an hour.

Distribution: Coastal islands of New Zealand.
Habitat: Underground burrows.
Food: Insects, small lizards and birds' eggs and chicks.
Size: 50–60cm (20–24in); 0.5kg (1.1lb).
Maturity: 20 years.
Breeding: 6–10 eggs once every 2–5 years.
Life span: 100 years.
Status: Lower risk.

LIZARDS

The most diverse and widespread group of reptiles is made up of the 3,000 species of lizards. They vary in size from just a few centimetres to almost 3m (10ft) long, and exhibit huge variation in shape, coloration and feeding habits. From legless burrowers to forest dwellers that "fly" from tree to tree, lizards manage to carve themselves a niche almost everywhere on earth.

Frilled lizard

Chlamydosaurus kingii

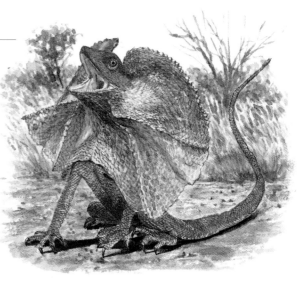

Distribution: Northern Australia and southern New Guinea.
Habitat: Woodland.
Food: Predominantly insects, but also small lizards and mammals.
Size: 55–70cm (22–28in).
Maturity: 2–3 years.
Breeding: 2 clutches of 10–20 eggs produced every year.
Life span: 20 years.
Status: Common.

In normal circumstances, the frilled lizard looks somewhat similar to other large lizards. It is drab-coloured, being able to blend into its background and remain hidden from its predators. However, should this hiding tactic not work, then the lizard's amazing, brightly coloured frill is brought into action. When the lizard opens its mouth, rods of cartilage attached to the jaw cause the frill to open out like an umbrella. At the same time the lizard makes a loud hissing noise. The combination of the loud hiss and opening frill is enough to frighten most predators into believing that this mostly harmless lizard is a fearsome creature not to be messed with.

Frilled lizards forage mainly on the ground but are also very good climbers, being able to chase their insect prey up trees. When on the ground, the frilled lizard has an enviable turn of speed, being able to outrun most humans.

Possibly one of the most spectacular lizards in the world, this animal uses its incredible frill to frighten would-be predators into believing that it is dangerous.

Thorny devil

Moloch horridus

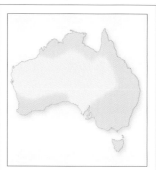

The incredibly spiny appearance of the thorny devil helps to protect and camouflage it, as well as collect water in its harsh desert habitat.

Australia plays host to many strange animals, and the thorny devil most definitely ranks among the most bizarre. Its entire body is covered by a barrage of spines, which are buff or grey in colour. These spines help to break up the lizard's outline, so it is difficult for birds of prey to spot it from above. However, the main benefit of the spines is less obvious – they are a source of water. Thorny devils live in extremely hot and arid areas, where water is at a premium. During the night, condensation collects on the lizard's skin; the spines help to channel this water down into grooves that run along the body to its mouth. This method of collecting water means that the thorny devil never needs to drink directly from a puddle or pond.

Thorny devils eat only ants, which they pick off one by one using their sticky tongues. They are very efficient at this process, being able to pick off up to 50 ants per minute. A single meal may contain as many as 3,000 ants.

Distribution: Western and central Australia.
Habitat: Desert.
Food: Ants.
Size: 15–18cm (6–7.2in); 90g (0.2lb).
Maturity: 3 years.
Breeding: 4–10 eggs laid in summer.
Life span: 20 years.
Status: Lower risk.

Water dragon

Physignathus cocincinus

With a prominent crest running from the back of the head down the spine, the water dragon is a large, impressive lizard. During the breeding season, males are bright green in colour, but become duller at other times of the year.

The water dragon is equally at home in water, on land and even in the trees. However, it will always head very swiftly for the comparative safety of water when it feels threatened. Having mated, females scrape out shallow hollows in which to lay their clutches of 10–15 eggs. They then cover the eggs with soil and leaves, and leave them to develop on their own. After two to three months the young hatch out of the eggs, measuring a mere 15cm (6in). However, they grow quickly and become sexually mature at just one year of age.

The bright green coloration of the male water dragon only lasts during the breeding season, at other times of the year he is duller, resembling the female.

Distribution: South-east Asia: Thailand, Vietnam and Cambodia.
Habitat: Tropical rainforest, near water.
Food: Invertebrates, small mammals, birds, lizards, frogs and fruit.
Size: 80–100cm (32–40in).
Maturity: 1 year.
Breeding: 5 clutches of 10–15 eggs laid each year, hatching after 2–3 months.
Life span: 15 years.
Status: Common.

Sailfin lizard (*Hydrosaurus pustulatus*): 80–100cm (32–40in)
Hailing from the Philippines, sailfin lizards are grey-green in colour. Adults have crests running down their backs and larger crests running down their tails. The tail crests can be up to 8cm (3.2in) high, and help the lizards to swim. Whilst they spend most of their time in trees, they run to water if threatened. The sail-like fin means that they can swim at high speed.

Crocodile lizard (*Shinisaurus crocodilurus*): 40cm (16in)
The only member of its family, the crocodile lizard is found solely in the Guilin and Guangxi regions of China. It gets its name from rows of large olive-green bony scales on its back and tail, which are reminiscent of a crocodile's skin. Local people call this species "the lizard of great sleepiness" because it can remain motionless, in a metabolic pause for hours or days on end.

Bearded lizard (*Pogona vitticeps*): 30–45cm (12–18in)
Inhabiting the dry, arid interior of Australia, bearded lizards are great survivors. They forage for their diet of small insects and vegetation in dry forest and scrubland. These lizards are territorial, defending their home patches from intruders. Within their territories they tend to have regular areas, where they rest and bask in the sun during the early mornings. When confronted with potential predators, bearded lizards puff out their black throat patches and open their mouths wide in the hope of intimidating their foe.

Flying lizard

Draco volans

Also known as flying dragons, flying lizards have sets of wing-like membranes, which are actually skin stretched over elongated ribs. The lizards do not really fly, but glide through the forest from tree to tree. A single glide can be up to 10m (33ft) long. When not gliding, the "wings" are folded away down the sides of the body. Flying lizards have a third flap of skin under their chins, which can be extended at will. These chin flaps are larger and coloured yellow in the males, being used in courtship dances.

These small lizards spend virtually their entire lives in trees. The females only come down to the ground for short amounts of time to bury their eggs in soil. Having laid their eggs and covered over the holes, the females will fiercely defend the eggs for approximately 24 hours, before returning to the trees and leaving the young to develop independently. Having hatched, the young immediately climb the nearest trees to start their arboreal lives; the males will probably never set foot on the ground again.

Distribution: South-east Asia, Indonesia, the Philippines and Borneo.
Habitat: Forest and woodland.
Food: Ants and other small insects.
Size: 15–22cm (6–8.8in).
Maturity: 1 year.
Breeding: Clutches of 5 eggs laid in holes in the ground.
Life span: 8 years.
Status: Common.

The skin stretched over its elongated ribs gives the flying lizard a pair of wing-like membranes, which it uses to glide from tree to tree.

Tokay gecko

Gekko gecko

The tokay gecko is among the largest species of gecko in the world, reaching lengths of almost 40cm (16in). It gets its name from its most common call, an explosive noise sounding like "to-kay, to-kay, to-kay". The gecko is nocturnal, coming out at dusk to forage for the insects and small vertebrates that make up its diet.

Tokays are fearsome fighters, with powerful bites which are enough to cause considerable discomfort to any predators attempting to make a meal of them. Male tokays are highly territorial and will attack any other males wandering into the wrong area after failing to heed the warnings given by the residents. Tokay fights are fast, furious and generally deadly to their enemies.

Like the majority of gecko species, tokay geckos have specialized pads on the ends of their toes that allow them to grip smooth surfaces with ease. In houses where they are welcomed as a sign of good luck, they climb up windows and across ceilings in search of food. Sometimes they can be found near lights, hoping to catch the moths that are attracted to them at night.

The tokay gecko is a grey-blue lizard with orange spots on its body. It is one of the world's largest geckos.

Distribution: South-east Asia.
Habitat: Bushes, trees and on or around rocks. Also commonly found in or near houses, where it is tolerated because it is believed to bring good luck.
Food: Insects, hatchling birds, and also small mammals and reptiles.
Size: 20–37cm (8–15in).
Maturity: 1–2 years.
Breeding: Females lay 1–2 eggs, usually in crevices in rocks or walls.
Life span: 10 years.
Status: Common.

Flying gecko

Ptychozoon kuhli

Distribution: South-east Asia.
Habitat: Tropical forests.
Food: Insects.
Size: 18–20cm (7–8in).
Maturity: 6 months.
Breeding: 5–6 clutches of 2 or 3 eggs laid throughout the summer.
Life span: 3 years.
Status: Common.

Unlike the flying lizard, the flying gecko uses webbing between its toes as parachutes to glide from tree to tree.

The flying gecko is another species of reptile, along with the flying snake and flying lizard, that has taken to gliding around the forests of South-east Asia by using flaps of skin as airfoils. However, unlike the other "flying" reptiles, the flying gecko doesn't use flaps of skin stretched over elongated ribs, but instead it has flaps which grow between its long toes, in the same manner as flying frogs. These flaps of skin give the gecko a very fat-handed appearance, and this has given rise to its alternative name, the thick-fingered gecko.

Flying geckos are exceptionally well camouflaged. They closely resemble the bark patterns on the trees upon which they rest motionless, with their heads facing downward for hours on end, waiting for their insect prey to come close enough to grab. They even have lighter patches on their skins, which look like the patches of lichen growing on the tree trunks.

Blue-tongued skink

Tiliqua scincoides

One of Australia's most familiar reptiles, the cosmopolitan habits of the blue-tongued skink mean that it is been able to make the best of most situations. It has a varied diet, including insects, snails, fruit and flowers, as well as carrion and the contents of rubbish bins.

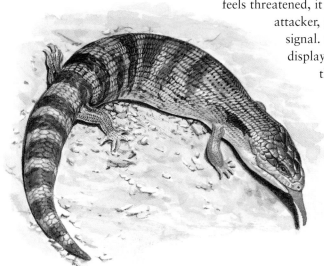

As its name suggests, the blue-tongued skink does indeed have a blue tongue. This is very large, almost the same size as the lizard's head, and when the lizard feels threatened, it will stick its bright tongue out at the attacker, presenting the predator with a warning signal. Combined with a fierce hiss, this display is often enough to discourage all but the most persistent predators.

During the breeding season, males set up territories from which they exclude other males. When females enter their territories, the males chase them around briefly, and then pin them down by the backs of their necks until they have finished mating.

The blue-tongued skink is a stocky reptile with a wide head, thick-set body and short limbs. The blue tongue discourages predators.

Distribution: Eastern Australia.
Habitat: Wide-ranging, including forest and parkland.
Food: Very varied, including insects, molluscs, carrion, fruit, flowers and food scraps from human settlements.
Size: 45–50cm (18–20in).
Maturity: 3 years.
Breeding: Up to 25 young born live.
Life span: 25 years.
Status: Common.

Knob-headed giant gecko (*Rhacodactylus auriculatus*): 20cm (8in)
On the Pacific islands of New Caledonia there is a group of bizarre geckos that have evolved in isolation for many thousands of years. The knob-headed giant gecko is one of them, and is so-called because it has a series of raised crests on its skull that give it a knobbed or horned appearance. It is highly variable in colour, from being mottled to having striking broad bands of brown and white running down its body. Unlike most geckos, which are predominantly insectivorous, adult knob-headed giant geckos eat mainly fruit.

Leach's giant gecko (*Rhacodactylus leachianus*): 30cm (12in)
This gecko is among the world's largest and is reputedly the only gecko in the world that growls. This strange nocturnal call may be one of the reasons why some locals consider this and other giant geckos to be "devils in the trees".

Long-tailed skink (*Mabuya longicauda*): 30–35cm (12–14in)
Living in open habitats such as gardens and parks, often near water, the long-tailed skink is aptly named. Its tail may be twice as long as the rest of its body and head combined. The long-tailed skink lives in South-east Asia, where it is a common sight rooting around leaf litter in search of insects and spiders. Female long-tailed skinks do not lay eggs, but give birth to live young. The young are miniatures of their parents, and receive no parental care after they are born.

Emerald tree skink

Lamprolepis smaragdina

Few reptiles can claim to be as brightly coloured as the emerald tree skink, which inhabits the tropical forests of South-east Asia and New Guinea. It is an adept climber, spending the majority of its time hiding among the dense foliage on tree trunks and branches, rarely venturing down to the ground. The emerald tree skink actively forages for its insect prey, which it catches with rapid, darting movements.

Like a lot of lizards, this species has the ability to shed its tail if grabbed – a phenomenon known as autotomy. This is a very useful tactic when attacked by predators. Once shed, the tail carries on moving and will often distract the predator, usually a bird of prey or snake, long enough for the rest of the lizard to make its escape.

Distribution: South-east Asia and New Guinea.
Habitat: Tropical forest.
Food: Insects.
Size: 18–25cm (7.2–10in).
Maturity: 6 months.
Breeding: Clutches of 9–14 eggs laid in summer.
Life span: 4 years.
Status: Common.

The bright green coloration of the emerald tree skink camouflages it very effectively among the foliage of its tropical forest habitats in South-east Asia and New Guinea.

Sand monitor

Varanus flavirufus

The sand monitor, or goanna, is one of the largest Australian lizards. It is also sometimes known as the racehorse monitor because it is capable of extreme speeds, often running only on its two back legs, using its long tail for balance.

Sand monitors are found throughout most of Australia, and have managed to be very successful by turning most situations into opportunities. They will eat virtually anything, searching for morsels of food with their long forked tongues, which are used for tasting the air. They will even dig up the nests of crocodiles when the mother's back is turned, and feast on the eggs within.

These lizards are not overtly aggressive, preferring to stay out of trouble whenever possible, but they can put up a serious fight if need be. They use their long whip-like tails, powerful jaws and long slashing claws to defend themselves from predators. Their claws also allow them to climb trees, usually in search of birds' nests.

Distribution: Australia.
Habitat: Woodland, shrubland and grassland.
Food: Lizards, insects, spiders, scorpions, centipedes and even small mammals and carrion.
Size: Up to 1.6m (5.5ft).
Maturity: Not known.
Breeding: 10 eggs laid into a deep burrow.
Life span: Not known.
Status: Common.

Sand monitors have flattened bodies, long powerful tails, stout limbs, long fingers and very sharp claws. Their well-developed hind legs help them achieve high speeds.

Lace monitor (*Varanus varius*): 1.5–2m (5–6.5ft)
Found in eastern Australia, the lace monitor is dark grey in appearance, with whitish markings, a long neck and tail and long, sharp claws, which it uses to climb trees. The long tail helps the monitor to balance while it is climbing, and it also can become a useful weapon when faced with a predator.

Borneo earless lizard
(*Lanthanotus borneensis*): 40–45cm (16–18in)
This lizard is nocturnal and highly secretive, and therefore its elongated red-brown form is rarely seen in its native range of north-west Borneo. The earless lizard belongs to a family of its own, but is most closely related to the monitor lizard. It is a good swimmer and a proficient burrower, having a long muscular tail, short stocky legs and a blunt snout. It is able to close its nostrils when diving underwater. Other than this, little is known about the lifestyle of this intriguing species.

Green tree monitor

Varanus prasinus

The green tree monitor blends wonderfully well into the foliage of the trees where it spends most of its days. It also has other adaptations that help it live an arboreal life, such as thick, rough scales on the soles of its feet, which help it to grip branches. Most importantly, it has a highly dextrous tail, which acts like a fifth limb while climbing. Many species of monitor will use their tails as a whip during defence. However, the tail is such an important organ to the green tree monitor that it actively defends it from predators.

Not much is known about the lifestyle of this lizard, due to its secretive nature and the inaccessibility of its habitat. However, it is known that it forages in the forest canopy, mainly for large insects. Some of these insects, such as some katydids, are very well protected with long spiny legs. Before attempting to eat these prickly morsels, green tree monitors therefore tend to strip the legs off and discard them, eating only the nutritious and less spiky body parts.

A long, graceful lizard with a pointed head and a whip-like tail, the green tree monitor can be many shades of green, from pale to very dark, depending on where it lives.

Distribution: New Guinea.
Habitat: Rainforests, palm forests, mangroves and cocoa plantations.
Food: Large insects and the occasional small mammal.
Size: Up to 1m (3.25ft).
Maturity: 2 years.
Breeding: 2 or 3 clutches of up to 5 eggs produced per year.
Life span: Not known.
Status: Common.

Komodo dragon

Varanus komodoensis

The Komodo dragon is probably the world's most infamous lizard. Not only is it the largest and most aggressive living lizard, but it is also one of the most endangered. It belongs to the same family as the monitor lizards, but has evolved separately for millions of years, becoming incredibly large in the process.

The Komodo dragon is just one of many giant species of animals that have evolved on islands around the world. It is also thought that Komodo dragons originally became so big that they were able to prey on a species of pygmy elephant that inhabited Indonesia thousands of years ago. These pygmy elephants have since become extinct, and the dragons now prey on other mammals, all of which have been introduced into their islands by human populations. The dragons lie hidden for hours upon end, waiting for prey animals to wander past, and then spring from their ambush positions with incredible bursts of speed.

Usually the prey is overpowered within seconds. However, should it escape, the problems for the victim are not yet over. Komodo dragons have a wealth of poisonous bacteria living in their mouths. When they bite prey animals, these bacteria are introduced to the wound, and often cause it to go septic and fester. This results in a slow, painful death.

Female Komodo dragons lay an average of about 20–25 soft, leathery eggs in September. About twice the size of chicken's eggs, they incubate for 8–9 months during the wet season. The young hatch out and immediately start to look for insect prey. However, they have to be careful, because they could well end up on the menus of larger dragons.

Distribution: Indonesian islands of Komodo, Rintja, Gillimontang, Padar and the western tip of Flores.
Habitat: Dry savannah and woodland.
Food: As adults, the bulk of the diet is made up of large mammals: goats, deer, pigs, horses and water buffalo. Birds and reptiles will also be taken.
Size: 3m (10ft); 150kg (330lb).
Maturity: 5 years.
Breeding: 20–25 eggs laid, incubation 8–9 months.
Life span: 30 years.
Status: Endangered.

This is the world's largest lizard. The huge form of the Komodo dragon belies the speed with which it can move.

Burton's snake lizard

Lialis burtonis

Distribution: Australia and southern New Guinea.
Habitat: Wide-ranging, from forests to desert.
Food: Lizards, mainly skinks.
Size: Up to 60cm (24in).
Maturity: Not known.
Breeding: 1 clutch of 2 eggs laid per year.
Life span: Not known.
Status: Common.

While it may look like a snake, this species is actually a legless lizard. Furthermore, it is a lizard that feeds on other lizards, which it catches in a cunning way. Having located a likely victim, the Burton's snake lizard keeps its body very still, but raises the tip of its tail slightly, and wiggles it. The skinks, upon which it feeds, are curious animals and are lured over to investigate. While the skink is preoccupied with the wiggling tail, it fails to notice the head watching it intently from a few centimetres away. Once in range, the snake lizard strikes, holding its prey tightly in its mouth until it suffocates to death. Burton's snake lizard likes to be hot; if the outside temperature drops down to about 21°C (70°F), it will enter an inactive (dormant) state in order to save energy.

Very variable in colour and markings, Burton's snake lizard is legless and has a broad, blunt snout used for burrowing.

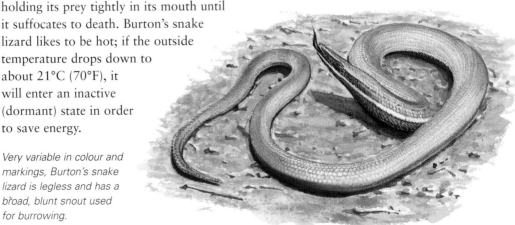

CROCODILIANS

Little-changed since the time of the dinosaurs, crocodiles are notorious for their stealth and ferocity while on the hunt. Despite their bloodthirsty reputation, female crocodiles are caring mothers. They guard their nest sites, help the young hatch from their eggs and carry them to the water. Even though they spend much of their time in water, crocodiles are also effective on the land, and can outrun humans.

Saltwater crocodile

Crocodylus porosus

The saltwater crocodile is probably the most fearsome reptile in the world. Better education is encouraging people to stay away from these giant animals.

This dark grey reptile is the largest of the crocodile species and the heaviest reptile in the world. A full-grown adult can weigh over 1,000kg (2,200lb) and be as much as 7m (23ft) long. It has a large head and powerful jaws, designed for holding and crushing. The crocodile eats pebbles, which are thought to aid digestion by grinding food, and they also act as a ballast for maintaining buoyancy.

The female "saltie" builds a nest from earth and grasses, which keeps the eggs safe from flooding. She guards the eggs from predators and carries the new hatchlings to the water. Juvenile crocodiles eat crustaceans, fish and reptiles, but as they grow larger, they often take creatures as big as a buffalo or domestic livestock. Humans are occasionally killed or injured.

Distribution: South-east Asia and Northern Australia.
Habitat: River mouths and swamps.
Food: Mammals, birds and fish.
Size: 5–7m (16–23ft); 500–1,000kg (1,100–2,200lb).
Maturity: 10–12 years.
Breeding: 40–60 eggs laid in summer.
Life span: 70 years.
Status: Common.

Gharial

Gavialis gangeticus

The gharial is easily recognized by its long, slender snout, which is filled with interlocking razor-sharp teeth. The male has a bulbous growth on the tip of the nose, used for making vocalizations and producing air bubbles when underwater. It uses bubble displays to attract females.

The gharial is poorly adapted to life on land because its leg muscles are not suitable for walking, and therefore it spends most of its life in water. It prefers quiet river backwaters, where its flattened tail and webbed hind feet make swimming easy.

Fish are the most common food for the gharial. The narrow jaws are well designed for quick snapping motions underwater, and the victims are swallowed head-first. Juveniles will often also eat small crustaceans and frogs. Gharials almost became extinct during the 1970s, and today they are protected throughout much of their range.

Distribution: Northern India, Bangladesh and Pakistan.
Habitat: Wide, calm rivers.
Food: Fish.
Size: 4–7m (13–23ft).
Maturity: 10 years.
Breeding: 30–50 eggs laid from March–May.
Life span: Not known.
Status: Endangered.

The bizarre-looking slender snout of the gharial helps it to grip its slippery fish prey. The reptile rarely comes on land except to nest.

Mugger

Crocodylus palustris

As its name suggests, the mugger crocodile rarely passes up an opportunity to grab a meal. Adults capture prey as large as buffalo.

This medium-sized crocodile is named from a Hindu word meaning "water-monster", and true to its name, the reptile poses quite a threat to any prey that catches its eye. The young crocodiles will take mostly small crustaceans and fish, but the adults will also prey on snakes, turtles and even deer and buffalo. They prefer slow-moving fresh water, not more than around 5m (16ft) deep, and will travel long distances over land in search of water during the dry season.

Mugger crocodiles look very similar to alligators, with broad snouts and flattened heads. However, their sharp teeth are perfectly aligned, and this is what distinguishes them from the alligators in appearance. They have flattened tails and are strong swimmers, but do not use their feet to swim, despite their being webbed.

Like all "crocs", muggers are social animals. The adults and juveniles often call to each other and, during the mating season, males establish territories and dominance by raising their snouts high above the ground and thrashing their tails.

Distribution: India, Pakistan and Sri Lanka.
Habitat: Shallow, slow-moving fresh water.
Food: Juveniles feed on fish, frogs and crustaceans; adults take a wide range of prey, including reptiles and mammals such as deer and buffalo.
Size: 2–5m (6.5–16ft).
Maturity: Females 6 years; males 10 years.
Breeding: Up to 28 eggs laid between February and April.
Life span: 40 years.
Status: Threatened.

Chinese alligator

Alligator sinensis

Distribution: Yangtze River in China.
Habitat: Slow-moving fresh water.
Food: Aquatic invertebrates and fish.
Size: 2m (6.5ft); 40kg (88lb).
Maturity: 4–5 years.
Breeding: 10–50 eggs laid from July–August.
Life span: Not known.
Status: Critically endangered.

Young Chinese alligators have bold markings of yellow and black, but these fade as the alligators mature, becoming more and more grey as time passes.

This small and secretive alligator is found only in one small part of China, along the banks of the Yangtze River. There are believed to be less than 200 Chinese alligators alive in the wild. Protection is in place, but to many farmers these alligators are nothing more than a nuisance, prone to attacking their wildfowl. Consequently, many are killed on sight. The loss of suitable habitat is also a major problem, and many captive breeding programmes have been postponed because there is not the space for the new specimens to be reintroduced to the wild.

Chinese alligators grow to around 2m (6.5ft) long and weigh up to 40kg (88lb). They are usually dark green or black in colour. Juveniles have bright yellow cross-banding. In common with the more familiar American species, *Alligator mississippiensis*, Chinese alligators have long, upturned snouts and bony ridges along their bodies and tails.

The teeth of Chinese alligators are well adapted for crushing, as they feed extensively on crustaceans and molluscs. They hunt mostly at night and during the summer months. They are opportunistic feeders, not averse to catching ducks or rats if they find them. They will rarely attack larger mammals.

SNAKES

The highly evolved snakes make fearsome and deadly predators of animals of all sizes, from insects to antelope. Snakes cannot chew their food, but can disassociate the two halves of their jaws and swallow their prey whole. Some species of snake produce the most potent natural toxins in the world, however they are in the minority, and only a small fraction of these reptiles pose any threat to humans.

Banded sea krait

Laticauda colubrina

Distribution: Pacific and Indian Oceans from Japan to Australia and Africa.
Habitat: Shallow coastal waters.
Food: Eels and fish.
Size: Typically 1–1.5m (3.3–5ft), up to 3.6m (12ft).
Maturity: 18–24 months.
Breeding: Clutches of 8–20 eggs laid on land.
Life span: Not known.
Status: Common.

The banded sea krait is a tropical marine snake, well adapted to life underwater and on land. It is a venomous but docile snake with distinctive black and yellow bands along its body and a creamy underbelly. It spends much of the time in water, but returns to the land to breed and shed its skin. On land, well-developed stomach scales known as scutes give the snake considerable terrestrial agility and tree-climbing ability, but once egg-laying is over, it returns to the sea.

Sea kraits stay mainly in shallow, tropical waters around South-east Asia and Australia, where they eat eels and small fish. They have flattened paddle-shaped tails for swimming, nostril flaps to keep out the water and specialized glands under their tongues for excreting salt from sea water. Average males, at 0.7cm (2.5ft) long, are dwarfed by females, which can easily reach 1.25m (4ft). As a result, females often venture into deeper waters in search of larger eels, avoiding competition for food.

Silver and black stripes cover the entire body of the banded sea krait, from the neck area to the tip of the tail.

Taipan

Oxyuranus scutellatus

The taipan of Australia is one of the most venomous snakes in the world, with a bite that can kill a mouse in three seconds and an adult human in 30 minutes. It is highly aggressive and employs a snap-and-release attack strategy, whereby a thrust and sudden bite is followed by withdrawal to avoid being crushed by the possible death throes of the victim.

Taipans thrive on the northern coasts of Australia, possibly because they only eat mammals. When the highly toxic cane toad was introduced to the area, it caused the numbers of frog-eating snakes to decline, leaving plenty of prey and vacant habitat for the taipan. Its lethal bite and athletic lunging have earned it the nickname the "poison pogo-stick".

The female taipan becomes sexually mature at a smaller size than the male, and will often lay two clutches of 10–20 eggs during the breeding season. The hatchlings are around 45cm (18in) long. They are usually a light olive colour, with creamy underbellies and reddish eyes.

Distribution: North Australian coast.
Habitat: Open grassland and woodland.
Food: Small mammals.
Size: 1.5m (5ft).
Maturity: 6–12 months.
Breeding: Females lay 1 or 2 clutches of 10–20 eggs per year.
Life span: Not known.
Status: Common.

Taipans are very variable in colour, ranging from sandy and light russet through to jet black.

Malayan pit viper

Calloselasma rhodostoma

The Malayan pit viper probably bites more humans each year than any other species of snake in Asia, and there is a good reason why this is so. It is a nocturnal hunter and spends the day curled up in leaf litter on the forest floor, well camouflaged by its red-brown triangular markings. Unfortunately this behavioural trait means that the snake will not move out of the way or give any kind of warning if a human is walking towards it; it will bite.

Like all vipers, the Malayan pit viper has long, hinged fangs, which lie pointing backwards when the snake has its mouth closed, and snap forward into position when the snake opens its mouth and rears up to strike. It has heat-sensing pits located between its eyes and nostrils, which are so sensitive they can detect the warmth given off by the bodies of their prey. This allows the snake to hunt in darkness.

A well-camouflaged and deadly beauty, the Malayan pit viper is one of Asia's most dangerous snakes.

Distribution: South-east Asia.
Habitat: Rubber plantations and rainforests.
Food: Small mammals.
Size: 0.7–1m (2.3–3.3ft).
Maturity: 1 year.
Breeding: 2 clutches of 13–25 eggs laid per year.
Life span: Not known.
Status: Common.

Red-tailed pipe snake (*Cylindrophis rufus*): 0.7–1m (2.3–3.3ft)
This harmless pipe snake is usually found underground but sometimes takes to water, actively hunting small eels and other snakes. When attacked, it raises its tail, showing the red underside, thus mimicking a cobra raising its head. Not only does this make the snake appear more dangerous than it actually is, but it also confuses predators as to which end is the head and which is the tail.

Sunbeam snake (*Xenopeltis unicolor*): 1–1.3m (3.3–4.3ft)
Under dull light this snake appears dark brown to black, but under sunlight it displays an iridescence of red, blue, green and yellow. The highly polished, glimmering scales give the sunbeam snake its name. It spends most of its time underground, coming out at night to feed on frogs, lizards and small mammals. It is found throughout southern China and South-east Asia.

Pacific ground boa (*Candoia carinata*): 0.7–1m (2.3–3.3ft)
Highly variable in colour and patterning, the Pacific ground boa – from Papua New Guinea and the Solomon Islands – can be striped, blotched or banded. However, most individuals have a flowery, blotched pattern and range in colour from yellow, grey and beige to black or even orange and red. The ground boas living in the Solomon Islands never leave the ground, while those found in New Guinea will climb trees and bushes quite readily in search of the small animals upon which they feed.

King cobra

Ophiophagus hannah

The king cobra is one of the largest snakes in the world, sometimes reaching 5.5m (18ft). It can rear up as tall as a human. It has flaps of loose skin around the head that can be flattened out to form a narrow hood. The king cobra is not strictly a true cobra and, as such, has an unmarked hood.

Depending on its habitat, the king cobra may vary its colour, and it is often darker when in forest than when in open savannah. It has good eyesight and will chase down fleeing prey over long distances. Unusually, king cobras eat only reptiles – mostly other snakes.

The intelligent king cobra is the only snake known to build a nest, which is fiercely guarded by the female. Once hatched, the young are just as deadly as the adults, ready to hunt from only ten days old. The smaller young are vulnerable to mongooses and giant centipedes, but the only threat to the adults tends to come from humans, who kill them for use in medicinal drugs.

The open hood of a king cobra is a sure sign of trouble. Being able to lift its head over 1.5m (5ft) from the ground, the snake is a fearsome predator. Its scientific name means "eater of snakes".

Distribution: Northern India to Hong Kong and Indonesia.
Habitat: Tropical rainforest and savannah.
Food: Reptiles, especially snakes.
Size: 4–5.5m (13–18ft).
Maturity: 5 years.
Breeding: 20–40 eggs laid between January and April.
Life span: 20 years.
Status: Threatened.

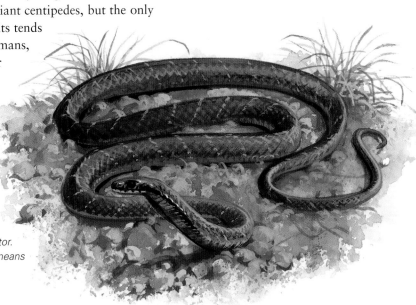

Green tree python

Morelia viridis

Distribution: Papua and Iran Jaya in New Guinea and the Cape York Peninsula of Australia.
Habitat: Tropical forest.
Food: Birds are the main prey item.
Size: 1.8–2.4m (6–8ft).
Maturity: Over 12 years.
Breeding: Females lay clutches of 6–30 eggs in hollow tree trunks.
Life span: Not known.
Status: Common.

Masters of disguise: green tree pythons are virtually impossible to spot among the foliage when they are coiled motionless in a tree.

This beautiful bright green snake spends almost its entire life in the treetops. Most functions – from eating and drinking to mating and egg laying – are performed off the ground. The green coloration gives good camouflage against the leaves, and the prehensile tail lets the snake cling firmly to branches. It will often wait, coiled around a branch and with its head hanging downwards, ready to pounce on passing birds. Vertical pupils make its eyes very sensitive to movement, and the scales around its mouth have heat-sensitive pits which pick up the body heat of animals to aid prey detection.

This species displays the body shape characteristic of pythons: a thick body with a small head, covered with many small scales. Eggs are usually laid in clutches of anywhere from 6–30, in holes in tree trunks. The green coloration of mature snakes is not present in the young, which tend to be bright yellow or occasionally red. They are hunted by birds of prey.

Reticulated python

Python reticulatus

The reticulated python is easily recognized by its unmarked head and sheer size. It is the longest snake in the world. It is a strict carnivore, and kills most effectively by waiting in trees to ambush unsuspecting victims. It tends not to hunt actively, preferring to conserve its energy. It will usually eat birds and small mammals, as well as deer and pigs. Like all reptiles, it has a low metabolic rate and can go for long periods without eating. A captive reticulated python once refused food for 23 months, and then resumed normal feeding.

The reticulated python has a striking net-like pattern of markings, made up of darker triangular shapes along its sides, and patterns of yellow or cream running down its back. The head is largely unmarked, apart from a thin black stripe running across the top.

Reticulated pythons are strong swimmers, although they prefer to spend most of their time on land, hiding in trees. They are nocturnal, and usually breed during the winter months. Large eggs are laid in hollow trees or burrows, then the female coils around them and shivers to keep the eggs warm. Once the baby snakes are hatched, however, they are left to fend for themselves.

Distribution: South-east Asia.
Habitat: Tropical rainforest.
Food: Mainly mammals.
Size: 6–10m (20–33ft); up to 200kg (440lb).
Maturity: 2–4 years.
Breeding: 25–80 eggs.
Life span: 30 years.
Status: Common.

The beauty of the world's longest snake is matched by its strength and power. The reticulated python gets its name from its distinctive skin markings.

Mangrove snake

Boiga dendrophila

Distribution: South-east Asia.
Habitat: Forest near coasts and rivers.
Food: Lizards, birds and frogs.
Size: 2–2.5m (6.5–8.5ft).
Maturity: 1–2 years.
Breeding: Clutches of 4–15 eggs.
Life span: Not known.
Status: Common.

The brightly coloured mangrove snake is easily recognized – it is mainly black, but with bright yellow bands along the length of its body. These bands do not form complete circles around the body, but are interrupted by a pronounced ridge running down the length of the back. It also has yellow lips and throat.

Mangrove snakes are nocturnal hunters, and usually take small vertebrates such as frogs and lizards. They are mildly venomous, and keep their fangs pointing towards the backs of their mouths. As their name suggests, mangrove snakes tend to live in or around mangrove swamps, choosing trees either in coastal waters or near rivers farther inland. They spend most of their time coiled in tree branches and are often fairly docile during the day. The females lay their eggs in piles of rotting leaf litter or old hollow tree stumps.

The bright yellow markings on its jet-black body make the mangrove snake one of the world's most striking reptiles.

Golden tree snake (*Chrysopelea ornata*): 1–1.2m (3.3–4ft)
Also known as the ornate flying snake, this dramatic snake can spread its ribs to form a concave wing shape, allowing it to glide over long distances. When threatened, it will leap from its perch and glide safely to the ground, leaving its hungry predator at the top of the tree. The golden tree snake has only a very mild poison, preferring to kill its mainly lizard prey by crushing it in its powerful jaws.

Tentacled snake (*Erpeton tentaculatum*): 0.7–1m (2.3–3.3ft)
This sluggish, nocturnal snake has two short soft tentacles on its snout. It lives in water and hunts by ambush – lying still and hidden by weeds and waiting for its prey to swim past. When fish or amphibians come within range, the tentacled snake rapidly strikes with a sideways motion, clinging tightly on to its prey before it has a chance to escape.

Blue coral snake (*Maticora bivirgata*): 1.2–1.4m (4–4.5ft)
The highly venomous nature of the blue coral snake is advertised by the bright orange markings on its head and tail. The rest of its body is black, with two beautiful light blue stripes running down each flank. Despite its venom, this species of snake is relatively docile and rarely bites humans, preferring to use its toxins to overpower the other species of snake upon which it feeds. Whilst being primarily nocturnal, it can occasionally be found lying stretched out on forest trails in the early morning, basking in the sunshine.

Red-tailed racer

Gonyosoma oxycephala

The red-tailed racer has a somewhat misleading name. It has a plain green body, fading into a tail which varies in colour from brown to orange or grey, but it is never truly red. It is an arboreal snake, active during the daylight hours. It spends most of its time foraging and hunting for birds, small mammals and bats, searching with its large eyes for any animal sizeable enough to form a good meal.

Its green coloration gives it excellent camouflage while moving through the tropical rainforests where it lives. It rarely comes down from the trees, and even mating takes place in the branches. Despite its relatively small size, the racer is an aggressive snake, always ready to defend itself. When it is threatened by birds or larger mammals, it will inflate its throat to look bigger, and lift itself into an S-shaped attacking posture, ready to strike.

Distribution: South-east Asia.
Habitat: Tropical forest.
Food: Birds and rodents.
Size: 1.6–2.4m (5.3–8ft).
Maturity: Not known.
Breeding: Clutch of 40 eggs.
Life span: Not known.
Status: Common.

Despite its name, none of the red-tailed racer's long, thin body is actually red.

CATS

Different species of cat can be found in many different habitats across the globe. The big cats are distinguished from the small cats by several visible characteristics, although size is not necessarily one of them. Also, the small cats cannot roar. However, cats around the world share the same lithe, sinuous grace and agility, combined with killer instincts and razor-sharp claws.

Tiger

Panthera tigris

The largest and most powerful of the cat family, the tiger's orange and black striped coat helps it to blend into dense undergrowth.

Tigers lack the speed of other cats, but their large and strong hind legs allow them to make leaps of up to 10m (33ft) in length. They have retractable claws, which means that they stay sharp, not getting worn down in day-to-day life. Their foreshortened jaws give them immense crushing power in their bites.

Predominantly solitary, tiger groups usually consist of mothers and their young, which stay with them for two years. Clearly marked home ranges keep accidental meetings and disputes to a minimum, but high levels of social tolerance have been observed, often at kill sites.

Tigers are now critically endangered due to poaching, logging and deforestation.

Distribution: India, Myanmar, Thailand, China and Indonesia.
Habitat: Tropical rainforest, coniferous forest and mangrove swamps.
Food: Hoofed mammals, including pigs, deer and cattle.
Size: 1.9–3.3m (6.25–11ft); 65–300kg (143–660lb).
Maturity: 3–4 years.
Breeding: 3–4 cubs.
Life span: 15 years.
Status: Critically endangered.

Leopard

Panthera pardus

Distribution: Sub-Saharan Africa and southern Asia.
Habitat: Forest, mountains and grassland.
Food: Antelope, deer and rabbits.
Size: 1–1.9m (3.25–6.25ft); 20–90kg (44–200lb).
Maturity: 33 months.
Breeding: 2–4 cubs.
Life span: 10–15 years.
Status: Common.

The leopard is widespread across most of Africa and southern Asia, ranging from open grassland to tropical rainforest and mountain highlands. It is an opportunistic feeder, choosing mainly large hoofed mammals, such as deer and antelope, but will take birds, rabbits and even dung beetles if prey is scarce.

Leopards are well adapted for climbing trees and have been seen hiding the corpses of prey high in the branches to eat later. They hunt mostly during the day to avoid competition with nocturnal lions and hyenas.

Leopards vary greatly in colour depending on their habitat. On the savannah they are usually a sandy ochre, while the high mountain leopards are very dark gold. They tend to have short legs on long bodies, and their fur is covered in black spots or rosettes. Completely black leopards – black panthers – are usually found only in forests, but they do not represent a different subspecies, merely an infrequent mutation.

Solitary and nocturnal, the beautiful form of the leopard is rarely seen, even though it often lives in close proximity to humans.

Clouded leopard

Neofelis nebulosa

The clouded leopard is not a close relation of the true leopard, and is believed to be an evolutionary link between the small cats and big cats. This shy and retiring creature has short legs, but a long tail and teeth. It has distinctive cloud-shaped markings on its pelt, which tends to be pale yellow to grey. It also has two large black bars on the back of its neck.

Not much study has been done on clouded leopards due to their shyness of humans. They have been observed running head-first down tree trunks and hanging underneath branches, and will often retire to the trees to digest their meals. They are carnivorous, eating mainly deer, cattle and monkeys. It is thought that most of their hunting is done on the ground.

Like most of the big cats, clouded leopards have no real predators, and their biggest threat comes from human activities. Loss of habitat and pressure of hunting for their beautiful pelts is driving them deeper into the forest. It takes around 25 animals to make a single fur coat. Their bones are also used in traditional medicine.

Distribution: South-east Asia.
Habitat: Deep tropical forest and jungle.
Food: Mainly deer, cattle and monkeys.
Size: 75–90cm (30–36in); 20–30kg (44–66lb).
Maturity: 9 months.
Breeding: 1–5 kittens born in summer.
Life span: 17 years.
Status: Vulnerable.

Elusive and agile, these handsome cats are little known and highly endangered.

Fishing cat (*Felis viverrinus*): 75–85cm (30–34in); 8–14kg (17–31lb)
The fishing cat lives mostly near the mangrove swamps, lakes and marshes of South-east Asia. Unlike a lot of cats, it actually likes water and is able to swim well, in addition to being able to scoop fish from the water with its paws. It is even capable of diving underwater and surfacing below unsuspecting waterfowl.

Flat-headed cat (*Felis planiceps*): 50–65cm (20–26in); 1.5–2kg (3.3–4.4lb)
The flat-headed cat of Indonesia has unusually small and flattened ears and partially webbed toes. It is a naturally good swimmer and hunts mainly for fish and other aquatic animals in mangrove swamps and lakes. In the wild, these cats are predominantly solitary, coming together only to breed. They have short, stumpy legs and, unlike the majority of cat species, cannot fully retract their claws.

Snow leopard (*Panthera uncia*): 1–1.3m (3.25–4.25ft); 25–75kg (55–165lb)
The snow leopard is found on upland steppe and forest in central Asia. It can take prey as large as a yak, but tends to feed on smaller creatures, such as sheep, goats, hares and birds. It is very secretive, hiding away in caves and crevices for much of the day. The snow leopard's luxuriantly thick coat keeps it warm and enables it to live at very high altitudes without suffering from the cold. However, this coat now carries a price: snow leopards are often hunted for their skins, which can be sold for very high prices in Asian countries.

Jungle cat

Felis chaus

Often found living around farms and other human settlements, the jungle cat is a fierce and robust little predator. It has a sandy grey to reddish coat with tabby stripes along its legs, a dark tail tip and black tufts on its large ears. It has good hearing and is very agile, often leaping almost 2m (6.5ft) into the air to catch birds as they fly past.

There is no distinct breeding season, so litters may be born throughout the year. Kittens are generally darker than the adults, with more pronounced stripes. Male jungle cats are often more protective of their young than females, and family groups are common.

This species, along with the African wildcat, was sacred to the ancient Egyptians, who trained them to catch birds – possibly the start of the domestication of cats.

While the jungle cat is common, it shows greater density in natural wetlands than near human habitations, and may be suffering from loss of habitat.

Distribution: Middle East, India and south-east China.
Habitat: Jungles and swamps.
Food: Small mammals, lizards and frogs.
Size: 50–75cm (20–30in); 4–16kg (9–35lb).
Maturity: 18 months.
Breeding: 3–5 young.
Life span: 15 years.
Status: Common.

Jungle cats were worshipped as guardians of the underworld by the ancient Egyptians. Their mummified remains have been found in tombs throughout ancient Egypt.

DOGS

Tough and adaptable, larger species of dog tend to be highly gregarious creatures, living in large and complex social groups called packs. Bonding behaviour in packs is common and important for the stability of relationships between animals of the group. These behaviours include licking, whining and tail-wagging – all traits still readily seen in domesticated dogs.

Asian red dog

Cuon alpinus

The Asian red dog's coat is cinnamon with white patches on the throat and face. The ears are lined with white fur.

The Asian red dog, or dhole, ranges from the alpine forests of Russia to the rainforests as far south as Java, but never lives in open habitats. A highly social animal, it is often seen in packs of around ten animals, sometimes as many as 25. In these packs it hunts large deer and sheep up to ten times as big as itself, and has been seen killing tigers and bears. Larger victims are often partially devoured while still alive. An adult Asian red dog can eat 4kg (8.8lb) of meat in one hour. The animal has a powerful square jaw, enabling it to disembowel its prey easily.

Whether hunting or resting, the Asian red dog leads a well-organized life. The existence of strict hierarchies in packs means that fighting is rare. Females are very sociable and will share their dens with other mothers while giving birth. The males of a pack will help out by hunting and regurgitating food for hungry pups and mothers to eat.

Distribution: Throughout Asia, from India to China.
Habitat: Tropical rainforest and forest steppes.
Food: Small to sizeable mammals, including deer and sheep, occasionally berries and reptiles.
Size: 90cm (36in); 17–21kg (37–46lb).
Maturity: Not known.
Breeding: 8 pups.
Life span: 12 years.
Status: Threatened.

Dingo

Canis dingo

Distribution: Mainland Australia, Burma, Philippines, Indonesia and New Guinea.
Habitat: Forests, woodlands and open arid grasslands.
Food: Rabbits, rodents and marsupials.
Size: 0.7–1.1m (2.25–3.5ft); 8.6–21.5kg (18–47lb).
Maturity: 1 year.
Breeding: 5–6 pups born from June–July.
Life span: 12 years.
Status: Common.

Thought to have arrived in Australia around 4,000 years ago, dingoes are believed to be the ancestors of various true dog breeds. They can be distinguished from dogs that have been descended from wolves by the shape of the skull and through genetic analysis. They usually have ginger coats with white markings.

In Australia, dingoes are widespread and classed as vermin in many states, due to their taste for livestock. When sheep are not available, they will hunt large marsupials, rabbits and lizards. In Asia they tend to exist on rice and other scavenged food, but will also catch small rodents. The Australian dingo is slightly larger than the Asian variety, and their main enemy in both cases are humans. In Australia, bounties are paid for skins and scalps, and in the Asian islands dingoes often make substantial meals for hungry people.

Dingoes were introduced into Australia so long ago that they have evolved into an entirely separate species from domesticated dogs.

Raccoon dog

Nyctereutes procyonoides

The raccoon dog originated in eastern Asia, across northern China and Japan, as well as Siberia and Manchuria. In 1927 it was introduced to eastern Europe for fur-farming and is now seen as far west as the French–German border and northern Finland.

Unusually for a member of the dog family, the raccoon dog is an agile climber, and even the cubs can regularly be seen playing amongst the branches of trees.

Adults form pair bonds and have distinct home ranges. However, these are relatively flexible and they will often roam into other raccoon dog territories. Males and females both help to care for offspring, taking it in turns to guard young while the others hunt for food. They eat whatever they can find, varying with the seasons. Their diet includes fish, amphibians, small mammals, birds, fruit and carrion. They are the only species of dog to "winter sleep". This behaviour resembles hibernation, but doesn't involve a lowering of body temperature.

The raccoon dog looks like a grey and black raccoon, with its characteristic black face mask and brindled greyish body fur.

Distribution: Siberia and north China. Introduced into eastern and central Europe.
Habitat: Damp lowland forest.
Food: Carrion, fruit, fish, frogs and birds. Scavenges food scraps from near human settlements.
Size: 50–60cm (20–24in); 4–10kg (8.8–22lb).
Maturity: 9–11 months.
Breeding: 4–9 young born from April–June.
Life span: 11 years.
Status: Widespread.

Golden jackal

Canis aureus

Distribution: Southern Europe, Middle East, northern Africa and southern Asia.
Habitat: Open savannah and grassland.
Food: Opportunistic feeders.
Size: 0.6–1.1m (2–3.5ft); 7–15kg (15–33lb).
Maturity: Females 11 months; males 2 years.
Breeding: 6–9 pups born after 63 days of gestation.
Life span: 6–8 years.
Status: Common.

Golden jackals can often be seen rummaging around landfill sites near human settlements, looking for tasty refuse.

The golden jackal is widespread, living across southern Europe, the Middle East and south Asia. It is the only jackal that ranges into North Africa, where it was held sacred to the Egyptian god Anubis in ancient times. It usually sports a golden-brown or yellow coat of short, coarse fur and a black-tipped tail.

Golden jackals mate for life and typically raise pups together for about eight years. They live in clearly defined scent-marked territories, often in small family groups. Some offspring remain as helpers, taking care of new-born pups and leaving their mothers free to gather food for their families.

These jackals are found mainly in open grassland terrain. Dominance fights are common, and golden jackals spend more time away from their groups than other social canids. The dominant cubs tend to be the ones that leave their groups, but in unfavourable conditions they will drive the weaker ones from their packs.

Jackals are opportunistic feeders, eating whatever carrion and small mammals they can find, as well as a lot of plant matter. However, golden jackals hunt more than other jackal species, and often come into competition with hyenas and lions, which will try to steal their prey. The jackals eat very quickly, without chewing their food, and will often bury their kills to hide them from other scavengers.

BEARS

Bears are the largest carnivores on land. However, many bears consume high proportions of vegetation in their diets – as much as 95 per cent in some species. Bears have small eyes and ears and large snouts. Their sense of smell is extremely well developed, and this serves them well while foraging and hunting. Bears tend to be exceedingly strong, and a single blow can break a human skull.

Sun bear

Helarctos malayanus

The world's smallest bear rarely stands taller than 1.5m (5ft) and has a short, glossy, black coat with an orange U-shaped marking on its chest. Very little is known about its behaviour and habitat in the wild or, indeed, about just how endangered it might be.

The sun bear is a stocky creature, with large, curved claws for climbing trees and an elongated tongue for eating insects which it finds in the canopy. It will also eat rodents, lizards, honey and the soft insides of palm trees. In more urban areas, it has been seen eating banana crops and refuse. In common with most bears, it is hunted for its medicinal value according to local beliefs, and a combination of hunting and habitat destruction has led to a serious decline in populations of sun bears, with possibly only a few thousand left in the wild.

Barely reaching 1.5m (5ft) in height, the sun bear is the smallest of the bear family.

Distribution: South-east Asia.
Habitat: Lowland tropical rainforest.
Food: Honey, insects and rainforest vegetation.
Size: 1.2–1.5m (4–5ft); 30–60kg (66–132lb).
Maturity: Not known.
Breeding: 2 cubs born after 3.5 months of gestation.
Life span: 25 years.
Status: Endangered.

Sloth bear

Melursus ursinus

The sloth bear is something of an anomaly. In terms of diet, this medium-size bear has more in common with anteaters than other bears. It was named for its ungainly appearance and long, curved claws, but in fact can run faster than a human and is very active and noisy at night. Its preferred food is termites, and to this end it has developed a gap in the front teeth through which it sucks up the insects. It can open and close its nostrils at will, and a hairless patch on the front of the snout protects it against the termites' defensive secretions. A sloth bear at work on a termite nest can be heard a long distance away through the forest. The bear usually lies alone at night. If surprised by humans in the undergrowth, it rears up on its hind legs and brandishes its heavy claws. Sloth bears have been known to injure humans, but they usually run away when disturbed.

The sloth bear is distinguished by its long, black, shaggy hair and its highly dextrous nose.

Distribution: India, Sri Lanka and Bangladesh.
Habitat: Low-altitude dry forest and grassland.
Food: Termites.
Size: 1.5–1.9m (5–6.25ft); 80–140kg (176–308lb).
Maturity: Not known.
Breeding: 2 cubs born each year.
Life span: 40 years.
Status: Vulnerable.

Giant panda

Ailuropoda melanoleuca

One of the most famous and easily recognized animals in the world, the giant panda is also one of the most endangered. Scarcely 1,000 individuals are believed to survive in the wild – in central and south-western China – with another 140 animals in zoos across the world. Habitat loss and poaching are the major dangers, and because the panda has a very slow reproductive cycle, it takes a long time for populations to recover. Females usually give birth to two cubs, one of which survives and stays with the mother for up to three years. In a lifetime, a female may raise only 5–8 cubs.

A panda's diet is almost exclusively bamboo, occasionally supplemented by other grasses and small rodents. Its digestive system is ill-equipped to digest the fibrous bamboo efficiently, so it has to spend most of its days foraging and eating. An elongated wrist bone with a fleshy pad of skin forms a functional but awkward thumb which is used to grasp the stems, and strong teeth then crush them into a more digestible pulp.

Pandas were once thought to be solitary creatures. However, new evidence suggests that small social groups may form outside the breeding season. These well-loved animals are the focus of much detailed research, always aimed at preserving the species. Recent research into in-vitro fertilization of pandas may help in the battle to prevent extinction.

Distribution: Mountain ranges in central China.
Habitat: High-elevation broadleaf forests with bamboo understorey.
Food: Bamboo.
Size: 1.2–1.8m (4–6ft); 110kg (242lb).
Maturity: 4–8 years.
Breeding: 1 cub born every 3–4 years.
Life span: 35 years.
Status: Critically endangered.

Black with white spectacle-like markings around its eyes, the giant panda is instantly recognizable to animal-lovers across the globe.

Asiatic black bear

Ursus thibetanus

The Asiatic black bear has the dubious accolade of being the bear most prized by poachers. Its organs are believed locally to be of particular medicinal potency. Formerly it roamed across most of Asia, from Afghanistan to Japan, but thanks to hunting pressure it is now restricted to small, isolated pockets of high-altitude woodland. It looks similar to the American bears, with black-brown hair and a cream-coloured V-shape across its chest. However, it has larger ears than most other bears.

In the wild, Asiatic black bears are omnivorous, eating small mammals and birds as well as invading bee nests and termite mounds. They are good tree-climbers, despite their short claws, and will spend most of their days aloft. In cooler regions they hibernate, sleeping from November until early April. Females lose nearly half of their body weight during hibernation, so they have to eat well beforehand. In warmer climes the bears often migrate to the lowlands to avoid a winter sleep.

The Asiatic black bear's whitish chest patch gives it the nickname "moon bear".

Distribution: Southern Asia, Russia, Korea and Japan.
Habitat: Deciduous tropical forest and brushland.
Food: Small mammals, insects, honey and fruit.
Size: 1.2–1.9m (4–6.25ft); 90–115kg (198–253lb).
Maturity: 4 years.
Breeding: 1–4 cubs born 6–8 months after mating.
Life span: 25 years.
Status: Endangered.

SMALL CARNIVORES

Small carnivores tend to have long, lithe, sinuous bodies, and are extremely efficient predators, often crucial in the control of rodent populations. Being very adaptable animals, they have been able to carve niches in a wide variety of habitats – from the otters of lakes and seas to the raccoons and martens, some of which now live alongside humans in cities.

Red panda

Ailurus fulgens

The beautiful and elusive red panda is known locally as the "fire fox" in its native country of Nepal.

The red panda is a smaller relative of the more familiar giant panda, although modern biologists are unsure exactly how closely related they are. The red panda is slightly bigger than a large housecat, with a very cat-like face, rusty coloured fur and a long, striped tail. It has partially retractable claws and very tough jaws for chewing the bamboo shoots that are an essential part of its diet. These shoots offer very little nutrition and, like other carnivores, the red panda's digestive system is very short, so it is unable to get the most out of its food. Because of this, the red panda has a low metabolic rate, and chews every mouthful thoroughly. In the wild, red pandas are usually solitary creatures, with clearly defined scent-marked territories. They roam through the forests on the slopes of the Himalayas, which are deciduous hardwoods and rhododendrons with a bamboo understorey. Unfortunately, this fragile ecology and their particular diet means that these beautiful creatures are no longer as widespread as they once were.

Distribution: Himalayas.
Habitat: Highland bamboo forests.
Food: Bamboo leaves, berries, mushrooms and occasionally eggs or young birds.
Size: 510–635mm (20–25in); 3–6kg (6.5–13lb).
Maturity: 18 months.
Breeding: 1–4 cubs per year.
Life span: 14 years.
Status: Lower risk.

Sable

Martes zibellina

Distribution: Siberia and northern Europe.
Habitat: Mountainous forests.
Food: Rodents, birds, fish, nuts and berries.
Size: 35–56cm (14–22in); 0.7–1.8kg (1.5–4lb).
Maturity: 16 months.
Breeding: Litter of 3–4 young born in summer.
Life span: 15 years.
Status: Lower risk.

This carnivore lives in mountainous wooded areas, usually near streams, and an individual may have several dens beneath rocks or large roots. The sable hunts by day or night, roaming across a territory that may be as large as 3,000ha (7,400 acres). Mostly it hunts rodents, but it will also eat small birds, fish, honey and berries.

Sables form individual territories, which are fiercely defended against intruders, but in the mating season the males are more forgiving to passing females. The young are born small and blind during the spring. They open their eyes after around 30 days and are independent by 16 months.

The sable has a luxurious silky coat, usually dark brown or black, and has been hunted for many years. During the 18th century, thousands of animals were trapped for their pelts, and the sable is now raised on farms for the fur industry.

An elegant relative of the pine marten, the sable was almost hunted to extinction for its sumptuous pelage (fur).

Short-clawed otter

Aonyx cinerea

The short-clawed otter is one of the smallest otters in the world and, as its name suggests, has very small claws. These claws are in fact tiny blunt spikes that barely protrude beyond the tips of its paws. Unusually, the feet are webbed only to the last knuckles – not to the ends of the toes, as in other otters. These adaptations mean that it has considerable manual dexterity and sensitivity of touch compared to other otters.

Short-clawed otters tend to catch food using their nimble paws rather than their teeth. They favour mostly crabs and molluscs, and have developed large, broad teeth for cracking the shells. Other food includes frogs and small aquatic mammals. They rarely eat fish, and so there is little competition for food when they live alongside other species of otter.

This Asian otter is highly social, and breeding pairs often stay together for life. Small social groups of up to 12 animals are common, and 12 distinct calls have been recorded. These otters also make rewarding pets, and some have even been trained to catch fish by Malay fishermen.

Distribution: South-east Asia, Indonesia and the Philippines.
Habitat: Freshwater wetlands and mangrove swamps.
Food: Crabs, molluscs and frogs.
Size: 450–610mm (18–24in); 1–5kg (2.2–11lb).
Maturity: 2 years.
Breeding: 1–6 young born yearly.
Life span: 20 years.
    Status: Threatened.

The short-clawed otter's finger-like front toes make this the most dextrous of the otters. Its front paws are more hand-like than any other otter, allowing it to feel for food in shallow water. It also has a strong tail, making it an excellent swimmer. The short-clawed otter has short dark brown fur with pale markings on its face and chest.

Burmese ferret badger (*Melogale personata*): 33–43cm (13–17in); 1–3kg (2.2–6.6lb)
This small, flexible badger has a long bushy tail and white or yellow markings on its cheeks and between its eyes. The ferret badger spends most of its days asleep in burrows, only stirring as night sets in, when it then forages. It eats insects, birds and small mammals and will often climb trees looking for insects, snails and fruit. The Lepcha and Bhotia peoples of northeast India keep Burmese ferret badgers in their homes to control cockroaches and other insect and rodent pests.

Palawan stink badger (*Mydaus marchei*): 32–46cm (12–18in); 3kg (6.6lb)
Found only on the islands of Palawan and Busuanga in the Philippines, the Palawan stink badger lives up to its name, squirting a noxious fluid from its anal glands when it feels threatened. Active by both day and night, it is a slow-moving creature with a stocky body and a long, flexible snout for sniffing out small grubs and worms. Due to its restricted range and secretive habits, little is known about the ecology of this species.

Hog-badger

Artonyx collaris

The hog-badger, or "bear-pig", roams across much of South-east Asia, living mainly in forested areas. It gets its name from its pink, hairless snout and its pig-like feeding behaviour. Rooting in the ground, using its canines and incisor teeth as pick and shovel, it finds small invertebrates and roots, as well as taking fruits and any small mammals that might wander past. Some local peoples have reported it to be a keen fisherman, taking crabs from rivers and streams.

The cubs of this nocturnal animal are playful creatures, but in maturity there is little social interaction. The hog-badger sleeps in deep burrows or caverns under large rocks, and can dig fast enough to escape from some predators – usually leopards or tigers. With strong jaws and sharp claws, it is not an easy meal to catch. In common with other badgers, it also employs a pungent defence mechanism, secreting noxious fumes from its anal glands when in danger.

Distribution: South-east Asia.
Habitat: Jungle and wooded highlands.
Food: Omnivorous: worms, fruit, roots and tubers.
Size: 55–70cm (22–28in); up to 14kg (30lb).
Maturity: 8 months.
Breeding: 2–4 young born in early spring.
Life span: 13 years in captivity.
    Status: Lower risk.

The hog-badger is much like the Eurasian badger in colour and appearance, but with much longer foreclaws and tail. These animals scavenge when food is scarce.

Palm civet (*Paradoxurus hermaphroditus*): 54cm (21in); 3.5kg (7.7lb)
Also known as the toddy cat, this carnivore is found throughout most of Southeast Asia, from Timor to India. The palm civet has distinctive markings, with black stripes down its back and small spots on its face. Civets divide their time between the ground and branches, where they feed on fruits, nuts and bulbs. They pick their fruit carefully, leaving less ripe fruit for eating at a later date.

Indian grey mongoose (*Herpestes edwardsi*): 43cm (17in); 1.5kg (3.3lb)
This mongoose ranges from Arabia to Sri Lanka, living in areas of bush and tall grass. It has a grey-brown coat speckled with flecks of black. The Indian grey mongoose is solitary by nature. A diurnal (day-active) species, it forages on grassland and in open woodland. Its diet is varied, including insects, eggs and small snakes, and it also eats some fruit.

Spotted linsang

Prionodon pardicolor

There are two species of linsang living in Asia, and they are the smallest of the viverrids, the family that includes the cat-like civets and genets. Unlike many other viverrids, they do not produce pungent scents used in defense.

Surprisingly little is known about these carnivores because they are very difficult to observe, especially in their natural forest habitats. They are nocturnal and spend a lot of time in the trees, where they move with sinuous agility through the branches, using their retractable claws to grip on to bark and their long tails for balance. They also forage for food on the ground. During the day, they shelter in nests constructed from sticks and leaves – either in tree hollows or in burrows. Nothing is known about their social behaviour; they are probably territorial like most other small carnivores.

Distribution: Eastern Nepal, southern China and northern Indochina.
Habitat: Forests.
Food: Small mammals, reptiles, birds' eggs and insects.
Size: 30–41cm (12–16in); 598–798g (1.3–1.75lb).
Maturity: 2–3 years.
Breeding: Up to 2 litters of 2–3 young per year.
Life span: 10 years.
Status: Endangered.

Spotted linsangs are sleek, with thick, velvety fur. Their black spots are arranged in rows along their flanks over an orange-buff or pale brown background. Their long tails have dark rings.

Binturong

Arctictis binturong

The binturong is the largest member of the civet family in Asia. Binturongs are nocturnal animals, and spend most of their time up in the trees. Although they are good climbers, they move slowly and carefully through the branches, and have never been observed to make leaps. They are the only carnivores, along with the kinkajou of South America, to have prehensile tails, which they use when climbing.

Binturongs are also capable swimmers, and sometimes dive and hunt for fish. They are easy to domesticate and make affectionate pets. However, surprisingly little is known about these animals in the wild. They can be active both night and day, and although they are usually solitary, one or two adults are sometimes seen together with young. Captive animals make a wide variety of calls. Like so many species, binturongs are declining because of habitat destruction.

The binturong has very long, black, coarse fur, often tipped with grey or buff colours. It has conspicuous tufts of long, straight fur on the backs of its ears, which project well beyond the tips.

Distribution: Sikkim, Indochina, Malaysia, Sumatra, Java and Borneo.
Habitat: Thick forests.
Food: Fish, birds, carrion, fruit, leaves and shoots.
Size: 61–96 cm (24–38in); 9–14 kg (19–30lb).
Maturity: 2.5 years.
Breeding: 2 litters of 1–6 young per year.
Life span: 25 years.
Status: Vulnerable.

RODENTS

The rodents are the largest group of mammals in the world, with over 2,000 species living in a variety of habitats. With the unintentional help of humans, many rodents have greatly expanded their ranges. All rodents have very distinctive incisor teeth, which are used for gnawing. These teeth keep growing throughout the animals' lifetimes to make up for wear and tear from cutting hard materials.

Australian water rat

Hydromys chrysogaster

The Australian water rat, also known as the beaver rat, is one of the few Australian mammals adapted to living in water. It can be found in freshwater rivers, brackish estuaries and saltwater coastal habitats. These rodents are excellent swimmers and hunt for their prey underwater, usually moving along the bottom in search of fish and large aquatic insect larvae. Australian water rats will tackle relatively large prey, including fish up to 30cm (12in) long. They usually carry their prey to feeding sites on logs or rocks.

Unlike many other Australian rodents, the water rat is not strictly nocturnal, and often hunts during the day, though it is most active in the evenings at sunset. This species is very common, and populations may have increased as a result of irrigation projects that have created more suitable watery habitats. However, four closely related species of water rat, which live only in New Guinea or on surrounding islands, are classified as vulnerable.

The Australian water rat has partially webbed hind feet used for paddling, and thick, sleek, seal-like fur.

Distribution: Australia, New Guinea and many surrounding islands.
Habitat: Rivers, streams, swamps and estuaries.
Food: Fish, amphibians and aquatic invertebrates.
Size: 12–35cm (5–14in); 0.3–1.3kg (0.6–2.8lb).
Maturity: 4 months.
Breeding: 1–7 young per litter; 2–3 litters per year.
Life span: 6 years.
Status: Common.

Golden hamster

Mesocricetus auratus

A number of species of small rodent are commonly referred to as hamsters, all of which belong to the same subfamily, the *Cricetinae*. Although wild populations of golden hamsters live in only a small area of Syria, people have introduced them into many other parts of the world. Golden hamsters are easy to keep, and have become very popular pets.

In the wild, this species lives in burrows in dry, rocky habitats. Burrows can be quite large and often comprise a number of chambers and entrances. Hamsters live alone in their burrows and are usually very aggressive towards one another. Indeed, captive hamsters must be kept apart in order to prevent them from killing one another.

Golden hamsters have huge cheek pouches for carrying food back to their burrows. If their young are threatened, female hamsters have been known to place as many as 12 baby hamsters in their cheek pouches. Although golden hamsters are common household pets and the third most common laboratory animal after rats and mice, the wild population inhabits such a small area that the species is listed as endangered.

Wild specimens have rich golden-brown fur on the upper side, but selective breeding in captive populations has produced a wide range of colours and fur types.

Distribution: Wild population restricted to Syria in the region of Aleppo.
Habitat: Semi-desert, rocky hills and scrubland.
Food: Wide variety of plant material, including leaves, seeds and fruit. Also known to eat meat.
Size: 15–20cm (6–8in); 97–200g (0.2–0.4lb).
Maturity: 2 months.
Breeding: 2–5 litters of 2–16 young produced annually.
Life span: 3 years.
Status: Endangered.

Flying squirrel

Petaurista elegans

Distribution: Nepal, Burma, South-east Asia, southern China, Sumatra, Java, Borneo and some surrounding islands.
Habitat: Mountain and hill forests.
Food: Fruit, nuts, leaves, shoots and maybe also insects and their larvae.
Size: 30.5–58.5cm (12–23in); 1–2.5kg (2.2–11lb).
Maturity: 1 year.
Breeding: 1 young.
Life span: 15 years.
Status: Common.

This animal, also known as the spotted giant flying squirrel, is one of the largest of over 40 species of flying squirrel found in the world. There are ten species of giant flying squirrel, all of which live in high-altitude forests in eastern Asia, at elevations usually exceeding 900m (3,000ft). In the Himalayas, the spotted giant flying squirrel lives as high up as 4,000m (13,000ft).

During the day, these animals hide in hollow tree trunks or in the thick foliage of high branches. At dusk, they start moving about in search of food. Usually, they move through the treetops in the same way as common tree squirrels, jumping from branch to branch. However, when they come to gaps in the trees too wide to cross by jumping, they leap from high branches and glide across the gaps on the broad webs of skin stretched between their limbs and tail. They have been known to make leaps as long as 450m (1,500ft). Although these animals don't actually fly, they are quite skilful in the air, making several banking turns in one leap and even riding rising air currents.

Giant flying squirrels have very long bushy "bottlebrush" tails, which are not flattened like those of some other species of flying squirrel. The tail acts as a rudder, both when the squirrel is leaping and when gliding through the air.

Giant squirrel

Ratufa indica

Distribution: Peninsular India.
Habitat: Forests.
Food: Fruit, nuts, bark, insects and birds' eggs.
Size: 25–46cm (10–18in); 1.5–3kg (3.3–6.6lb).
Maturity: 2 years.
Breeding: 1–5 young.
Life span: 20 years.
Status: Vulnerable.

The giant squirrel has dark brown fur on its upper side and buff-coloured underparts. It has particularly broad hands and long claws to help it grasp branches and climb.

This is the world's largest species of tree squirrel, with a head to tail length of up to 90cm (36in) and a weight of nearly 3kg (6.6lb). Giant squirrels spend most of their time in the treetops and are very agile, moving rapidly through the forest canopy. These squirrels are active during the day, and shelter in holes in trees at night.

During the breeding season, they construct large spherical nests from sticks and leaves, where the females give birth and care for their young. Giant squirrels live alone or in pairs, and are thought to have relatively small home ranges, centred on their nest sites. The squirrels make low "churring" calls when content, and loud chattering calls when alarmed. They are very wary and will dash into thick forest at the least indication of danger. As a result, they are very difficult to study, and relatively little is known about the species. They are now endangered due to the destruction of their habitats.

Beautiful squirrel
(*Callosciurius erythraeus*): 13–28cm (5–11in); 150–500g (0.3–1.1lb)
This is one of 15 species of so-called beautiful squirrels, found in the forests of India and eastern Asia. The squirrels are among the most brightly coloured of all mammal species, and often have a distinctive three-colour pattern. This species has an olive-coloured upper side and a rich red-brown underside.

Long-eared jerboa
(*Euchoreutes naso*): 7–9cm (2.8–3.6in); 30–50g (0.06–0.1lb)
This curious rodent from Mongolia and northern China has exceptionally large ears – longer than its head. Like other jerboas, it hops around on long back legs, like a miniature kangaroo, keeping its balance with the aid of a long, tufted tail. This little-known jerboa is now thought to have become endangered due to the loss of its habitat.

BATS

Bats are the second largest group of mammals – with 977 species – and the only mammals capable of true flight. Bats live in all temperate and tropical regions around the world and, because of their ability to fly, they have even colonized remote oceanic islands. Bat species are not evenly distributed around the world. For example, there are over 100 species of fruit bat living around Indonesia and New Guinea.

Flying fox

Pteropus edulis

Flying foxes are fruit bats with fox-like muzzles and ears, and large eyes.

This is one of 60 species of flying fox distributed over South-east Asia and Australia, as well as many islands of the western Pacific and Indian Ocean.

These bats spend their days roosting high up in tall trees, only emerging from the forest canopy at dusk, flying off in search of food. Fruit bats take off by dropping from their branches, so taller trees are preferred because they provide good launch sites. Sometimes fruit bats roost together in huge numbers. In the Philippines this species used to gather in groups of 100,000 before hunting and habitat loss drastically reduced its numbers.

Fruit bats are hunted for their meat, which is considered a delicacy in many countries. In some countries, fruit growers consider them pests. Isolated populations are vulnerable to local catastrophes such as tropical storms. In the last 50 years, two species have become extinct, and many more are seriously endangered.

Distribution: South-east Asia, Indonesia, the Philippines and the Nicobar and Andaman Islands.
Habitat: Lowland tropical forest and surrounding agricultural land with trees.
Food: Fruit, flowers, nectar and pollen.
Size: 1–1.8m (3.25–6ft); 0.6–1.6kg (1.3–3.5lb).
Maturity: 2 years.
Breeding: Single pup born annually.
Life span: 30 years in captivity.
Status: Common.

Schneider's leaf-nosed bat

Hipposideros speoris

There are 69 species of leaf-nosed bat which live in tropical and subtropical parts of Africa, Asia and Australia. These bats have strangely shaped noses which help them to focus their ultrasonic vocalizations – calls emitted from the nostrils and used in echolocation. These bats can locate flying insect prey and determine how fast they are moving, as well as detecting obstacles, such as branches, from the type of echoes returning from their calls.

Different echolocating bats make different types of call, depending on the kind of habitat in which they live. Schneider's leaf-nosed bats hunt insects in a particularly wide range of habitat types, including inside forests and the edges of more open areas. Although they can hunt and navigate in pitch darkness, these leaf-nosed bats often hunt around dusk and dawn when many species of swarming insects are most active. However, during these times they are more vulnerable to predators such as birds of prey. Although Schneider's leaf-nosed bats are fairly common throughout their range, 13 other species from the same genus are either declining in number or in danger of extinction.

The muzzles of these bats have strange leaf-like growths of skin, consisting of frontal horseshoe-shaped parts and leaf-like structures running across their centres. These structures focus the ultrasonic calls that help them catch insect prey.

Distribution: Southern India and Sri Lanka.
Habitat: Roost in hollow trees, caves and buildings.
Food: Insects taken in flight.
Size: 4–9cm (1.6–3.6in); 20–50g (0.04–0.11lb).
Maturity: 18–19 months.
Breeding: Single young born annually.
Life span: 12 years.
Status: Not known.

Short-tailed bat (*Mystacina tuberculata*): 60–68mm (2.4–2.7in); 12–15g (0.02–0.03lb)
This is one of two species of bat found in New Zealand – the only native mammals to live there. Like many forest bats, this species roosts in tree hollows but, unusually among bats, it is a ground forager and can move with great agility along the forest floor, where it preys on large invertebrates.

Bulmer's fruit bat (*Aproteles bulmerae*): 24cm (9.5in); 600g (1.3lb)
This rare fruit bat was first known from fossil remains in central Papua New Guinea, and living specimens were later discovered in the 1970s. Unlike most species of fruit bat, it roosts in caves rather than in trees. This species was thought to have gone extinct until some individuals were rediscovered in the early 1990s.

Pygmy fruit bat (*Aethalops alecto*): 65–73mm (2.5–2.9in); 19g (0.04lb)
This is the smallest of the fruit bats of Asia, and lives in high-altitude forests on the mountains of Malaysia and Indonesia. This nocturnal bat feeds on fruit and pollen, and during the day it roosts alone or in twos or threes. The species is threatened by the deforestation of its habitat.

Common blossom bat

Syconycteris australis

These small fruit bats are members of a group of similar bats, all of which have long, slender tongues with brush-like projections for picking up pollen and nectar from flowers. Although blossom bats usually roost alone, they may form "camps" like those of flying foxes, roosting together in groups at certain times of the year.

Some blossom bats stay in the same areas, apparently trying to defend their flowers from other bats, while others move freely between different foraging areas. Like many fruit bats, this species has large eyes, well adapted for seeing in low light.

At night, blossom bats congregate in areas with many flowers, and large numbers can be seen flying around some species of tree when they are in bloom. Perhaps surprisingly, relatively few blossom bats attempt to defend rich nectar sources because of the increased disturbance from the large number of bats attracted to such sites.

Distribution: North-eastern Australia, New Guinea and several island groups of Indonesia and the western Pacific.
Habitat: Wide range of forest types.
Food: Nectar, pollen and occasionally fruit.
Size: 5–7.5cm (2–3in); 11.5–25g (0.02–0.05lb).
Maturity: Not known; probably around 1 year.
Breeding: 1 young or very occasionally twins born.
Life span: Not known.
Status: Common.

Common blossom bats are one of the smallest fruit bats in the world. They have red-brown or grey-brown fur on top, and pale undersides. Like some species of fruit bat, they are important pollinators. There is concern that their numbers are declining in Australia.

Colugo

Cynocephalus variegatus

The colugo is also known as the flying lemur, but this name is somewhat misleading because these animals are not lemurs, and although they can glide almost horizontally for 100m (330ft) or more, they are not capable of true flight either.

Colugos have very well developed gliding membranes which, unlike those of other gliding mammals, stretch all the way to the tips of their fingers, toes and tails. As their wide eyes suggest, these animals are largely nocturnal, sleeping in holes or hollows high up in trees during the daytime. At dusk they leave their shelters, climbing up to find good take-off positions, and then glide away in search of food.

In the branches they hang upside down, moving hand over hand, with their tails tucked under their bodies. Little is known about the social behaviour of these animals, except that they usually live alone, but occasionally come together in small groups. A second species of colugo only lives on certain islands of the Philippines, and is now threatened by the loss of its habitat.

Colugos have dark fur with white spots on their upper side that makes them difficult to see against the bark of trees. The colugo's head is surprisingly similar to that of the flying fox.

Distribution: South-east Asia and the East Indies.
Habitat: Primary and secondary forest, coconut and rubber plantations.
Food: Young leaves and perhaps also fruit, flowers and buds.
Size: 32–42cm (12–17in); 1–1.75kg (2.2–3.8lb).
Maturity: Not certain, but probably around 3 years.
Breeding: 1 or 2 young are reared annually.
Life span: 15 years.
Status: Not known.

ELEPHANTS AND RELATIVES

The first ancestors of the elephants originated in Africa around 40 million years ago. From this prehistoric family, two different groups evolved: the mastodons and the modern elephant family. The relatives of the Asian elephant appeared in Africa, and then spread into Asia and Europe. Elephants have few relatives. They are thought to share ancestry with hyraxes and sea cows – dugongs and manatees.

Asian elephant

Elephas maximas

Asian elephants can be distinguished from their African cousins by their smaller ears, sloping backs and by having only one rather than two finger-like projections on the ends of their trunks.

The Asian elephant is one of the world's largest land animals, second only to its close relative, the African elephant. Asian elephants live in small groups of 15–40 individuals, consisting of related females and their young, led by old matriarchs – head females.

Asian elephants are intelligent animals, and they have been reported to be able to use tools. For example, they sometimes use sticks held in their trunk to scratch themselves or to swat insects. They have been domesticated for many thousands of years and have been used as draught and war animals up to modern times. However, the Asian elephant can be an agricultural pest, eating up to 150kg (330lb) of crops per day.

Distribution: Originally found in the Middle East, India, southern China, South-east Asia, Java, Sumatra, Borneo and Sri Lanka.
Habitat: Tropical forest, open woodland and grassland.
Food: Grass, leaves, roots, stems, fruit and other crops.
Size: 5.5–6.4m (18–21ft); 2,720–6,700kg (6,000–14,750lb).
Maturity: 9 years.
Breeding: 1 calf born every 2–8 years.
Life span: 80 years.
Status: Endangered.

Dugong

Dugong dugon

The dugong is a very distant relative of the elephant, and is placed in its own order – the *Sirenia* – along with the manatees. Dugongs live in shallow coastal regions where the sea grass on which they feed is abundant. They rarely make long-distance migrations, though in some places they make daily movements from feeding areas to resting sites in deeper water.

Dugongs have unusually shaped mouths, with overhanging upper lips that are specially designed for cropping sea grasses. They can dive for up to three minutes before coming up to breathe, and will swim at up to 20kph (12mph) if pursued.

The young are born underwater, after which they ride on their mothers' backs, breathing when the females come to the surface.

Sharks attack dugongs, but groups of dugongs will gang up on them and ram them with their heads. Orcas (killer whales) have also been known to attack dugongs, but by far their greatest enemy is human beings, who have hunted them extensively for their meat, hides and ivory.

Dugongs have thick, smooth hides, usually dull grey-brown in colour. Unlike the closely related manatees, which have rounded paddle-shaped tails, dugongs have fluked tails like those of whales and dolphins.

Distribution: Coasts of tropical East Africa, tropical Asia and Oceania.
Habitat: Shallow coastal waters.
Food: Sea grass and occasionally algae and crustaceans.
Size: 2.4–2.7m (8–9ft); 230–908kg (500–2,000lb).
Maturity: 9–15 years.
Breeding: 1 or 2 young born after about 1 year's gestation, every 3–7 years.
Life span: 70 years.
Status: Vulnerable.

HOOFED ANIMALS

Hoofed animals are separated into two main groups by the shape of their hooves. The Perissodactyla, *which includes the horses, zebras, tapirs and rhinos, have hooves with an odd number of toes, with most of the animal's weight supported on the middle toe. The* Artiodactyla, *in contrast, have an even number of toes, and include animals such as deer, cattle, antelope, pigs, camels, giraffes and hippopotamuses.*

Muntjac

Muntiacus reevesi

Only the males of these dainty deer carry antlers, and these rarely exceed 15cm (6in) in length. However, the male muntjac's main weapons are its long upper canine teeth, which curve outwards from its lips like tusks. The teeth are usually used in fights to settle territorial disputes with other males, but can also inflict savage injuries on dogs and other attacking animals.

Male muntjacs defend territories of around 20ha (50 acres) in size, usually close to water, and try to encompass as many of the smaller female territories as possible. When they are nervous, muntjacs make a call that sounds like a dog barking, giving muntjacs their other common name, "barking deer". These calls are probably aimed at predators that use ambush tactics to catch their prey. By calling, the muntjacs let the predators know that they have been spotted, and therefore are unlikely to succeed in their ambushes. Muntjacs were introduced into Britain in 1901, and feral populations have established themselves well.

As well as the protruding canine teeth that are also found in a few other species of deer, the lower portions of a male muntjac's antlers are covered in fur. Instead of antlers, females have small bony knobs with a coating of fur.

Distribution: Southern China and Taiwan. Introduced to Britain.
Habitat: Forest and farmland surrounded by vegetation.
Food: Grass, tender leaves and shoots.
Size: 0.6–1.4m (2–4.75ft); 14–33kg (30–73lb).
Maturity: Females 1 year; probably older for males.
Breeding: Single fawn born each year.
Life span: 15 years.
Status: Common.

Sambar

Cervus unicolor

This large Asian deer has particularly stout six–pointed antlers that can measure as much as 1m (3.25ft) along the outside curve. Sambars are very cunning and can live close to human habitation.

The sambar is one of ten closely related species of deer, all in the genus *Cervus*, which includes the European and American red deer and the oriental sika deer. Like red deer, male sambars fight during the mating season. Victorious males set up small territories marked with scent, and mate with any females that pass through. In some nature reserves in India, sambars are important prey animals for dholes (Asian red dogs), Asiatic lions and tigers. Although they are an important prey for some rare predators, sambars can also be troublesome to nature reserve managers because they sometimes kill large trees by stripping their bark, leading to considerable habitat destruction. In some countries where sambars have been introduced, such as New Zealand, they are hunted for sport.

Distribution: India to south-eastern China, Malay peninsula, Sri Lanka, Taiwan, Hainan, Sumatra, Borneo and surrounding islands. Introduced into Australia, New Zealand, California, Texas and Florida.
Habitat: Forests.
Food: Leaves, buds, berries, twigs, grass and fallen fruit.
Size: 1.6–2.5m (5.25–8.25ft); 109–260kg (240–570lb).
Maturity: Females 2 years; first mating older in males.
Breeding: Single fawn.
Life span: 25 years.
Status: Abundant.

Przewalski's horse

Equus przewalskii

Distribution: Altai Mountains of Mongolia.
Habitat: Grassy plains and deserts.
Food: Grass, leaves, twigs, buds and fruit.
Size: 2.2–2.8m (7.25–9.25ft); 200–300kg (440–660lb).
Maturity: Females 4 years; males 5 years.
Breeding: Single foal born every 3 years.
Life span: 38 years.
Status: Extinct in the wild.

Some scientists consider this horse as simply a subspecies of the domestic horse – *Equus caballus* – rather than a separate species. Most certainly, Przewalski's horse represents a unique animal, either as the last remaining truly wild variety of domestic horse, or as a unique species. In fact, Przewalski's horse, named after the Russian explorer who discovered it in 1879, has very similar habits to feral populations of domestic horses.

It lives in groups of around ten individuals, consisting of females with their young and a single dominant male or stallion. The stallion may lead his harem of females and young for many years, taking great care to protect them from rival males and other dangers such as predators.

These horses spend their days in dry areas, and in the evenings move to wetter areas with better grazing and drinking water. In some parts they make seasonal migrations to track the rainfall and the richest grazing sites. The horses have not been seen in the wild since 1968, and it is feared that they are now extinct in their former range. However, the species survives in zoos.

Przewalski's horses are slightly smaller than domestic horses, with light reddish-brown-coloured upper parts, pale flanks and white undersides. Plans have been made to reintroduce these horses to their former range.

Sika deer (*Cervus nippon*): 0.9–1.4m (3–4.75ft); 80kg (176lb)
This species of deer lives in eastern Asia, including most of China and Japan. Like red deer, male sika deer fight during the rutting season in order to control harems of up to 14 females. Sika deer are very vocal, and can produce at least ten different sounds, ranging from soft whistles to loud screams.

Giant muntjac (*Megamuntiacus vuquangensis*): 96cm (38in); 34–50kg (75–110lb)
This animal was unknown to science until 1994, when descriptions of a few individuals found in Vietnam were first published. Like other species of muntjac deer, the males have sharp elongated canines used in fighting. Giant muntjacs are hunted for their meat, and may also be suffering from habitat loss.

Four-horned antelope or **chousingha** (*Tetracerus quadricornis*): 0.8–1m (3–3.25ft); 17–21kg (15–46lb)
This small antelope lives in Nepal and India in open forests, usually close to water. The males are unique among the *Bovidae* – the family including antelope, cattle and goats – in that they have four horns. These horns are smooth and cone-shaped, and have made this species sought after by trophy hunters.

Babirusa

Babyrousa babyrussa

There are probably little more than 4,000 of these wild pigs roaming the Indonesian forests of Sulawesi and its surrounding islands.

Babirusas are most active during daylight hours. Males usually live alone, while females and young go about in groups of about a dozen. The tusks are not well designed for combat, and although males are aggressive when they meet, they rarely use their tusks in fighting. Females do not usually fight among themselves, but they sometimes attack by trying to bite the front legs of their opponents. Babirusas are fast runners and good swimmers. They sometimes swim out to sea to reach small islands.

Distribution: Sulawesi, Indonesia, and some nearby islands.
Habitat: Damp, tropical forests.
Food: Leaves and fallen fruit.
Size: 0.9–1.1m (3ft); up to 100kg (220lb).
Maturity: 1 year.
Breeding: 2 litters of 1 or 2 young produced annually.
Life span: 24 years.
Status: Vulnerable.

Unlike any other species of wild pig, whose tusks grow from the sides of the jaw, the upper tusks of the babirusa grow upwards through the muzzle. These pigs often visit salt licks, where scientists observe their behaviour.

Bactrian camel

Camelus bactrianus

Archaeological evidence has revealed that bactrian, or two-humped, camels were first domesticated around 2500 BC. It used to be believed that the one-humped, or dromedary, camel evolved from domesticated bactrian camels. However, 3,000-year-old rock drawings in the Arabian peninsula show horsemen hunting dromedaries, and 7,000-year-old dromedary remains suggest that one-humped camels had wild-living ancestors.

Bactrian camels and dromedaries can interbreed, and their young have either a long single hump with a slight indentation, or a large hump and a small hump. Camel humps contain fat deposits that provide the animal with energy when there is no available food.

Over the last hundred years there has been a great reduction in wild bactrian camel numbers. Although there are around a million domesticated animals, only 1,000 or so wild ones remain, and these are affected by hunting and herders who prevent them from reaching water holes. Camels have many adaptations to cold and heat, and can survive for long periods without water. They have very few sweat glands, so lose little liquid through their skins. They are able to drink brackish water, which would make other animals sick.

Distribution: Wild populations now only found in Mongolia and north-western China, but domestic animals found in many parts of central Asia and beyond.
Habitat: Dry steppes and semi-deserts.
Food: Unpalatable plants and carrion.
Size: 2.2–3.4m (7.25–11.25ft); 300–690kg (660–1,500lb).
Maturity: Reach maturity after more than 3 years.
Breeding: Single calf produced every 2 years. Occasionally twins are born.
Life span: Probably around 20 years in the wild.
Status: Endangered.

Wild bactrian camels are quite different in appearance from domestic ones, and have much lighter coats, shorter fur, leaner bodies and smaller humps.

Indian rhinoceros

Rhinoceros unicornis

This is the largest of three different species of rhinoceros living in Asia. Apart from mothers with their calves, these rhinos live alone, though occasionally several come together at muddy wallows or good grazing areas. They live in home ranges of 2–8sq km (0.75–3sq miles), which overlap with those of other rhinos. Meetings between neighbouring rhinos are often aggressive affairs. Although Indian rhinoceroses usually flee when disturbed, they sometimes charge at humans. Females with calves are particularly dangerous, and several fatal attacks are recorded every year in Nepal and India.

This species used to be common in north-western India and Pakistan until around 1600, when large areas of lush lowland grasslands were turned into farmland. As well as losing much of their prime habitat, rhinos came into conflict with farmers and sportsmen. By the early 1900s the species was close to extinction. International law now protects these rhinos, and their numbers have increased. There are now around 2,000 individuals in the wild.

Distribution: Originally found in northern Pakistan, Nepal, northern India, northern Bangladesh and Assam.
Habitat: Grasslands, swamps, forests and farmland.
Food: Grass, leaves, fruit, twigs and crops.
Size: 3.1–3.8m (10–12.5ft); 1,600–2,200kg (3,500–4,800lb).
Maturity: 7–10 years.
Breeding: Single calf born every 3–5 years.
Life span: 40 years.
Status: Endangered.

Both males and females have horns that can grow up to 53cm (21in). The skin is greatly folded, and is covered in rivet-like knobs that make it look like armour.

Yak

Bos grunniens

Yaks are closely related to cattle, and have been domesticated since around 1000 BC. There are nearly 13 million domestic yaks around the high plateaux of Central Asia, where they are used as draught animals and for milk, meat and wool production.

Yaks are well suited to cold, high-altitude conditions, being powerful but docile. There are probably only a few thousand wild yaks, ranging from eastern Kashmir along the Tibetan–Chinese border into the Qinghai province of China.

Yaks spend the short summers feeding in sparse alpine meadows, and in winter they descend into the valleys. Females usually live together in large herds that used to be thousands strong when wild yaks were more abundant. Males live alone or in small groups of less than 12 animals until the breeding season, when they join the herds to fight over females.

Distribution: Originally found in highlands of Siberia, Nepal, Tibet, western China and adjacent areas around the Himalayas.
Habitat: Highland and mountainous steppes.
Food: Grass, herbs and lichens.
Size: 3.3m (11ft); 400–1,000kg (880–2,200lb).
Maturity: 6–8 years.
Breeding: Single calf every 2 years.
Life span: 25 years.
Status: Endangered.

Yaks have stocky bodies and very long black-brown woolly fur that almost reaches to the ground, to help keep them warm. Wild yaks are larger and have stronger horns than domestic yaks.

Gaur (*Bos gaurus*): 2.5–3.3m (8–11ft); 650–1,000kg (1,400–2,200lb)
The gaur is closely related to domestic cattle, and is characterized by its short red-brown or black-brown fur, with white lower legs. This species lives from Nepal and India to South-east Asia, including the Malay peninsula, inhabiting forested hills. In some places the gaur is diurnal, in others it is nocturnal, depending on the level of persecution by humans.

Mountain anoa (*Bubalus quarlesi*): 1.6–1.7m (5–5.5ft); 150–300kg (330–660lb)
There are thought to be two species of anoa, both restricted to the island of Sulawesi. Mountain anoas live in dense forests and are very secretive. Usually anoas will flee when disturbed, but occasionally they have been known to charge. These animals have a very restricted range and have suffered from excessive hunting and habitat loss.

Axis deer or **chital** (*Axis axis*): 1–1.7m (3.25–5.5ft); 27–110kg (60–240lb)
Found in India, Nepal and Sri Lanka, these deer are characterized by their slender body shape. At certain times of the year they have white spots on their fawn-coloured fur. They live mostly in open habitats, presumably so that they can see approaching predators. Indeed, axis deer are the favourite prey of tigers in many parts of India.

Nilgai

Boselaphus tragocamelus

Nilgai used to be widespread across the Middle East but in recent years they have disappeared from Bangladesh, though they continue to survive in India, Pakistan and Nepal, and have been introduced into Texas.

During the mating season, males compete for territories, usually by aggressive displays or ritualized fighting, involving pushing each other with their necks. Occasionally, proper fighting occurs, and they drop to their knees, lunging at each other with their short stabbing horns. The winners have the opportunity to gather harems of up to ten females.

Distribution: Eastern Pakistan, India, and Nepal. Introduced into Texas.
Habitat: Forests, jungles and occasionally open grasslands.
Food: Grass, leaves, twigs, and will also eat fruit and sugar cane.
Size: 1.8–2.1m (6–7ft); up to 300kg (660lb).
Maturity: Females 2 years; males 5 years.
Breeding: Occasionally 3 calves born at a time; twins very frequent.
Life span: 10 years.
Status: Conservation-dependent.

Only the male nilgai have horns, but both sexes possess manes on their necks. The wiry coat is reddish-brown in males and a paler colour in females.

Serow (*Capricornis sumatraensis*): 1.4–1.8m (4.75–6ft); 50–140kg (110–308lb)
This is the most widespread of three species of serow living in large parts of China, the Himalayan region, South-east Asia and parts of Indonesia. The other two species are restricted to the islands of Taiwan and the Japanese archipelago. Serows are related to goats, and similarly live on rocky slopes. Both males and females possess sharp horns rarely more than 25cm (10in) long, which can inflict deadly injuries to hunting dogs.

Sao la (*Pseudoryx nghetinhensis*): 1.5–2m (5–6.5ft); 100kg (220lb)
Despite its large size and striking colours, the sao la, with its long, straight, smooth horns and striped facial pattern, was unknown to science until 1992. This animal was first identified from several sets of horns obtained from hunters in a nature reserve on the Laos-Vietnam border. Unfortunately, shortly after its discovery it was classified as endangered, and is threatened by poaching and habitat loss.

Tibetan antelope or **chiru** (*Pantholops hodgsoni*): 1.3–1.4m (4.25–4.5ft); 25–55kg (55–120lb)
This animal is actually more closely related to goats than to true antelopes, and lives on the high plateau of Tibet, Kashmir and north-central China. The males have slender, ridged horns up to 70cm (28in) long, rising straight upwards. They use these sabre-like horns when fighting for control of females during the rutting season, sometimes inflicting fatal injuries.

Himalayan tahr

Hemitragus jemlahicus

Himalayan tahrs are closely related to goats. There are two other species of tahr: the Arabian tahr, which is only found in Oman, and the Niligri tahr, which lives around the Niligri Hills in southern India.

Both male and female Himalayan tahrs have luxuriant manes over their necks and shoulders, presumably as a defence against the cold mountain air. Tahrs are very wary, and at the least alarm they will scamper off over rocks and through forest, moving easily over the steep terrain.

Tahrs live in herds usually consisting of around ten individuals. During the mating season, males lock horns and wrestle one another in order to win the right to mate with females.

Competition with domestic goats and hunting has begun to reduce all three species of tahr. Arabian and Niligri tahrs are now officially classified as endangered by the IUCN.

Distribution: The Himalayas, from Kashmir to western Bhutan. Introduced into New Zealand.
Habitat: Forested hills and mountains.
Food: Mostly grass.
Size: 0.9–1.4m (3–4.75ft); 50–100kg (110–220lb).
Maturity: Females around 1.5 years; probably older for males.
Breeding: 1 or 2 young at a time.
Life span: 21 years.
Status: Vulnerable.

Himalayan tahrs resemble goats, but unlike goats, males do not sport goatee beards and do not have twisted horns.

Saiga

Saiga tatarica

Saigas are related to goats and sheep, and around two million years ago, in the Pleistocene epoch, these animals were very abundant, ranging right across Europe and Asia from Britain to Alaska. Nowadays, saigas are not so common. They have been exterminated from some parts of their range, such as Crimea, by over-hunting and habitat loss.

Saigas are nomadic, constantly moving about in search of food. In autumn, many saiga populations migrate south to warmer climes and better feeding grounds, returning north in the following spring. Saigas move rapidly, covering 80–120km (50–75 miles) per day during their migrations.

Adult saigas can run at up to 80kph (50mph), and even two-day-old saiga kids can outrun humans. In winter, after the migration is over, males try to herd females into their territories, and successful males gather between 5–15 females. Competition is intense, and fights between saiga males are sometimes fatal.

The saiga has an unusually shaped nose with large, downward-pointing nostrils. The strange internal structure of this nose is only found in one other type of mammal – whales. It is thought to warm inhaled air in cold winters, and to help cool the saiga during hot summers.

Distribution: Western Ukraine to western Mongolia.
Habitat: Steppes and dry grassy plains.
Food: Grass, herbs and shrubs.
Size: 1–1.4m (3.25–4.75ft); 26–69kg (57–150lb).
Maturity: 12–20 months.
Breeding: 1–2 calves.
Life span: 10–12 years in the wild.
Status: Vulnerable.

Water buffalo

Bubalus bubalis

Distribution: Nepal, India, Sri Lanka, South-east Asia, Malay peninsula, Borneo, Java and Sumatra. Introduced into many other areas, including South America, Europe, Australia and Hawaii.
Habitat: Wet grasslands, swamps and lush river valleys.
Food: Green grass and water vegetation.
Size: 2.4–3m (8–10ft); 700–1,200kg (1,540–2,640lb).
Maturity: 18 months.
Breeding: Single calf every 2 years.
Life span: 25 years.
Status: Endangered in the wild; domestic population is common.

These large animals were domesticated as long ago as 5000 BC in southern China, 3000 BC in the Indus valley and 2000 BC in other parts of the Middle East. There are now estimated to be around 150 million domestic water buffalo around the world. So useful are these beasts that they have been introduced into many new areas, including Australia, South America, southern Europe and Hawaii.

Domestic water buffalo are very docile, produce excellent milk and meat, and are strong and easily managed work animals. In some areas, they form an important part of agricultural economies and ecosystems by providing a reliable and easily maintained source of power and by conserving wallowing sites that harbour a wide diversity of animal and plant life.

Wild water buffalo from original undomesticated stock are very rare, and very few populations remain. These wild buffalo live in herds of up to 30 individuals, consisting of females and their young, led by elder females. During the dry season males live in bachelor groups away from the females, and in the wet season the dominant males enter herds to mate. The female herd leaders remain in charge of their groups even when bulls are present, and after mating the males are driven away.

Wild water buffalo have the longest spread of horns of any cattle – up to 2m (6.5ft), measured along the outside edge.

Markhor

Capra falconeri

The markhor is one of seven species of wild goat, all of which live in mountainous regions of Europe and Asia. This species lives in certain mountain ranges of Central Asia. As a protection against the cold continental winters, markhors have thick white and grey coats and long shaggy manes covering their necks and shoulders. In summer, markhors lose their winter coats, which are replaced by shorter red-grey coats, and they move higher up the mountains to feed on the rich spring growth.

Females live in small herds, usually comprising about nine individuals, but occasionally up to 100. Males are solitary, only joining the female herds in the mating season. During this time, they fight one another for females, lunging at one another and locking horns.

Markhors are sought by trophy hunters and are also killed for their meat and hides. There are three subspecies, the rarest of which numbers only around 700 individuals. The political instability that has plagued some of the countries in the markhor's range has made it difficult to control illegal poaching.

Male markhors are characterized by their long corkscrew-shaped horns that can reach up to 1.6m (5.25ft) in length. Females also have horns, but they rarely grow longer than 25cm (10in).

Distribution: Mountainous areas of central Asian countries, including Turkmenistan, Uzbekistan, Tajikistan, Afghanistan, Pakistan and Kashmir.
Habitat: Mountainous areas close to the treeline, rocky areas, dry country and steep meadows.
Food: Grass, leaves and twigs.
Size: 1.4–1.8m (4.75–6ft); 32–110kg (70–240lb).
Maturity: 2.5 years.
Breeding: 1 or 2 young born at a time.
Life span: 12 years.
Status: Endangered.

TREE SHREWS

Tree shrews are not closely related to other shrews and are placed in an entirely different group, or order, called the Scandentia. *Tree shrews are an important group of mammals because it is from their ancestors that the primates evolved. Unlike other shrews, they have large eyes and good vision, and look more like squirrels with long snouts. There are now only 16 species, all living in forested areas of eastern Asia.*

Lesser tree shrew

Tupaia minor

Distribution: Malaysia, Sumatra and Borneo.
Habitat: Forests.
Food: Insects, small vertebrates, fruit, seeds and leaves.
Size: 14–23cm (5.5–9in); 100–300g (0.2–0.6lb).
Maturity: 3 months.
Breeding: 1–3 young.
Life span: 12 years.
Status: Not known.

This is the smallest of 11 species of tree shrew from the genus *Tupaia*, named after the Malay word for squirrel, *tupai*. These tree shrews do indeed resemble squirrels, with their long, bushy tails. Unlike most other species of small mammal, they are active throughout the day, though they also have short rests at regular intervals.

Their main predators are eagles, other birds of prey and snakes. Tree shrews are inquisitive, and are constantly searching in holes and crevices for food. Like squirrels, they hold their food in their front paws and eat while sitting on their haunches. Although they are called tree shrews and are capable climbers, they spend a lot of time on the ground or in the branches of bushes.

Tree shrews are highly territorial, with males defending an area of just over 1ha (2.5 acres), which covers the ranges of one or more females. They repel intruders of the same sex by chasing them and making loud squeals of aggression. Tree shrews also make other calls, which include chattering in response to disturbance, and clucking and whistling during courtship and mating.

Lesser tree shrews' fur colour ranges from a rusty-red colour through dark browns to grey. They have squirrel-like bushy tails and sharp claws for climbing trees.

Indian tree shrew

Anathana ellioti

Walter Elliot, an English civil servant based in Madras during the mid-19th century, was the first person to describe this species, hence its Latin name. However, very little has been learned about it since then, even though it seems to occur over much of southern India.

Unlike other species of tree shrew, this species is rarely found in close proximity to human dwellings. It has been seen in the dry deciduous forests on India's Deccan Plateau, and presumably has very similar habits to other tree shrews. It has also been found living in rocky upland habitats, without trees, at altitudes of 1,400m (4,600ft).

The Indian tree shrew spends a large part of the day searching for food and then returns to a hole among rocks before nightfall, where it shelters until dawn. These shrews appear to be solitary animals, almost always foraging alone and rarely, if ever, sharing shelters. However, occasionally small groups of three or four individuals have been observed playing together for short periods.

The Indian tree shrew, also sometimes called the Madras tree shrew, can be distinguished from other species of tree shrew living in India by its larger and more thickly haired ears.

Distribution: India, south of the Ganges River.
Habitat: Forests.
Food: Insects, earthworms and fruit.
Size: 17–20cm (7–8in); 160g (0.3lb).
Maturity: 3 months.
Breeding: 1–3 young born in related species.
Life span: Not known.
Status: Threatened.

PRIMITIVE PRIMATES

Although these primates have simpler social structures and smaller brains than the monkeys and apes, in other ways they are well adapted for their particular habitats. There are 57 species of primitive primate, the majority living in Madagascar, with some living in tropical Asia. They are all nocturnal tree-dwellers, and are characterized by their large, round eyes.

Tarsier

Tarsius bancanus

These little primates are nocturnal hunters, living in forests with thick ground-level vegetation. During the day, they sleep clinging to vertical branches, and slowly wake up as it gets dark. They move about through the branches like tree frogs, making leaps between branches. They have round pads on their fingertips and toes that help them grip on to surfaces.

As well as their round eyes and long naked tails, tarsiers have very powerful back legs with extremely long anklebones – or tarsals – which give them their name.

When hunting at night, they scan for prey with their huge eyes, which measure 16mm (0.6in) across. Thanks to special vertebrae, they can turn their heads almost 180 degrees in either direction. When they spot prey, which may be an insect, a small bat or even a poisonous snake, they jump, catch their prey in their hands and kill it with a bite to the back of its neck.

Usually tarsiers live alone, but sometimes adult males and females live together. Tarsiers make a whole range of calls that serve to attract mates and warn off competitors. Females carry their babies in their mouths, or sometimes the babies ride on their mother's back. Baby tarsiers become independent very quickly, and after only 26 days they are able to hunt by themselves.

Distribution: Southern Sumatra, Borneo and possibly Java.
Habitat: Forests, mangroves and scrub.
Food: Insects and small vertebrates.
Size: 9–16cm (3.6–6.4in); 80–165g (0.17–0.36lb).
Maturity: Not known.
Breeding: 1 young per year.
Life span: 13 years.
Status: Common but decreasing, partly due to habitat loss.

Slender loris

Loris tardigradus

The slender loris and its cousins the slow lorises are closely related to the bushbabies of Africa. Unlike the bushbabies, which have long fluffy tails, lorises lack tails. Like the tarsiers and other primitive primates, the slender loris is a tree-dwelling animal, mostly active at night. But unlike the tarsiers, the slender loris moves through the branches very slowly and deliberately, always supported by at least three of its limbs. The slender loris has opposable thumbs and big toes which it uses to grasp branches while climbing. When it spots prey, it cautiously stalks and, once it gets within range, grabs it with both hands.

Lorises usually live alone and, if forced to share space with others in captivity, they will fight one another. These animals make a variety of calls, including squeals and growls that indicate distress and disturbance, and whistles that are often heard when familiar males and females meet. The slender loris is threatened in India because its forest habitat is becoming increasingly fragmented, and because it is hunted for use in traditional medicines.

The slender loris differs from the slow loris in having a much more slender body and limbs. All lorises have thick woolly fur.

Distribution: Southern India and Sri Lanka.
Habitat: Mountain and lowland forests.
Food: Insects, young leaves, shoots, fruit, birds' eggs and small vertebrates.
Size: 18–26cm (7–10.5in); 85–348g (0.19–0.75lb).
Maturity: Females 10 months; males 18 months.
Breeding: 1–2 young born every 10 months.
Life span: 15 years or more in captivity.
Status: Vulnerable.

APES

There is only one species of great ape living outside of Africa – the orang-utan of Sumatra and Borneo. In contrast, all 11 species of lesser ape, or gibbon, live in tropical China, South-east Asia and the East Indies. Like the great apes, the gibbons are tailless and move in the treetops by swinging from branch to branch (brachiating), though with considerably more agility than their heavier, more terrestrial relatives.

Orang-utan

Pongo pygmaeus

Old adult male orang-utans can sometimes get very fat, and these have very round faces because of deposits of fat under their skin.

The orang-utan is unique among large primates because it is relatively solitary and lives in trees, whereas other large primates, such as humans, chimps, gorillas and baboons, live in social groups and spend most of their time on the ground. The name orang-utan means "forest people" in the Malay language.

Female orang-utans sometimes accompany each other while travelling and will eat together. Males, on the other hand, usually avoid one another. Orang-utans travel less than 1km (0.6 miles) per day through their home ranges, moving from branch to branch at a leisurely pace. These apes sleep in nests high in trees, made from leafy branches. Like the other great apes, orang-utans are intelligent animals, and have often been observed using tools. For example, they use large leaves as umbrellas to keep the rain off, and smaller leaves as pads to protect their hands and feet when moving through thorny vegetation.

Distribution: Sumatra and Borneo.
Habitat: Primary rainforests.
Food: Mostly fruit, but also other vegetable matter, insects, small vertebrates and birds' eggs.
Size: 1.25–1.5m (4–5ft); 30–90kg (66–200lb).
Maturity: 12–15 years.
Breeding: Single young born every 3–4 years.
Life span: 60 years.
Status: Vulnerable, due to habitat loss.

Siamang

Hylobates syndactylus

Distribution: Peninsular Malaysia and Sumatra.
Habitat: Rainforests up to 1,800m (6,000ft) altitude.
Food: Leaves, fruit, flowers, buds and insects.
Size: 75–90cm (30–36in); 8–13kg (17–29lb).
Maturity: 8–9 years.
Breeding: Single young born every 2–3 years.
Life span: 40 years.
Status: Threatened.

Siamangs are the largest of the lesser apes or gibbons. All species of gibbon live in trees, and are among the most agile animals in the world. The distance across the outstretched arms of a siamang can be up to 1.5m (5ft) – far greater than its standing height.

Gibbons use their long arms to swing, or brachiate, through the trees, and can move 3m (10ft) in a single swing. They do not tolerate other gibbons in their territories, and use loud calls which can be heard from several kilometres away to warn away intruders. Both male and female siamangs possess naked throat sacks that inflate with breath and resonate their calls. Sometimes male and female siamangs sing together in duets, the male making booms and loud screams and the female barking and booming.

To help grasp wide branches, gibbons have long thumbs, which attach at the wrist rather than the palm – like those of great apes and humans.

Lar gibbon

Hylobates lar

Lar gibbons live in small social groups consisting of an adult male and female, and up to four immature offspring. Like the siamangs, adult lar gibbons defend their territories from intruders by calling, often in duets with males and females alternating their calls. However, lar gibbons spend much more time calling than siamangs, making calls nearly every day.

Female lar gibbons are much less social than female siamangs and, although the males spend a lot of time showing apparent signs of affection such as embraces and grooming behaviour, the females rarely reciprocate. Males are probably more likely to lose their partners to competitors than siamangs, hence the greater amount of calling.

Lar gibbons sleep in the highest trees in the forest, usually those giants that emerge from the forest canopy. They almost never sleep in the same place from night to night, and this is thought to be a strategy to prevent predators, such as pythons and birds of prey, from learning their position.

All lar gibbons have white hands and feet, giving them their alternative name, the white-handed gibbon.

Distribution: Southern China, eastern and southern Burma, Thailand, Malaysian peninsula and northern Sumatra.
Habitat: Lowland tropical forest.
Food: Fruit, leaves and insects.
Size: 45–65cm (18–26in); 5–8kg (11–18lb).
Maturity: 8–9 years.
Breeding: 1 young born every 2–2.5 years.
Life span: 25 years.
Status: Endangered.

Kloss's gibbon (*Hylobates klossi*): 45–65cm (18–26in); 6kg (13lb)
This species is found only on a few islands in the Mentawai group, near western Sumatra. Due to its restricted range and low numbers, it is classified as vulnerable by the IUCN. Like other gibbons, this species defends territories in the forest, the males advertising their presence and strength to rivals by singing just before dawn.

Javan gibbon (*Hylobates moloch*): 45–65cm (18–26in); 4–9kg (9–20lb)
Javan gibbons are found only on Java, where they have lost over 95 per cent of their original forest habitat in recent decades. As a result, it is estimated that only 250 adults remain, making this the world's rarest gibbon.

White-browed gibbon (*Hylobates hoolock*): 45–65cm (18–26in); 4–9kg (9–20lb)
This gibbon has the most westerly distribution of all the gibbons, living as far west as Bangladesh. The white-browed gibbon is the only species of gibbon that can swim, while all other species avoid water. Although gibbons can walk upright, they almost never cross open ground on foot. This means that features such as rivers and open spaces will act as barriers to the spread of gibbon populations.

Crested gibbon

Hylobates concolor

This species used to be much more widespread than it is today; at one time it lived in much of southern China, and was found as far north as the Yellow River in eastern China. It has suffered considerably from the loss of its forest habitat to logging and agriculture. It has also been hunted for its meat, which is considered a delicacy by some Chinese people, and for its bones, which are prepared as a local medicine to treat rheumatism.

Wars in South-east Asia have helped throw this species into decline, so that it now numbers less than 2,500.

Like other gibbons, the crested variety moves around the treetops searching for fruit and tender leaves during the day. However, unlike any other species, crested gibbons sometimes live in polygamous groups, with one adult male sharing a territory with up to four adult females.

Distribution: South-eastern China, Hainan, north-western Laos and Vietnam.
Habitat: Tropical forest.
Food: Fruit, leaves and insects.
Size: 45–65cm (18–26in); 5–9kg (11–20lb).
Maturity: 8–9 years.
Breeding: Single young born every 2–3 years.
Life span: 25 years.
Status: Endangered.

Male crested gibbons are black, while females are golden or grey-brown in colour. Females are born almost white, and only attain their adult colour at between 2 and 4 years of age.

MONKEYS

Around half of the 96 species of Old World monkey live in south-central Asia, South-east Asia, Japan and Indonesia, where they are commonly known as langurs and macaques. Most Old World monkeys live in hot, tropical climates, but a few species, such as the Japanese macaque, can be found in very cold habitats at northerly latitudes.

Proboscis monkey

Nasalis larvatus

Scientists are not sure why proboscis monkeys, particularly older males, have evolved such strange noses, but they may be involved in attracting females or even used to radiate excess heat. Proboscis monkeys are very social and sometimes feed together in bands of up to 60 or more animals. Usually they live in smaller groups of 2–27 animals, consisting of a single dominant male, a harem of 1–9 females and their young.

Young females stay with the group, while young males move away to join bands of bachelor males. Proboscis monkeys rarely move more than 1–2km (0.6–1.2 miles) away from fresh water. They sleep close to rivers or in mangrove trees in coastal areas. These monkeys are among the best swimmers of all primates. They even have partially webbed feet, which help them to paddle or walk across soft mud.

Proboscis monkeys have peculiar protruding noses that become particularly long and bulbous in old males. The infants have blue faces.

Distribution: Borneo.
Habitat: Lowland rainforest and mangroves.
Food: Leaves, fruit, flowers and seeds.
Size: Females 53–61cm (21–24in), 7–11kg (15–24lb); males 66–76cm (26–30in), 16–22kg (35–48lb).
Maturity: Not known.
Breeding: Usually single young born at a time after a gestation of about 166 days.
Life span: 23 years.
Status: Vulnerable.

Crab-eating macaque

Macaca fascicularis

The crab-eating macaque is one of the most widespread of the 20 species of macaque, most of which live in parts of the Indian subcontinent, southern China, South-east Asia and Indonesia. Crab-eating macaques live in groups of around 30 individuals, which consist of adult males and females and their young. Crab-eating macaques live in ordered societies based on dominance hierarchies. Dominant individuals often force lower-ranking animals away from the best feeding and resting sites and give them few opportunities to mate. Indeed, low-ranking females take longer to reach sexual maturity than high-ranking females because they eat less food.

Although crab-eating macaques prefer mangroves and forests around rivers, they have adapted to a range of habitats and sometimes live among people in towns. These monkeys sometimes raid crops and orchards, and they can be aggressive to humans.

Crab-eating macaques have tails that are longer than their bodies, giving them their alternative name, the long-tailed macaque.

Distribution: Malaysia, Indonesia and the Philippines.
Habitat: Forests, coastal mangroves and urban areas.
Food: Leaves, fruit, flowers, crustaceans, molluscs, insects, birds' eggs and small vertebrates.
Size: 40–47cm (16–19in); 3–7kg (6.6–15lb).
Maturity: Females 4 years; males 6 years.
Breeding: 1 young born every 2 years.
Life span: 35 years.
Status: Near threatened.

Distribution: Tibet, Nepal, Sikkim, northern Pakistan, Kashmir, India, Bangladesh and Sri Lanka.
Habitat: Tropical and temperate forests, savannah, farmland, alpine scrub and desert edges.
Food: Leaves, fruit and flowers.
Size: 41–78cm (16–31in); 5.5–23.5kg (12–52lb).
Maturity: Females 3–4 years; males 6–7 years.
Breeding: 1 or 2 young born every 2 years.
Life span: 25 years.
Status: Near threatened.

Hanuman langur

Semnopithecus entellus

These monkeys live in a wide variety of habitats, from hot tropical forests to cold mountain habitats, up to 4,000m (13,000ft) above sea level. Although they are principally tree-living animals, langurs are happy to live on the ground in habitats with few trees.

In areas with lots of food, hanuman langurs live in groups that may include a number of adult males as well as females and young, but in areas with less food, such as certain mountain habitats, there is only one adult male per group.

Like the crab-eating macaque, both sexes show a dominance hierarchy, though it is less pronounced in female hanumans than in female macaques. Males sometimes form groups of up to 30 individuals. Occasionally all-male groups attack male–female groups, and if they succeed in overthrowing the alpha male or males, the newcomers kill all the infants in the group. This makes the females come into oestrus quicker, so the new leaders can start to father their own offspring.

Hanuman langurs have dark faces and prominent brow ridges. They usually have grey, brown or buff-coloured upper-parts, and orange-white or yellow-white heads and chests. Their tails are longer than their bodies.

Pig-tailed langur (*Simias concolor*): 45–52cm (18–20in); 6.5–8kg (14–18lb)
This rare monkey is only found on a few islands in the Mentawai group off the south-west coast of Sumatra, and gets its name from its short naked tail with a tuft of fur on the tip. It lives in thick forest in hilly country. It is not as social as many other langur species and usually lives in pairs with 1–3 young.

Douc langur (*Pygathrix nemaeus*): 56–76cm (22–30in); 10kg (22lb)
This brightly coloured monkey is found in Cambodia, Vietnam and Laos. Like most monkeys it is very social, living in groups of 4–15 individuals consisting of mostly females, but including one or more adult males. This is one of the most brightly coloured species of monkey, with some varieties sporting bright yellow faces surrounded by pure white whiskers, and rich red-chestnut coloured legs.

Banded leaf monkey (*Presbytis femoralis*): 42–61cm (16–24in); 5–8kg (11–18lb)
This is the most widespread of eight species of leaf monkey from the same genus. It is found throughout the Malay peninsula, parts of Sumatra and Borneo and surrounding islands. Despite its broad range, this monkey is becoming rare. These leaf monkeys are characterized by crests of hair on the top of their heads. Sometimes they are forced out of their feeding areas by the smaller but more aggressive crab-eating macaque.

Snub-nosed monkey

Rhinopithecus roxellana

This is one of the few species of primate living exclusively outside the tropics, inhabiting the cold mountain forests on south-eastern slopes of the Tibetan plateau in China.

These monkeys are mostly tree-living, but will come to the ground occasionally to search for wild onions and to eat grass. In summer, when food is relatively abundant, up to 600 snub-nosed monkeys may live together, but as winter falls and food becomes more scarce, these large gatherings split up into smaller groups of 60–70 animals.

Snub-nosed monkeys have many vocalizations, the most common being a loud "ga-ga" call made when food is found.

There are probably fewer than 15,000 left in the wild because they have been hunted for their beautiful fur and for other parts that are used in medicines.

Distribution: Mountainous areas of the Tibetan plateau in south-western China.
Habitat: Mountain broadleaf and conifer forests.
Food: Leaves, buds, bark, grass and lichens.
Size: 57–76cm (22–30in); 12–21kg (26–46lb).
Maturity: Females 4–5 years; males 7 years.
Breeding: 1 or occasionally 2 young.
Life span: Not known.
Status: Vulnerable.

Although these monkeys have dull, grey-black fur on the top of their head, shoulders, back and tail, other parts of the body are covered in a rich, golden fur, giving them their other name, the golden monkey.

MONOTREMES

Some scientists do not consider the monotremes to be true mammals, but intermediate forms between mammals and reptiles. Indeed, their anatomy, digestion, reproductive organs and excretory systems have many similarities to those of reptiles, for example they lay eggs. However, monotremes also show mammalian characteristics: they have fur, they nourish their young with milk and they are warm-blooded.

Short-nosed echidna

Tachyglossus aculeatus

The short-nosed echidna is one of two species of echidna. It is found throughout Australia and parts of New Guinea. The other rarer species, the long-nosed echidna, lives only in the highlands of New Guinea. The short-nosed species regularly feasts on ants or termites, thus earning its common nickname, the spiny anteater.

Short-nosed echidnas live alone, foraging during both the day and the night. They locate their food by smell, and it is also thought that they may be able to pick up electric signals from prey animals using sensors in the tip of their snout. They are powerful diggers, using their clawed front paws to dig out prey or create burrows for shelter. The short-nosed echidna lays a single egg with a leathery shell into a pouch on its abdomen, and the young hatches soon afterwards. The baby is incubated in the pouch for 10–11 days, and finally leaves the pouch after around 55 days. The mother will continue to suckle her young even after it has left the pouch.

Distribution: Widespread throughout Australia, including Tasmania.
Habitat: Most habitats, from semi-desert to highlands.
Food: Ants, termites and earthworms.
Size: 30–45cm (12–18in); 2.5–7kg (5.5–15.5lb).
Maturity: Not known.
Breeding: Single young at a time, incubated in a pouch on the mother's abdomen.
Life span: 50 years.
Status: Low risk.

The short-nosed echidna has a long, hairless snout. The protective spines are enlarged hairs. They cover its back and sides, and are much thicker than those of the long-nosed echidna.

Platypus

Ornithorhynchus anatinus

Platypuses live in burrows in stream banks, which they excavate with their powerful front legs. There are two kinds of burrow: one for shelter and one for incubation. The incubation burrows can be up to 18m (60ft) long and rise 1–7m (3–23ft) above the waterline. As part of the courtship ritual, females carry bundles of wet leaves to their incubation chamber, at the ends of the burrow. Females then plug the tunnel with soil and lay 1–3 eggs in the incubation chamber. The eggs hatch after ten days and the young stay in the burrow, where the mothers keep them warm and suckle them. They finally emerge after four months.

Males possess spurs on their hind feet that are attached to venom glands, which produce poison strong enough to kill dogs. These are thought to be used in fighting.

This is surely one of the strangest living mammals, with a snout resembling a duck's bill, a tail like a beaver's, and clawed, webbed feet. The bill is thought to contain an organ for detecting the electric pulses produced by prey.

Distribution: Eastern and south-eastern Australia and Tasmania.
Habitat: Freshwater streams and lakes.
Food: Freshwater crustaceans, insect larvae, snails, tadpoles and small fish.
Size: 30–45cm (12–18in); 0.5–2kg (1.1–4.4lb).
Maturity: 2–3 years.
Breeding: 1–3 eggs laid at a time.
Life span: 13 years in the wild; up to 21 years in captivity.
Status: Fairly abundant, though may be declining.

MARSUPIALS

The marsupials are a group of mammals with a peculiar reproductive method. The young are very small and underdeveloped when born, and after making their way to their mother's nipples, they grow and develop in safety inside a pouch. Nearly 75 per cent of all marsupial species are found in and around Australia and New Guinea, with the rest being found in the Americas.

Squirrel glider

Petaurus norfolcensis

This is one of five closely related species of gliding possums, including the sugar glider, that live in Australia and New Guinea. These animals resemble flying squirrels, they are mostly nocturnal and have large eyes to help them see in low light. They are arboreal, and during the day they sleep in nests made from leaves in the hollows of trees.

Squirrel gliders have membranes of skin that stretch from their wrists to their ankles, which form gliding surfaces (aerofoils) when their legs and arms are spread out. The closely related but smaller sugar gliders can glide for distances of up to 45m (150ft), and the larger fluffy glider of the same genus can glide up to 114m (375ft).

Squirrel gliders live in social groups, usually consisting of one adult male, several adult females and their young. These animals communicate with a variety of calls, including chatters, nasal grunts and repetitive short grunts, which seem to serve as alarm calls and warnings to squirrel gliders from other groups. During the breeding season, females develop pouches in which the young stay for around six months. After this time, the pouches wither away.

Squirrel gliders have beautiful long tails, grey fur on top and pale fur underneath. They have attractive dark stripes from their noses all the way to their rumps, and stripes across their eyes.

Distribution: Eastern and south-eastern Australia.
Habitat: Open forests.
Food: Nectar, pollen, sap, insects and other invertebrates and small vertebrates.
Size: 12–30cm (5–12in); 200–260g (0.4–0.6lb).
Maturity: Females end of first year; males beginning of second year.
Breeding: 1 young, or occasionally twins, annually.
Life span: 12 years.
Status: Threatened.

Long-clawed marsupial mouse

Neophascogale lorentzii

This is one of over 50 species of marsupial mice, all of which live in Australia and New Guinea. All are carnivorous, taking any prey small enough to be overpowered. Very little is known about this species, probably because it lives in the remote and inaccessible wet forest habitat of the interior of New Guinea, at elevations of up to 3,000m (10,000ft). However, the long-clawed marsupial mouse is quite similar in appearance and habits to the better-known species living in Australia, such as the brush-tailed marsupial mouse.

Like the Australian species, the long-clawed marsupial mouse is nocturnal and arboreal, though it is also sometimes active during the day. It is highly territorial, with females occupying huge territories – about double the size of male territories. Females are very aggressive with one another and can usually dominate males. Daughters sometimes inherit parts of their mothers' territories when they become independent, but sons are always driven away to seek their own territories.

The long-clawed marsupial mouse resembles a tree shrew, with its long, thin muzzle and large, bushy tail. As its name suggests, it has particularly long claws on all four feet.

Distribution: Western and central mountains of New Guinea.
Habitat: Upland wet moss forests.
Food: Insects and perhaps other small animals.
Size: 17–23cm (7–9in); 110–230g (0.25–0.5lb).
Maturity: 8 months.
Breeding: 8 young.
Life span: 1–2 years.
Status: Not known.

Koala

Phascolarctos cinereus

Distribution: South-eastern Australia.
Habitat: A range of habitats, from coastal islands and tall eucalyptus forests to low woodlands inland.
Food: Eucalyptus leaves.
Size: 60–85cm (24–34in); 4–15kg (8.8–33lb).
Maturity: Sexual maturity at 2 years in females and males, but first breeding probably not until 5 years old in males.
Breeding: 1 young, or occasionally twins, born annually.
Life span: 20 years.
Status: Near threatened.

Koalas are placed in their own family, which shows how different they are from other marsupials. These animals live practically their whole lives in stands of eucalyptus trees that form the core of their territories. Eucalyptus leaves are by far the most important food for koalas. The animals even smell of eucalyptus oil. A problem with eucalyptus leaves is that they are very fibrous and difficult to digest, so koalas have cheek pouches and long intestines, and occasionally eat soil or gravel. All these traits are adaptations to help them break down the tough eucalyptus leaves.

Koalas are very solitary animals and, although the territories of males and females overlap, males will not tolerate intruders of the same sex. Resident koalas usually attack intruders savagely. Males mark out their territories with strong-smelling scent, and make loud calls to warn off other males.

During the breeding season, males try to guard as many female territories as they can. The single young or joey stays in its mother's pouch for seven months, then rides on its mother's back until the next season's joey matures. Koalas used to be very common in south-eastern Australia, but a mixture of hunting for fur in the early 20th century, habitat loss and severe forest fires have reduced their numbers.

Koalas have dense grey fur, which is paler on their undersides. They have two opposable thumbs and three fingers on each of their hands, which helps them to grip strongly on to branches.

Common wombat

Vombatus ursinus

This is the most common of three species of wombat, all of which live in Australia. Wombats resemble small bears and have large heads, short, stocky bodies and short, powerful legs. The common wombat can be distinguished from the other two species by its hairless nose and rounded ears. Unlike bears, wombats are not predators, and tend to be shy and timid animals. In fact, they make good pets, being playful and affectionate.

In the wild, wombats dig out large burrows that may be up to 30m (100ft) long. Although there is only one entrance, a burrow may branch off into different chambers. The wombat makes a nest out of leaves or bark in one of the chambers.

Wombats are usually nocturnal, but sometimes they sunbathe in specially prepared spots, close to the entrances of their burrows. Common wombats live in large home ranges and, although they tend to be solitary, neighbouring territories overlap considerably. Although wombats are sometimes aggressive towards each other in captivity, some observations in the wild suggest that wombats sometimes make visits to one another's burrows.

Wombats resemble small, chubby bears, having compact bodies covered with a dense coat of grey-brown hair. Evidence from fossils suggests that there were once hippo-sized wombats.

Distribution: Originally found throughout south-eastern Australia and Tasmania.
Habitat: Hilly or mountainous coastal country, creeks and gullies.
Food: Grass, roots of shrubs and trees, and fungi.
Size: 0.7–1.2m (28–48in); 15–35kg (11–77lb).
Maturity: 2 years.
Breeding: 1 or occasionally 2 young born in late autumn after 20 days' gestation.
Life span: 25 years.
Status: Common.

Brush-tailed possum

Trichosurus vulpecula

Large numbers of Australasian marsupials are commonly referred to as possums, which belong to several families. These are not to be confused with opossums, which are marsupials from an entirely separate group, living in the Americas.

This possum is the most common of three possum species, all known as brush-tailed possums due to their long, furry prehensile tails. It is closely related to the cuscuses of Sulawesi, New Guinea and surrounding islands.

The brushed-tailed possum is nocturnal and arboreal. It is a very adaptable animal, and can live in semi-desert areas in the Australian interior by sheltering in eucalyptus trees and along rivers. It even lives in large numbers in most Australian cities, hiding under the roofs of houses.

Possums generally live alone and defend well-defined territories marked with scent. Encounters often result in fights. When these animals are disturbed, they rear up to their full height on their back legs, spread their forelimbs and make piercing screams. They are fierce fighters.

Brush-tailed possums come in a variety of colours, including grey, brown, black, white and cream. Males tend to have red-brown coloration on their shoulders.

Distribution: Most of Australia, including Tasmania. Introduced into New Zealand.
Habitat: Forests, rocky areas, semi-deserts with scattered eucalyptus trees and suburban habitats.
Food: Shoots, leaves, flowers, fruit, seeds, insects and occasionally young birds.
Size: 32–58cm (12–23in); 1.3–5kg (2.8–11lb).
Maturity: Females 9–12 months; males 24 months.
Life span: 13 years.
Status: Common.

Numbat (*Myrmecobius fasciatus*): 17–27cm (7–11in); 300–600g (0.6–1.3lb)
This marsupial from southern parts of Australia is also known as the banded anteater and, as the name suggests, it specializes in eating ants and termites. Like other anteaters, it has a long snout, a sticky tongue, which can extend at least 10cm (4in), and powerful claws for ripping open rotting logs to expose termite nests.

Marsupial mole (*Notoryctes typhlops*): 9–18cm (3.5–7in); 40–70g (0.08–0.15lb)
This unusual species is not related to other moles, and is only distantly related to other marsupials. It is white or cream in colour, but otherwise resembles a placental mole. It spends a lot of time underground and has long, spade-like claws on its forelimbs for digging, and tiny eyes hidden under its skin. This is a good example of "convergent evolution" between marsupial mammals and placental mammals – having evolved similar adaptations for the same lifestyle.

Native cat or **quoll** (*Dasyurus geoffroi*): 29–65cm (11–26in); 500g (1.1lb)
This is one of six species, all from the same genus, that are called native cats or quolls. They are not related to the true cats, but get their name from their somewhat cat-like appearance and their predatory behaviour. All species of native cat have coats with white spots. They are unpopular with farmers because they occasionally raid chicken coops. As a result of habitat loss, persecution and possibly competition and predation by introduced red foxes, all species of native cat are declining.

Tasmanian devil

Sarcophilus harrisii

The Tasmanian devil comes from a family of carnivorous marsupials that includes marsupial mice and native cats, or quolls, which used to live all over Australia. They are now restricted to the island of Tasmania, which was never colonized by dingoes.

The Tasmanian devil is nocturnal and spends a lot of its time snuffling over the ground trying to pick up the scent of food. It is a very efficient scavenger, and uses its powerful jaws to crush bones and chew up tough skin.

During the day, Tasmanian devils take refuge in nests of bark, grass or leaves inside hollow logs, old wombat burrows or other sheltered spots. The ferocity of Tasmanian devils has been greatly exaggerated, and although they will sometimes fight savagely amongst themselves when feeding, they are apparently docile and safe to handle.

Distribution: Originally found over much of Australia, but now only occurs in Tasmania.
Habitat: Coastal heath and forest.
Food: Carrion, small invertebrates and vertebrates.
Size: 52–80cm (20–32in); females 4.1–8.1kg (9–17lb); males 5.5–12.8kg (12–28lb).
Maturity: 2 years.
Breeding: Litter of 1–4 young.
Life span: 8 years.
Status: Common.

These stocky little carnivores look like tiny bears, but have long tails. They usually have black or dark brown fur, with white markings on their throat, rump and sides.

Musky rat kangaroo

Hypsiprymnodon moschatus

Musky rat kangaroos have dense rich brown or rusty grey fur that is lighter on their undersides. Compared to other rat kangaroos, their back legs are less well developed. These animals carry seeds away from the area where the fruit falls and bury them for eating later when food is scarce. Some seeds germinate, and produce trees for future seed supplies.

This is the smallest of ten species of rat kangaroo, all of which live in Australia. Most rat kangaroos have short fur on their long tails, but some have tails that are hairless and scaly. Like kangaroos, these animals have large feet and well-developed hind legs. However, unlike other species in the family, this rat kangaroo usually moves about on all fours rather than hopping kangaroo-fashion.

Both the males and females emit musky scents, probably to attract mates. Although they usually live alone, they do not seem to defend territories. Unlike all other rat kangaroos, they are most active during the day, when they forage on the forest floor, looking for insects and worms by turning over forest debris and rummaging in the leaf litter with their forepaws. Sometimes they take a break from foraging and stretch out to sunbathe in bright spots in the forest. At night, musky rat kangaroos sleep in nests between the buttress roots of trees or in tangles of vines. The range of these animals is contracting because of forest clearance for agriculture.

Distribution: North-eastern Queensland, Australia.
Habitat: Dense vegetation in tropical rainforest.
Food: Insects, worms, roots, seeds, palm fruit, fungi, flowers, twigs, leaves, lichen and bark.
Size: 21–34cm (8–14in); 337–680g (0.75–1.5lb).
Maturity: Between 18 and 21 months.
Breeding: Usually 2 young born at a time.
Life span: Not known.

Red kangaroo

Macropus rufus

Distribution: Most of Australia.
Habitat: Grassland and savannah with some cover.
Food: Grass.
Size: 0.8–1.6m (32–64in); 20–90kg (44–180lb).
Maturity: 2 years.
Breeding: 1 or 2 born when conditions are favourable.
Life span: 27 years.
Status: Common.

Like other members of the family, red kangaroos have large bodies with a relatively small head, large ears, well-developed hind legs, huge feet and a long muscular tail. Males are usually a rich red-brown colour, while females are blue-grey.

The red kangaroo is the largest of the 61 species comprising the kangaroo and wallaby family, and stands up to 1.8m (6ft) tall on its hind legs. This marsupial mammal has a unique way of travelling. When grazing, it moves around slowly by supporting its body on its forelegs and tail and swinging its back legs forwards. When moving fast however, it hops on its powerful back legs and can make single leaps of more than 9m (30ft).

This is a very efficient way of moving across rough terrain, and kangaroos bounce along at speeds of up to 48kph (30mph) on their springy back legs, using much less effort than a running placental mammal of similar size.

Kangaroos live in dry conditions and can live for long periods without water. They are able to survive on low-quality vegetation found in dry habitats, thanks to a digestion process that uses gut bacteria to help break down tough plant material. However, unlike other large species of kangaroos, reds usually move in search of better feeding conditions during droughts, sometimes travelling more than 200km (125 miles). Red kangaroos are not territorial, but males will fight one another by boxing with their arms and kicking with their back legs, to win control of groups of females during the breeding season.

Doria's tree kangaroo

Dendrolagus dorianus

Distribution: Western, central and south-eastern New Guinea.
Habitat: Mountainous rainforests.
Food: Mostly leaves and fruit.
Size: 52–81cm (20–32in); up to 20kg (40lb).
Maturity: Not known.
Breeding: 1 young born at a time.
Life span: 20 years.
Status: Vulnerable.

There are ten species of closely related tree kangaroo, all of which live in New Guinea and on a few surrounding islands, or in tropical northern Queensland in Australia. This species is the largest of the tree kangaroos and, like others in the group, it has a thick tail that can be longer than the body. Unlike most ground-living kangaroos, which have well developed back legs, the front and back limbs of tree kangaroos are almost the same size.

As their name asserts, tree kangaroos live in trees, but they frequently come to the ground to search for food and to move to new trees. Indeed, this species actually spends most of its time on the ground, while smaller species may spend as much as 98 per cent of their time in the branches of trees.

Tree kangaroos are very agile, and can jump between trees, dropping as much as 9m (30ft) from one branch to another. They are able to jump to the ground from as high up as 18m (60ft). Most species of tree kangaroo live alone, but related females of this species sometimes gang together to drive away unfamiliar males. Most species of tree kangaroo are declining because of increased hunting and habitat loss.

This species of tree kangaroo has fur in various shades of brown, but other species are among the most colourful of all marsupials, with bright yellow markings and different shades of red.

Large Celebes cuscus (*Ailurops ursinus*): 0.5–0.6m (20–24in); 7–10kg (15–22lb
This animal only lives on the Indonesian island of Sulawesi (Celebes) and belongs to the same family as the Australian possums. It has a stocky body with thick, dark-coloured fur above and pale fur below. Unlike the other two species of cuscus living on Sulawesi, this species lives in trees and has a long prehensile tail to help it climb.

Rock wallaby (*Petrogale lateralis*): 50–80cm (20–32in); 3–9kg (6.6–18lb)
There are 14 species of rock wallaby, all from Australia and all characterized by long, powerful hind legs, long tails and large ears. These animals live in dry rocky habitats, close to cover. They are incredibly agile on cliffs and rocky outcrops. They can make leaps of 4m (13ft) and easily bound up the steepest slopes.

Mountain pygmy possum (*Burramys parvus*): 10–13cm (4–5.2in); 30–60g (0.06–0.13lb)
This species was only known from fossils until 1966, when a live specimen was caught in a ski hut on Mount Hotham in south-western Australia. It is now known that around 1,000 individuals survive high up in the mountains, and pass the cold winters in hibernation. In spring and summer, the animals forage for seeds, fruit, insects and worms at night, sometimes climbing into bushes with the help of their prehensile tails.

Bilby

Macrotis lagotis

Bilbies, or rabbit-eared bandicoots, belong to a distinct group of marsupials with 22 species, all of which live in Australia, Tasmania, New Guinea and on some of the surrounding islands. They are characterized by their long, pointed muzzles, and have hind legs that are larger and more well developed than their front legs, though not to the same degree as the kangaroos.

There used to be two species of bilby, but the smaller of the two has not been seen since 1931 and is probably extinct. Unlike other species of bandicoot, bilbies are powerful diggers and excavate spiral-shaped burrows.

Bilbies are nocturnal, sleeping in their burrows during the day. They live alone or in small colonies, usually with one adult male, several females and a number of young. Bilbies have the shortest gestation of any mammal – 14 days. Once born, the babies spend around 80 days in their mother's pouch, followed by a further two weeks in the burrow.

Distribution: Originally found over most of temperate and arid Australia; now restricted to pockets in Western Australia, Northern Territory and south-western Queensland.
Habitat: Dry habitats, including dry woodland, scrub, savannah and semi-desert.
Food: Insects, small vertebrates and some vegetable material.
Size: 29–55cm (11–22in); 0.6–2.5kg (1.3–5.5lb).
Maturity: Females 5 months; males 12 months.
Breeding: 1 or 2 young.
Life span: 7 years.
Status: Endangered.

Males are usually bigger than females, but both have very long finely furred ears. Bilbies have long grey, black and white tails with a crest of long hair on the end.

INSECTIVORES

Insectivores are perhaps the oldest mammal group, dating back 135 million years. Today, the group includes the smallest mammals in the world. All insectivores have five digits on each limb and they usually have small eyes, long snouts and primitive teeth. As their collective name suggests, insectivores commonly feed on insects and other small invertebrates.

Moonrat

Echinosorex gymnura

Moonrats are related to hedgehogs and are one of the largest insectivores. Females tend to be larger than males, but both sexes are otherwise similar in appearance, with narrow bodies, long snouts and coarse black fur with white markings on their heads. Their exceptionally narrow bodies allow the creatures to search for prey in tight spaces. Moonrats are nocturnal, and during the day they sleep in protected spots, such as hollow logs, under tree roots or in holes. At night they search through the leaf litter for small prey.

Moonrats usually live close to water and sometimes swim in streams in search of fish, frogs, crustaceans and other aquatic prey.

Moonrats have long, hairless and scaly tails up to 30cm (12in) long.

They sometimes carry parts of their prey to their resting sites, to be eaten later. Moonrats are solitary animals and except during mating, they do not tolerate each other's presence. They mark out their territories with strong-smelling scents to warn off intruders. Moonrats often respond to encounters by making hissing noises and low roars.

Distribution: South-east Asia.
Habitat: Lowland forests, plantations, mangroves and agricultural land.
Food: Worms and other leaf litter invertebrates, fish, amphibians and aquatic invertebrates.
Size: 26–46cm (13–23in); 0.5–2kg (1.1–4.4lb).
Maturity: 1 year.
Breeding: 2 litters of twins born every year.
Life span: 4 years.
Status: Common.

Indian hedgehog

Paraechinus micropus

The Indian or desert hedgehog is similar in appearance to the common European hedgehog, except that it tends to be smaller in size. Indian hedgehogs come in different colours; some have banded spines of dark brown, with black and white or with yellow, and there is also an unusually large proportion of black and white individuals.

As their alternative name suggests, these animals are well adapted to living in dry desert conditions. They escape the heat of the day by lying up in burrows about 1–2m (3–6ft) deep, which they dig themselves. When the temperatures drop at night, they come out and search the desert floor for prey. If they are alarmed or are chasing frogs, these hedgehogs can move surprisingly fast considering their short legs, reaching speeds exceeding 2kph (1.25mph).

They often bring food back to their burrows for later use. When water or food is scarce, Indian hedgehogs may stay sleeping in their burrows for long periods to conserve energy and water. These hedgehogs stay in the same places all year round and live alone.

Some Indian hedgehogs have a banded appearance with a brown muzzle and a white forehead and sides. Unlike European hedgehogs, which have smooth spines, they have rough spines.

Distribution: Pakistan and India.
Habitat: Deserts and other dry habitats.
Food: Insects, small vertebrates and birds' eggs.
Size: 14–27cm (5.6–13.5in); up to 435g (1lb).
Maturity: 1 year.
Breeding: 1–6 young born per litter.
Life span: 7 years.
Status: Lower risk.

Tibetan water shrew

Nectogale elegans

There are several species of shrew that are at home in water. All of these have silky fur that repels water, long tails and fringes of stiff hairs along the edges of their feet, toes, fingers and tails that help them swim. In smaller species, these hairs allow the shrews to run across the surface of the water for short distances, supported by the surface tension.

The Tibetan water shrew is the only species of shrew to have webbed feet. It also has disc-like pads that may help it keep its footing on slippery wet stones. This shrew lives in a burrow dug in a stream bank.

Most aquatic shrews forage by making repeated dives in the same spot, each dive lasting usually less than 20 seconds. After each dive, they shake their fur dry. If no prey is found, they move along the stream 1m (3ft) or so and dive in a new position. The Tibetan water shrew has sharp teeth that seem to be specialized for catching fish, which are its main prey.

The Tibetan water shrew has a long dark coloured tail with several fringes of short, stiff white hairs that shine with rainbow iridescence when wet.

Distribution: Tibet, south-central China, Nepal and northern Burma.
Habitat: Mountain forest streams.
Food: Small fish and aquatic invertebrates.
Size: 9–13cm (3.5–5in); 25–45g (0.05–0.09lb).
Maturity: 6 months.
Breeding: Not known.
Life span: Not known.
Status: Common.

Asian musk shrew (*Suncus murinus*): 7.5–12cm (3–4.8in); 10–32g (0.02–0.07lb)
This species lives in large numbers in and around human settlements, and is very common in houses throughout its range. It originated in India, but has been spread by people, right the way down the coast of East Africa and all the way east across Asia to Indonesia and a number of oceanic islands, including Mauritius and Guam, where it threatens small native reptiles.

Mole shrew (*Anourosorex squamipes*): 8.5–11cm (3.4–4.5in); 14–25g (0.03–0.05lb)
This strange shrew lives in large parts of China and South-east Asia and, although it is in the shrew family, it looks and behaves much more like a mole. It lives in mountain forests up to 3,100m (10,000ft) above sea level, and spends its time underground, burrowing among the roots of plants, searching for insects and earthworms that form its diet.

Asian mole

Euroscaptor micrura

There are six species of mole living in South-east Asia, southern China and Japan. Like the more familiar European moles, they spend much of their time underground and their bodies have a number of special adaptations to suit their subterranean lifestyle.

Members of the mole family, the *Talpidae*, generally dig tunnels in soil where earthworms are in abundance, along with other prey, and where they are safe from marauding predators. They possess large, powerful front paws on short, stocky forelimbs, which enable them to dig rapidly through even hard ground while using their shovel-like snouts to push loose soil aside.

The Asian moles have the largest front paws in relation to body size of all the moles. In the darkness of their tunnels they have no need of sight and so their eyes are tiny, and probably only able to detect light and dark. However, like many other moles they are very sensitive to ground vibrations, and can use them to find moving prey.

Two species of Asian mole have become rare due to habitat destruction, and one of these species, from a small region of Vietnam, is considered to be critically endangered.

Like other moles, Asian moles have short, velvety hair that will lie in the direction in which it is brushed. This makes it easy for moles to move both forward and backwards through tight tunnels.

Distribution: Nepal, Sikkim, Assam, northern Burma and southern China.
Habitat: Forests with deep soils in mountainous regions.
Food: Insects, earthworms and other soil invertebrates.
Size: 10–16cm (4–6.5in); 29g (0.06lb).
Maturity: Not known.
Breeding: Litters of 2–5 young.
Life span: Not known.
Status: Lower risk.

SEA MAMMALS

There are two main groups of sea mammals: the cetaceans (whales and dolphins) and the pinnipeds (seals, sea lions and walruses). The cetaceans evolved from a primitive group of hoofed mammals and became the masters of the oceans. The pinnipeds evolved from a carnivore ancestor and, although they can stay submerged for over an hour, they still have to come on to land to give birth.

Ganges river dolphin

Platanista gangetica

This species has a long, slender snout and a very low, ridge-like dorsal fin. The side, or pectoral, fins of this species have very square back edges.

The large majority of dolphins live in saltwater marine habitats. However, there are at least seven species of dolphin that regularly visit or permanently live in the freshwater habitats of large rivers, including the Ganges in India, the Yangtze in China and the Amazon in South America.

Because rivers often carry a lot of cloudy sediment, especially during times of heavy rain, visibility can be very poor. Indeed, these dolphins have very small deep-set eyes that lack lenses and are probably only useful for detecting light and dark. Ganges river dolphins emit clicks frequently and rely strongly on echolocation to find their way around. These dolphins also hunt for prey using echolocation and by probing in the mud on the river bottom using their sensitive snouts.

These dolphins may inhabit fast-flowing rivers, where the flow can be violent, especially during times of flood. This means that they have to be able to be swim 24 hours a day to avoid being washed away and injured.

Distribution: Ganges, Brahmaputra, Meghna Rivers and Karnaphuli River of India, Nepal and Bangladesh.
Habitat: River habitats, from the foothills of the Himalayas to tidal limits.
Food: Fish, shrimp and other bottom-dwelling invertebrates.
Size: 2–3m (6.5–10ft); 51–89kg (1122–195lb).
Maturity: 10 years.
Breeding: Single young born at a time.
Life span: 30 years.
Status: Endangered.

Hector's dolphin

Cephalorhynchus hectori

Distribution: New Zealand.
Habitat: Muddy waters.
Food: Fish, crustaceans, squid and invertebrates.
Size: 1.1–1.8m (3.5–6ft); 26–86kg (57–190lb).
Maturity: 6–9 years.
Breeding: Every 2–3 years.
Life span: 20 years.
Status: Vulnerable.

Hector's dolphins are among the rarest species of marine dolphin, with probably less than 5,000 individuals remaining. These dolphins only live in shallow areas around the coast of New Zealand.

Hector's dolphins live in groups of 2–8 individuals, though they may occasionally come together in aggregations of as many as 50 individuals. They hunt for fish and squid from the surface to the sea floor, and sometimes they follow the nets of trawlers in search of stray fish.

The critically endangered population around New Zealand's North Island has only 100 adults, but is unlikely to be helped by individuals from populations around the South Island because of very low migration rates. The northern population is almost certainly doomed to extinction.

Like other species in the same genus, Hector's dolphins are characterized by distinctive black and white markings. Their heads, pectoral and dorsal fins and tails are black and their flanks are grey, but their undersides are white. There are also two characteristic fingers of white going from their bellies and along their sides towards their tails – a pattern unique to this species.

Sperm whale

Physeter catodon

The sperm whale is supremely well adapted to life in the deep oceans. These are the largest hunting predators in the world, with teeth up to 20cm (8in) long and the largest brains of any mammal, weighing over 9kg (20lb). They prefer areas of ocean with cold upwellings at least 1km (3300ft) deep where squid – their favourite food – are most abundant. Sperm whales can dive to incredible depths to hunt, occasionally up to 2.5km (1.5 miles). They are social animals, and they live in groups of between 20 and 40 females, juveniles and young. Sperm whales have been hunted for their oil since the mid-18th century, and after serious population declines between the 1950s and 80s, this species is now protected.

Distribution: Ranges throughout oceans and seas worldwide.
Habitat: Deep oceans.
Food: Mostly squid, including giant deep-sea squid, but also several species of fish and shark.
Size: 12–20m (40–65ft); 12,000–50,000kg (12–50 tonnes).
Maturity: Females 7–13 years; males 25 years.
Breeding: 1 calf born every 5–7 years.
Life span: 77 years.
Status: Vulnerable.

The box-like head of the sperm whale contains the spermaceti organ, which is filled with the fine oil so valued by whalers. The purpose of this organ is unclear.

Leopard seal (*Hydrurga leptonyx*): 2.4–3.4m (8–11.25ft); 200–591kg (440–1,300lb)
These predatory seals live all around the Antarctic and occasionally they can be found in temperate waters around New Zealand, southern Australia and Argentina. They have large, sleek bodies, almost reptile-like heads and long canine teeth. Leopard seals eat krill, which they filter from the water using their cheek teeth. They are fearsome predators too, and also eat other seals and penguins.

Australian sea lion (*Neophoca cinerea*): 2–2.5m (6.5–8.25ft); up to 300kg (660lb)
This species lives around the coast of southern Australia, from Shark Bay in Western Australia to the south-eastern edge of Australia. The Australian sea lion eats fish, squid and crustaceans. It forms breeding colonies of around 100 individuals on small offshore islands, where dominant males defend small territories centred on females. As well as being strong swimmers, these sea lions are surprisingly adept on land, and can even climb steep cliffs.

Chinese river dolphin (*Lipotes vexillifer*): 1.4–2.5m (4.75–8.25ft); 42–167kg (92–334lb)
This freshwater dolphin lives in the Yangtze River in China from its estuary to around 1,900km (1,200 miles) upriver. Like the Ganges river dolphin, it has small eyes, a long, thin snout and a reduced dorsal fin. This species has suffered extensively from boat traffic strikes, hunting and the decline of its prey brought about by the construction of dams and pollution. It is probably the most endangered of all the dolphins.

Baikal seal

Phoca sibirica

This is the only one of 33 species of seal and sea lion that lives exclusively in fresh water. It has one of the most restricted distributions of all the pinnipeds, only being found in Lake Baikal in south-central Siberia.

In winter the lake is entirely covered in a thick layer of ice. During this period, the seals spend most of their time under the ice, coming up to breathe through access holes which they keep open by scratching with the claws on their front flippers and by abrading the edges with their teeth and heads.

Baikal seals dive for about 25 minutes when foraging for fish, but can remain submerged for an hour if frightened. During the breeding season in May, successful males gain access to harems of several females. Mating occurs underwater, and the pups are born in late winter or early spring. Females construct a chamber in the snow, where they give birth to and suckle their young.

Distribution: Lake Baikal.
Habitat: Fresh water.
Food: Fish and aquatic invertebrates.
Size: 1.1–1.4m (3.5–4.75ft); 50–130kg (110–260lb).
Maturity: 6–7 years.
Breeding: Usually 1 pup, but occasionally twins.
Life span: 55 years.
Status: Near threatened.

The long whiskers are very sensitive to touch and are probably very important for locating prey in the dark conditions under the winter ice.

CLASSIFICATION

Scientists classify all living things into categories. Members of each category share features with each other – traits that set them apart from other animals. Over the years, a tree of categories and subcategories has been pieced together, showing how all living things seem to be related to each other.

Taxonomy, the scientific discipline of categorizing organisms, aims to classify and order the millions of animals on Earth so that we can better understand them and their relationship to each other. The Greek philosopher Aristotle was among the first people to do this for animals in the 4th century BC. In the 18th century, Swedish naturalist Carolus Linnaeus formulated the system that we use today.

By the end of the 17th century, naturalists had noticed that many animals seemed to have several close relatives that resembled one another. For example lions, lynxes and domestic cats all seemed more similar to each other than they did to dogs or horses. However, all of these animals shared common features that they did not share with frogs, slugs or wasps.

Linnaeus devised a way of classifying these observations. The system he set up – known as the Linnaean system – orders animals in a hierarchy of divisions. From the largest division to the smallest, this system is as follows: kingdom, phylum, class, order, family, genus, species.

Each species is given a two-word scientific name, derived from Latin and Greek. For example, *Panthera leo* is the scientific name of the lion. The first word is the genus name, while the second is the species name. Therefore *Panthera leo* means the *"leo"* species in the genus *"Panthera"*. This system of two-word classification is known as binomial nomenclature.

Below: The tiger (Panthera tigris) *belongs to the genus* Panthera, *the big cats, to which lions also belong. All cats are members of the larger order of* Carnivora (carnivores) *within the class of* Mammalia *(mammals).*

Above: Like the tiger, the lion (Panthera leo) *belongs to the cat family,* Felidae. *This is divided into two main groups, the big and small cats. The group of small cats includes cougars, bobcats and domestic cats.*

Lions, lynxes and other genera of cats belong to the *Felidae* family. The *Felidae* are included in the order *Carnivora*, along with dogs and other similar predators. The *Carnivora*, in turn, belong to the class *Mammalia*, which also includes horses and all other mammals.

Mammals belong to the phylum *Chordata*, the major group which contains all vertebrates, including reptiles, amphibians, birds, fish and some other small animals called tunicates and lancelets. In their turn, *Chordata* belong to the kingdom *Animalia*, comprising around 31 living phyla, including *Mollusca*, which contains the slugs, and *Arthropoda*, which contains wasps and other insects.

Although we still use Linnaean grouping, modern taxonomy is worked out in very different ways from the ones Linnaeus used. Linnaeus and others after him classified animals by their outward appearance. Although they were generally correct when it came

Close relations

Cheetahs, caracals and ocelots all belong to the cat family *Felidae*, which also includes lions, tigers, wildcats, lynxes and jaguars. Although big cats can generally be distinguished from *Felis* by their size, there are exceptions. For example the cheetah is often classed as a big cat, but it is actually smaller than the cougar, a small cat. One of the main behavioural differences between the two groups is that big cats can roar but not purr continuously, while small cats are able to purr but not roar.

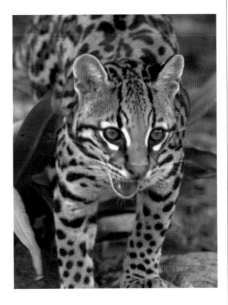

Above: The cheetah (Acinonyx jubatus) differs from all other cats in possessing retractable claws without sheaths. This species is classed in a group of its own, but is often included within the group of big cats.

Above: The caracal (Caracal caracal) is included in the group of small cats, (subfamily Felinae), but most scientists place it in a genus of its own, Caracal, rather than in the main genus, Felis.

Above: The ocelot (Felis pardalis) is a medium-sized member of the Felis or small cat genus. Like many cats, this species has evolved a spotted coat to provide camouflage – unfortunately attractive to hunters.

Distant relations

All vertebrates (backboned animals) including birds, reptiles and mammals such as seals and dolphins, are thought to have evolved from common fish ancestors that swam in the oceans some 400 million years ago. Later, one group of fish developed limb-like organs and came on to the land, where they slowly evolved into amphibians and later reptiles, which in turn gave rise to mammals. Later, seals and dolphins returned to the oceans and their limbs evolved into paddle-like flippers.

Above: Fish are an ancient group of aquatic animals that mainly propel themselves by thrashing their vertically aligned caudal fin, or tail, and steer using their fins.

Above: In seals, the four limbs have evolved into flippers that make highly effective paddles in water but are less useful on land, where seals are ungainly in their movements.

Above: Whales and dolphins never come on land, and their ancestors' hind limbs have all but disappeared. They resemble fish but the tail is horizontally – not vertically – aligned.

to the large divisions, this method was not foolproof. For example, some early scientists believed that whales and dolphins, with their fins and streamlined bodies, were types of fish and not mammals at all. Today, accurate classification of the various genera is achieved through a field of study called cladistics. This uses genetic analysis to check how animals are related by evolutionary change. So animals are grouped according to how they evolved, with each division sharing a common ancestor somewhere in the past. As the classification of living organims improves, so does our understanding of the evolution of life on Earth and our place within this process.

GLOSSARY

Aestivation A period of dormancy during hot and dry weather.

Amphibian One of a group of backboned animals that spend part of their lives on land, part in water, and are dependent on water to breed. Amphibians include frogs, toads, newts, salamanders and caecilians.

Anatomy The study of how bodies are constructed.

Animal A complex organism that collects food from its surroundings.

Arthropod A member of the large group of invertebrate animals, including insects, spiders, crustaceans and centipedes.

Bacterium A microscopic, usually single-celled organism. Many are parasitic and cause disease.

Baleen The horny plates found inside the mouths of some whales, which are used to strain the animal's food.

Biome A large area with a distinctive climate and community of wildlife.

Blubber A layer of fat found under the skin of many aquatic animals that live in cold environments. It provides insulation, helping the animal to retain body heat.

Caecilian A worm-like amphibian.

Camouflage The colour and patterns on an animal's skin that help it to blend in with its surroundings and so hide from predators or prey.

Canine A member of the dog family; or a long, pointed tooth.

Carnivore An animal that eats mainly meat, or a member of the group of mammals of the order *Carnivora*, most of which are carnivorous.

Cartilage A tough, gristly substance found in the skeletons of vertebrates. In fish such as sharks, almost the whole skeleton is composed of cartilage, not bone.

Cell One of the tiny units from which living things are made. Some living things consist of just one cell; others consist of millions of cells.

Circadian A lifestyle with a daily rhythm.

Colony A group of animals that live together and cooperate to find food and rear their young.

Continent A large landmass.

Crepuscular Active at dawn or dusk, or both.

Diurnal Active during the daytime.

DNA A molecule found inside the cells of living organisms, which contains instructions to form the bodies of offspring when the organism reproduces. The instructions take the form of coded sequences called genes. DNA is short for deoxyribonucleic acid.

Drey A squirrel's nest.

Echolocation A technique that allows animals such as bats and dolphins to orientate themselves in darkness or murky water, and locate their prey. The animal emits a stream of high-pitched sounds and listens out for the echoes that bounce back off solid objects.

Egg The female reproductive cell; or the earliest stage of development for reptiles, amphibians and many other animals.

Embryo Any developing young animal in an egg or womb. In mammals, this is the stage before the unborn animal becomes a foetus.

Evolution The process by which living things gradually adapt in order to become better suited to their environment.

Extinction When all the individuals in a species die out, so that none is left.

Foetus A baby mammal developing in the womb, which is older than an embryo.

Fossil The remains or imprint of a once-living organism that has been preserved in stone.

Fungi A group of organisms that includes mushrooms, toadstools and yeasts.

Gene A section of DNA that carries the coded instructions for a particular trait in a living thing.

Genetics The study of heredity and variation.

Genus The second smallest division in taxonomy.

Gestation The period between mating and birth, during which young mammals develop inside their mother.

Gland A structure on the inside or outside of the body that secretes a chemical substance.

Habitat The external environment in which animals and other organisms live. Deserts and rainforests are examples of habitats.

Herbivore An animal that eats mainly plant matter.

Hibernation A period of dormancy that enables animals such as dormice to survive cold weather. During true hibernation the animal's body temperature, heart rate and breathing slow right down, so that it appears to be dead.

Incisor One of the sharp chisel-shaped teeth found at the front of some mammals' jaws, which are used to gnaw or nibble food.

Invertebrate An animal without a backbone. Invertebrates make up about 95 per cent of the animal kingdom. This huge supergroup includes insects, crustaceans, molluscs, worms, jellyfish, sponges and starfish.

Kingdom In taxonomy, the initial and largest grouping into which living things are divided. All life on Earth is grouped within five kingdoms: animals, plants, fungi, protists and monerans, which include bacteria.

Larva An immature stage in an animal's lifecycle, e.g. in amphibians the larvae are tadpoles, which occur after hatching and before they become adults. The larvae differ greatly from the adult form.

Mammal A vertebrate animal with hair on its body, which feeds its young on milk.

Marsupial One of a group of mammals whose young are born early and complete their development in a pouch on the mother.

Migration A regular seasonal journey undertaken by an animal or group of animals to avoid adverse weather, to find food or a mate, or to reach a favourable site for raising offspring.

Monotreme One of a small group of unusual mammals that lay eggs instead of giving birth to live young.

Mutation A variation in the genetic code. Mutations occur naturally and may be harmful, beneficial or have no effect.

Natural selection The process by which unsuited organisms are weeded out, leaving only the strongest or most suitable to breed, thereby passing on their genes. Over time, natural selection helps to bring about evolution, resulting in organisms that are best adapted to the environment.

Nocturnal Active at night.

Organ A part of an animal's body with a distinct function, such as the heart, kidney or eye.

Organism A living thing, such as a plant, animal or fungus.

Pampas A grassland in South America.

Parasite An animal that lives on or inside another animal, and feeds on its flesh or its food.

Permafrost The permanently frozen ground that lies beneath the topsoil in cold biomes.

Photosynthesis The process by which plants turn carbon dioxide and water into glucose, using the energy in sunlight.

Phylum The second largest taxonomic division after kingdom.

Placenta A blood-rich organ that develops within the womb of a pregnant female mammal to nourish the unborn young.

Plankton Microscopic plants and animals that float near the surface of oceans and lakes, and provide food for many larger animals. Microscopic plants are known collectively as phytoplankton; microscopic animals are known as zooplankton.

Plant A complex organism that photosynthesizes.

Population The total number of individuals in a species, or the number in a group that is geographically separated from other groups of the same species.

Prairie A grassland in North America.

Predator Any animal that catches other animals – its prey – for food.

Protein A complex chemical made up of chains of smaller units and used to construct the bodies of organisms.

Protist A single-celled organism.

Reflex A fast, involuntary muscular movement made in response to an external stimulus such as pain, involving nerve signals but not normally routed through an animal's brain.

Reptile One of a group of scaly-skinned vertebrate animals most of which breed by laying eggs. Reptiles include lizards, snakes, crocodiles, turtles and tuataras.

Retina The light-sensitive layer at the back of the eye.

Rodent One of a group of mammals with long front teeth called incisors. The group of rodents includes rats and mice.

Salinity Salt content.

Savannah A grassland or open woodland in Africa or Australia.

Scavenger An animal that feeds on decaying organic matter.

Social Living with others of the same kind in a cooperative group.

Solitary Living alone.

Species A particular kind of organism. Members of a species can interbreed to produce more of the same kind.

Spinal cord The main nerve in the body of vertebrates that runs down inside the backbone to link the brain with smaller nerves throughout the body.

Steppe A grassland in eastern Europe or Asia.

Symbiosis A relationship between two different types of living things, from which both organisms benefit.

Taxonomy The scientific discipline of categorizing organisms.

Territory An area which an animal uses for feeding or breeding, and defends against others of its species.

Timberline The zone on a mountain beyond which the climate is too cold for trees to grow.

Toxin A chemical which is poisonous.

Tundra The barren, treeless lowlands of the far north.

Veldt A grassland in southern Africa.

Venom A cocktail of poisons made by a variety of animals to defend themselves.

Vertebrate An animal with a backbone.

INDEX

Page numbers in *italic* refer to the illustrations.

A

aardvark *164*
aardwolf *150*
Acinonyx jubatus 7, 52, 53, 148, 247
addax 57, 173
Addax nasomaculatus 57, 173
adder *144*
Aepyceros melampus 53, 171
Aethalops alecto 222
Afrixalus fornasinii 135
Agalychnis callidryas 7, 11, 74
agama, starred or sling-tailed 141
Ailuropoda melanoleuca 37, 39, 61, 215
Ailurops ursinus 241
Ailurus fulgens 39, 216
ajolote *81*
Alces alces 50, 51, 66, *108*
alligator *24*
American *82*
Chinese *205*
Alligator
A. mississippiensis 82
A. sinensis 205
Alouatta seniculus 112
Alytes obstetricans 134
Amblyrhynchus cristatus 18, *42, 59, 79*
Ambystoma
A. macrodactylum croceum 71
A. mexicanum 70
A. tigrinum 70
Ammodorcas clarkei 170
amphibians 6, 7, 9, 11, 15, 17, 19, 22, 23, 24, 43, 45, 51, 55, 65, 186, 246
aestivation 32–3
endangered status 37
intelligence 24
reproduction 20, 21
tropical forests 47
amphisbaenians 25
Amphiuma tridactylum 69
amphiuma, three-toed *69*
anaconda, green 6, *44,* 45, 66, *84,* 147

Anathana ellioti 230
anatomy 11, 14–15, 41
Andrias japonicus 188
Anguis fragilis 139
Anilius scytale 85
anoa, mountain 227
anole, green *79*
Anolis carolensis 79
Anomalurus derbianus 161
Anourosorex squamipes 243
anteater
giant *52, 115*
lesser 115
scaly 164
spiny *58,* 236
antelope 18, 19, 41, 53
four-horned 225
royal 171
saiga *53*
Tibetan 228
Antilocapra americana 52, 109
Antrozous pallidus 105
Aonyx cinerea 217
Aotus lemurinus 113
ape 21, 31, 37, 46, 126, 174–5, 232–3
Barbary *62,* 177
Aproteles bulmerae 222
arachnids *10*
Arctictis binturong 218
Arctocebus calabarensis 179
armadillo 7
giant *114*
long-nosed or nine-banded *114*
Arthroleptis stenodactylus 135
Artonyx collaris 217
Arvicola terrestris 158
Ascaphus truei 73
ass 57, 167
Ateles geoffroyi 111
auroch 34
Australophocaena dioptrica 121
Axis axis 227
axolotl *70*
aye aye *179*

B

babirusa *225*
baboon 31
hamadryas *176*
Babyrousa babyrussa 225
badger *155*
American *30, 95*
Burmese ferret 217
Palawan stink 217
Baiomys taylori 103
Balaena mysticetus 123
Balaenoptera musculus 9, 26, 42, 123

bandicoot, rabbit-eared *241*
Basiliscus plumifrons 79
basilisk
double-crested *66*
green *79*
Bassaricyon gabbii 98
Bassariscus astutus 99
bat 9, 26, *27,* 33, 59, 104–5, 162–3, 221–2
Angolan free-tailed *162*
Bulmer's fruit 222
butterfly 163
common blossom *222*
common vampire *104*
fishing bulldog 105
ghost 105
greater mastiff *162*
hammer-headed fruit *162*
long-tailed 163
New World sucker-footed 105
noctule *163*
pallid *105*
pipistrelle *163*
pygmy fruit 222
Schneider's leaf-nosed *221*
short-tailed 222
tent-building *104*
velvety free-tailed *105*
Batrachuperus
B. mustersi 189
B. pinchonii 189
bear 15, 18, 19, 32, 37, 92–3, 214–15
American black *48, 93*
Asiatic black *215*
brown 6, *50,* 51, 59, *92*
grizzly 51, *66,* 92, 93
Kodiak *66,* 92
polar 26, *54, 55, 92*
sloth *214*
spectacled *93*
sun *214*
beaver, American *44, 45, 101*
beluga *121*
bilby *241*
binturong *218*
Bipes biporus 81
birds 6, 9, *11,* 16, 24, 28, 30, 39, 47, 55, 59, 61, 246

bison *18,* 35, *41, 52,* 53
American *107*
European 7, *173*
wood *48*
Bison
B. bison 107
B. bonasus 7, 173
Blarina brevicauda 119
blindsnake, Schlegel's *145*
boa
constrictor 85
emerald tree *6,* 25, *46, 84*
Pacific ground 207
rosy 85
round island *58*
Boa constrictor 85
boar, wild 37, *49,* 126, *169*
bobcat 89
Boiga dendrophila 209
Bombina
B. bombina 133
B. orientalis 190
bongo 171
bonobo *175*
boomslang *143*
boreal forests 6, 40, 41, 50–1
Bos
B. gaurus 227
B. grunniens 61, 227
Boselaphus tragocamelus 227
Bothrops atrox 87
Brachylagus idahoensis 117
Brachyteles arachnoides 113
Bradypus tridactylus 115
Breviceps adspersus 133
Bubalus
B. bubalis 229
B. quarlesi 227
buffalo
African 173
water *229*
Bufo
B. americanus 75
B. bufo 49, 75, *132*
B. calamita 133
B. marinus 43, 74, 192
B. melanostictus 194
bullfrog
African *131*
Goliath *131*
North American 73
South American 73
Burramys parvus 241
bushbaby 179

C

Cacajao calvus 113
cacomistle 99
caecilian 22
Cayenne 71

Ceylon *188*
ringed *71*
caiman 24
  black *82*
  Cuvier's dwarf 83
  spectacled *83*
Caiman crocodilus 83
Callicebus molloch 113
Calliosciurius erythraeus 220
Calloselasma rhodostoma 207
camel 26, *56*, 57, 61, 186
  bactrian *226*
  dromedary *166*
Camelus
  C. bactrianus 226
  C. dromedarius 166
Candoia carinata 207
cane rat, great 161
canids 90–1, 151–3, 212–13
Canis
  C. aureus 213
  C. dingo 34, 57, 212
  C. latrans 30, 91
  C. lupus 17, 32, 37, 34, 41,
    50, *90*
  C. mesomelas 152
  C. simensis 151
Capra
  C. falconeri 229
  C. ibex 34, 60, 167
Capreolus capreolus 170
Capricornis sumatraensis 228
capuchin, brown *110*
capybara 6, *44*, 66, *102*
caracal *149*, 247
Caracal caracal 149, 247
Carettochelys insculpta 197
caribou or reindeer 33, 51, *55*,
    66, 170
carnivores 18–19
Castor canadensis 44, 45, 101
cat 14, 17, 18, 34, 46, *63*, 88–9,
    148–9, 210–11, 246
  fishing 211
  flat-headed 211
  jungle *211*
  native 239
  pampas 89
Cavia aperea 63, 103
cavy *63, 103*
Cebuella pygmaea 110

Cebus apella 46, 110
Centrolenella valerioi 75
Cephalorhynchus hectori 244
Ceratobatrachus guentheri 193
Cercocebus torquatus 177
Cercopithecus aethiops 63, 177
Cervus
  C. elaphus 170, 225
  C. nippon 49, 225
  C. unicolor 224
cetaceans 120–3, 183–6, 244–5
chameleon *11, 19*
  giant *58*
  panther *138*
chamois 7, *60, 172*
Charina trivirgata 85
cheetah *7, 52*, 53, *148, 247*
Chelodina longicollis 196
Chelonia mydas 77
Chelys fimbriatus 76
chimpanzee *174*
chinchilla 103
Chinchilla brevicaudata 103
chipmunk, Eastern American 101
Chiromantis xerampelina 134
Chironectes minimus 118
Chiropotes satanas 113
chiru 228
chital 227
Chlamydosaurus kingii 198
Choloepus hoffmanni 115
chousingha 225
Chrysemys picta 77
Chrysocyon brachyurus 90
Chrysopelea ornata 209
chuckwalla *80*
civet
  African 157
  palm 218
Civettictis civetta 157
Clemmys insculpta 77
cnidarians *10*
coati
  mountain 99
  ring-tailed *99*
cobra 87
  forest 147
  king *207*
  spitting *146*
Coleonyx variegatus 79
Colobus guereza 177
colugo 222
Condylura cristata 119
Congo eel 69
Connochaetes taurinus 18, 30,
    33, 171
Conraua goliath 131
Corallus caninus 6, 25, *46, 84*
Cordylus cataphractus 138
Coronella austriaca 145
cottontail, eastern *117*
cougar *60, 88*
coyote *30*, 91
Cricetus cricetus 159

crocodile 14, *20*, 24, 25, 142
  American *83*
  broad-fronted 142
  Cuban *83*
  dwarf *142*
  Nile *45, 142*
  Orinoco *83*
  saltwater *43, 204*
crocodilians 82–3, 204–5
Crocodylus
  C. acutus 83
  C. intermedius 83
  C. niloticus 45, 142
  C. palustris 205
  C. porosus 43, 204
  C. rhombifer 83
Crocuta crocuta 150
Crossarchus obscurus 157
Crotalus
  C. atrox 86
  C. cerastes 86
Cryptobranchus alleganiensis
    22, *68*
Cryptoprocta ferox 157
Ctenodactylus gundi 161
Cuon alpinus 212
Cuora flavomarginata 197
cuscus 239
  large Celebes 241
  spotted *59*
cusimanse 157
Cyclemys dentata 197
Cyclorana australis 195
Cyclura cornuta 78
Cylindrophis rufus 207
Cynocephalus variegatus 222
Cynomys ludovicianus 52, 53, 101
Cynops orientalis 189
Cystophora cristata 125

D

Dama dama 49, 170
Darwin, Charles 12, 13, 59
Dasypeltis scabra 143
Dasypus novemcinctus 114
Dasyurus geoffroi 239
Daubentonia madagascariensis
    179
deer 19, *20*, 27, 49
  axis 227
  fallow *49, 170*
  mouse 170
  pampas 53, 109
  red 170, 225
  red brocket 109
  roe 170

sika *49*
white-tailed *108*
Delphinapterus leucas 121
Dendroaspis polylepis 53, 146
Dendrobates pumilio 75
Dendrolagus dorianus 59, 241
Dermochelys coriacea 36, 136
deserts 6, 40, 41, 54, 56–7
desman, Russian *45, 182*
Desmana moschata 44, 182
Desmodus rotundus 104
dhole 212
dibatag 170
Dicamptodon tenebrosus 69
Diceros bicornis 168
Diclidurus albus 105
Didelphis virginiana 118
dingo *34, 57, 212*
Dispholidus typus 143
dog 14, 17, 18, 27, 31, 36, 63,
    90–1, 151–3, 212–13, 246
  African hunting *151*
  Asian red *212*
  bush *91*
  raccoon *213*
Dolichotis patagonum 103, 109
dolphin 7, *26*, 27, 31, *42, 43*,
    65, 120–3, *247*
  Amazon river *44, 120*
  Atlantic humpback *184*
  Chinese river 245
  Ganges river *244*
  Hector's *244*
  La Plata 121
  Risso's *121*
  white-beaked *43, 185*
donkey 57, 167
dormouse *32*, 49
  edible *158*
douroucouli 113
Draco volans 199
dragon
  flying 199
  Komodo *58, 59*, 65, *203*
  painted *141*
  water *199*
dugong 17, *43*, 123, *223*
Dugong dugon 17, 43, 123, *223*
dung beetles *30*
Dusicyon
  D. thous 91
  D. vetulus 91
Dyscophus antongilii 131

E

echidna
  long-nosed 236
  short-nosed *28, 59, 236*
echinoderms *10*
Echinosorex gymnura 242
ecology 30–1
  grasslands 52–3
Eira barbata 97
eland, common *173*

Elaphe
  E. guttata 87
  E. situla 145
elephant *8–9, 15, 19,* 21, 26, *27,*
    31, *38, 41,* 52, 126, 186
  African *8–9, 165*
  Asian *47, 223*
Elephantulus myurus 182
Elephas maximas 47, 223
Eleutherodactylus planirostris 73
elk *50, 51,* 66, 108
Emys orbicularis 136
endangered species 6, 36–7
Enhydra lutris 42, 43, 96
Equus
  E. asinus 57, 167
  E. burchelli 166
  E. przewalskii 53, 186, *225*
Eremitalpa granti 181
Erethizon dorsatum 48, 102
Erinaceus europaeus 39, *181*
Erpeton tentaculatum 209
Eschrichtius robustus 123
Euchoreutes naso 220
Eumeces lagunensis 81
Eumetopias jubatus 55, 125
Eunectes murinus 6, *44,* 45, 66,
    84, 147
Euroscaptor micrura 243
Eurycea lucifuga 69
eutherians 27
evolution 12–13, 30, 43, 59, 247
extinctions 36

F
Felis
  F. chaus 211
  F. colocolo 89
  F. concolor 60, 88
  F. pardalis 46, 89, 247
  F. planiceps 211
  F. rufus 89
  F. sylvestris lybica 149, 211
  F. sylvestris sylvestris 149
  F. viverrinus 211
  F. wiedii 88
  F. yagouaroundi 89
ferret, black-footed 95
filter-feeders 19
fish 9, *11,* 14, 27, 43, 45,
    246, 247
fisher *97*
flying fox *221*
foliovores 18, 63
food chains 30, 31, 42–3

forests 6, *38,* 40, 41, 46–7,
    48–9, 50–1
fossa *157*
fox
  Arctic *41, 54*
  bat-eared *41, 153*
  Cape 153
  crab-eating 91
  fennec *56, 57, 153*
  hoary 91
  kit *91*
  red *41, 62, 152,* 239
  royal or hoary 153
  sand or pale 153
  swift 91
fresh water 6, 40, 44–5
frog *11, 16,* 17, 19, *20,* 21, 22,
    23, 33, 39, *46,* 47, 57, 72–5,
    130–6, 190–5, 246
  African "hairy" 131
  Asian blue-web flying *194*
  Asian horned *190*
  Asian painted 191
  banded rubber *135*
  brown-striped 191
  Bushveld rain *133*
  Cape ghost *130*
  corroboree *193*
  crab-eating 194
  Darwin's *72*
  European common *132*
  European tree *133*
  Fijian ground 193
  flying *12*
  foam-nesting *134*
  four- or false-eyed 73
  giant *195*
  giant tree *191*
  greater leaf-folding *135*
  greenhouse 73
  Hochstetter's *193*
  holy cross, catholic
    or crucifix *192*
  Indonesian floating 194
  marsh 133
  Mexican burrowing 75
  mountain ghost 131
  ornate narrow-mouthed 193
  paradoxical 9, *75*
  red-eyed tree *7, 46, 74*
  red-legged pan 135
  reticulated glass 75
  Solomon Islands horned 193
  southern gastric brooding
    191
  strawberry poison-dart *75*
  tailed 73
  tomato 131
  tree *7, 11, 46,* 47
  trilling reed 135
  White's tree *194*
  wood 51
frugivores 18, 37
Furcifer pardalis 138

G
Galago senegalensis 179
Galictis vittata 95
Gallotia simonyi 141
gaur 227
Gavialis gangeticus 44, 204
Gazella thomsoni 12, 171
gazelle
  Thomson's *12,* 171
  Tibetan *61*
gecko 25, 57
  crocodile 141
  fat-tailed 139
  flying *200*
  knob-headed giant 201
  Leach's giant 201
  Moorish *141*
  sand *57*
  tokay *200*
  western banded 79
Gekko gecko 200
gelada 18, 177
genet
  aquatic 157
  common or small-spotted *157*
Genetta genetta 157
Geochelone
  G. elegans 197
  G. elephantopus 24, 36, *58,*
    59, 65, *77*
  G. pardalis 137
  G. radiata 137
Gerrhosaurus validus 139
gharial *45, 204*
gibbon 21
  crested *233*
  Javan 233
  Kloss's *233*
  lar *233*
  white-browed *233*
gila monster 12, *56,* 57, *78*
Giraffa camelopardalis 18, 36,
    53, 167
giraffe 18, 36, *53, 167*
Glaucomys volans 101
Glauconycteris variegata 163
glider
  squirrel *237*
  sugar 237
Glis glis 158
gnu, blue 18, 30, *33,* 171
goanna *202*
goat 34
  mountain 33, *60, 61*

Gonyosoma oxycephala 209
gopher, Northern pocket *101*
gorilla *15, 37,* 38, 46
  mountain *60, 61, 175*
  western-lowland *174*
Gorilla
  G. gorilla beringei 60, 61, 175
  G. gorilla gorilla 174
Grampus griseus 121
grasslands 6, 40, 41, 52–3
grisón, greater 95
groundhog 32, 100
guanaco *106*
guinea pig *63, 103*
Gulo gulo 50, 51, 95
gundi, north African 161

H
hamster
  common 159
  golden *219*
hardun 141
hare
  brown *180*
  snowshoe *54, 116*
hedgehog 39, *181*
  Indian or desert *242*
Helarctos malayanus 214
Heleophryne
  H. purcelli 130
  H. rosei 131
hellbender 22, *68*
Heloderma suspectum 12, *56,*
    57, *78*
Hemechatus haemachatus 147
Hemitheconyx caudicinctus 139
Hemitragus jemlahicus 228
herbivores 18, 19
Herpestes edwardsi 218
Heterocephalus glaber 161
Hexaprotodon liberiensis 169
hibernation 6, 32–3, 49, 51
Hippocamelus antisensis 109
hippopotamus 26, *44, 45, 168*
  pygmy 169
Hippopotamus amphibius 168
Hipposideros speoris 221
hog, giant forest 169
hog-badger *217*
hoofed animals 106–9, 166–73,
    224–9
horse 7, 34, *35,* 36, 246
  Przewalski's *52,* 53, 186, 225
huemul 109
humans 18, 21, 26, 34, 35, 36,
    37, 38–9, 46, 65, 174
  human settlements 6, 62–3
Hydrochaerus hydrochaeris 6,
    44, 66, *102*
Hydromys chrysogaster 219
Hydrosaurus pustulatus 199
Hydrurga leptonyx 245
Hyemoschus aquaticus 170
hyena, spotted *150*

Hyla arborea 133
Hylobates
   H. concolor 233
   H. hoolock 233
   H. klossi 233
   H. lar 233
   H. moloch 233
   H. syndactylus 232
Hylochoerus meinertzhageni 169
Hyperolius parkeri 135
Hypsignathus monstrosus 162
Hypsiprymnodon moschatus 240
Hystrix africaeaustralis 160
hyrax, rock *165*

I
ibex 34, *60*, 167
Ichthyophis glutinosus 188
Ictonyx striatus 154
iguana *25*
   green 47
   marine 18, *42*, 59, 79
   rhinoceros *78*
impala *53*, 171
indri *178*
Indri indri 178
Inia geoffrensis 44, 120
insectivores 119, 181–2, 242–3
insects 9, 12, 16, 30, 33, 36, 46,
   55, 246
International Union for the
   Conservation of Nature and
   Natural Resources (IUCN)
   36–7
introduced species 6, 34–5
invertebrates 9, 10, 14, 16, 36, 246
islands 6, 58–9

J
jackal 57
   black-backed *152*
   golden *213*
jackrabbit *117*
jaguar *89*
jaguarundi 89
javeline 107
jellyfish 6, *10*, 16
jerboa 57
   long-eared 220
jumping animals 12

K
Kaloula pulchra 191
kangaroo 26, *28*, *53*, *186*
   Doria's tree *241*
   red 7, 29, *240*
   tree *59*
Kassina maculata 135
kingsnake *85*
kinkajou *99*, 218
koala 7, *29*, *49*, *186*, *238*
krait, banded sea *206*
krill *10*, 19
kudu 173

L
Lacerta
   L. agilis 139
   L. vivipara 140
Lagenorhynchus albirostris 43, 185
lagomorphs 116–17, 180
Lagothrix lagotricha 111
Lama guanicoe 106
Lamprolepis smaragdina 201
Lampropeltis
   L. getulus 85
   L. triangulum 87
Lamprophis fuliginosus 147
lancehead, common 87
lancelets 246
Langaha madagascariensis 147
langur
   douc 235
   hanuman *235*
   pig-tailed 235
Lanthanotus borneensis 202
Laticauda colubrina 206
Laudakia stellio 141
Leiopelma hochstetteri 193
lemming, Siberian 33, *55*, *159*
Lemmus sibericus 33, *55*, *159*
lemur *6*, *59*
   flying *222*
   ring-tailed 179
   ruffed *6*, *58*, *59*, *178*
Lemur catta 179
Leontopithecus rosalia 37, 111
leopard *39*, 46, *210*
   clouded *211*
   snow *61*, 211
Lepidochelys kempii 137
Lepidophyma flavimaculatum
   81
Leptodactylus pentadactylus 73
Leptotyphlops dulcis 85
Lepus
   L. americanus 54, 116
   L. californicus 117
   L. europaeus 180
Lialis burtonis 203
Limnodynastes peronii 191
Linnaeus, Carolus 246
linsang, spotted *218*
lion 7, *18*, *21*, 30, 31, *41*, 53,
   126, *148*, 246
   mountain *60*, 88

Lipotes vexillifer 245
Litoria
   L. caerulea 194
   L. infrafrenata 191
livestock 34–5, 52, 53, 62
lizard 9, *14*, *17*, 19, 20, 24, *25*,
   47, 57, 58, 65, 78–81,
   138–41, 197–203
   African plated 139
   armadillo *138*
   bearded 199
   Borneo earless 202
   Burton's snake *203*
   crocodile 199
   desert horned *80*
   European glass *140*
   flying *199*
   frilled *198*
   Hierro giant 141
   Ibiza wall 141
   Middle American night 81
   sailfin 199
   sand 139
   viviparous *140*
llama *60*, 61
loris
   slender *231*
   slow *16*, 231
Loris tardigradus 231
Loxodonta africana 8–9, *165*
Lutra canadensis 44, *97*
Lycaon pictus 151
Lygosoma fernandi 141
Lyncodon patagonicus 97
lynx
   desert 149, 247
   Eurasian *51*, *149*, 246
Lynx lynx 50, *149*, 246

M
Mabuya longicauda 201
Macaca
   M. fascicularis 234, *235*
   M. sylvanus 62, 177
macaque 63
   Barbary *62*
   crab-eating *234*
Macroclemys temminckii 76
Macroprotodon cucullatus 145
Macropus rufus 7, *29*, *240*
Macrotis lagotis 241
Malacochersus tornieri 137
Malpolon monspessulanus 145
mamba 87
   black *53*, *146*
mammals 6, 9, 11, 17, 20,
   21, 24, 36–7, 43, 59,
   65, 246
   anatomy *15*, 26, 41
   evolution 13
   placental 6, 26–7
manatee, West Indian *123*, 223
mandrill *47*, *126*, *176*
Mandrillus sphinx 47, *176*

mangabey, red-capped *177*
Manis temmincki 164
mapache 99
mara 103, 109
margay *88*
markhor *229*
marmoset, pygmy *110*
marmot, Alpine *50*, 51, 53, 159
Marmota
   M. marmota 50, 51, 53, 159
   M. monax 32, *100*
marsupials 6, 26, 28–9, 34, 118,
   237–41
marten
   American pine *48*, *49*, 97
   beech 155
Martes
   M. americana 48, *49*, 97
   M. foina 155
   M. pennanti 97
   M. zibellina 155, *216*
matamata *76*
Maticora bivirgata 209
Mazama americana 109
meerkat *31*, *156*
Megamuntiacus vuquangensis
   225
Megaptera novaeangliae 122
Megophrys montana 190
Melanosuchus niger 82
Meles meles 155
Melogale personata 217
Melursus ursinus 214
Mephitis mephitis 94
Mesocricetus auratus 219
Microhyla ornata 193
Micruroides euryxanthus 87
milksnake 87
mink, American *94*
Mirounga leonina 125
mole 26, 53
   Asian *243*
   blind 182
   golden *181*
   marsupial 239
   star-nosed *119*
mole rat 53
   giant 151
   naked *161*
molluscs 9, *10*, 246
Moloch horridus 57, *198*
Molossus ater 105
Monachus monachus 183
monerans 10
mongoose 18
   banded *156*

Indian grey 218
monitor 25
  green tree *202*
  lace 202
  sand *202*
  savannah *139*
monkey 6, 16, 17, 18, 26, 27, 31, 32, 37, 39, 41, 47, 63
  banded leaf 235
  black-handed spider *111*
  capuchin *46*, 63, 110
  colobus 177
  golden *60*, 235
  howler *112*
  Humboldt's woolly 111
  New World 110–13
  night *113*
  Old World 176–7, 234–5
  proboscis *234*
  snub-nosed *61*, *235*
  squirrel 31, *111*
  titi 113
  woolly spider 113
Monodon monoceros 184
monotremes 6, 26, 28, 236
moonrat *242*
moose *50*, *51*, 66, *108*
Mops condylurus 162
Morelia viridis 208
mountains 6, 40, 60–1
mouse 51
  brush-tailed marsupial 237
  house 21, 35, 36, 63, *159*
  long-clawed marsupial *237*
  marsupial 239
  pygmy *103*
  southern birch 159
mudpuppy *69*
mugger *205*
Mungos mungo 156
Muntiacus reevesi 224
muntjac *224*
  giant 225
muriqui 113
Mus musculus 21, 35, 36, 63, 159
musk ox *54*, 55, 107
muskrat *44*, 103
mussels 9
mustangs 35
Mustela
  M. erminea 154
  M. nigripes 95
  M. nivalis 155

M. vison 94
mustelids 94–7, 154–5, 216–17
Mydaus marchei 217
Myrmecobius fasciatus 239
Myrmecophaga tridactyla 52, 115
Mystacina tuberculata 222

N
Naja
  N. melanoleuca 147
  N. pallida 146
Nanonycteris veldkampii 163
narwhal 184
Nasalis larvatus 234
Nasua nasua 99
Nasuella olivacea 99
Natrix natrix 49, 144
Nectogale elegans 243
Necturus maculosus 69
Neofelis nebulosa 211
Neophascogale lorentzii 237
Neophoca cinerea 245
Neotragus pygmaeus 171
newt *11*, 22–3
  Chinese fire belly 189
  crocodile *189*
  eastern 71
  great crested *129*
  marbled 129
  paddletail 189
  palmate 129
  red-spotted *71*
  sharp-ribbed *129*
nilgai *227*
Noctilio leporinus 105
Notaden bennetti 192
Notophthalmus viridescens 71
Notoryctes typhlops 239
numbat 239
nutrient cycles 30
Nyctalus noctula 163
Nyctereutes procyonoides 213

O
Occidozyga lima 194
oceans 6, 40, 41, 42–3
ocelot *46*, *89*, 247
Ochotona princeps 60, 116
Odobenus rosmarus 54, 125
Odocoileus virginianus 108
okapi *36*, *47*, 167
Okapia johnstoni 36, 47, 167
olingo *98*
olm *128*
omnivores 18–19
Ondatra zibethicus 44, 103
Ophiophagus hannah 207
Ophisaurus apodus 140
opossum
  Virginia *118*
  water *118*
orang-utan 39, *47*, 174, 186, *232*
orca or killer whale 19, 41, *42*, 122
Orcinus orca 19, 41, 42, 122

Ornithorhynchus anatinus 26, 28, 65, 236
Orycteropus afer 164
Oryctolagus cuniculus 180
oryx, Arabian *56*, *172*
Oryx leucoryx 56, 172
Osbornictis piscivora 157
Osteolaemus tetraspis 142
Otaria flavescens or byronia 124
Otocyon megalotis 41, 153
otter 45
  giant 6, *96*, 120
  North American river *44*, *97*
  sea *42*, *43*, *96*
  short-clawed *217*
Ovibos moschatus 55, 107
Ovis canadensis 107
Oxyuranus scutellatus 206
Ozotoceros bezoarticus 53, 109

P
Pachytriton labiatus 189
Pagophilus groenlandicus 183
Paleosuchus palpebrosus 83
pampas 52
Pan
  P. paniscus 175
  P. troglodytes 174
panda
  giant *37*, *39*, *61*, 215
  red *39*, 216
pangolin, Cape *164*
panther *60*, 88
Panthera
  P. leo 7, 18, 21, 30, 31, 41, 53, 126, *148*, *246*
  P. onca 89
  P. pardus 210
  P. tigris 7, 19, 46, 50, 51, 65, 210, 246
  P. uncia 61, 211
Pantholops hodgsoni 228
Papio hamadryas 176
Paradoxurus hermaphroditus 218
Paraechinus micropus 242
peccary, collared 107
Pedetes capensis 161
Pedostibes hosii 195
pekan 97
Pelodiscus sinensis 196
Pelusios subniger 137
Perodicticus potto 179
Petaurista elegans 220
Petaurus norfolcensis 237
Petrogale lateralis 241
Phacochoerus africanus 169

Phascolarctos cinereus 7, 29, 49, 238
Phoca
  P. sibirica 245
  P. vitulina 42, 185
Phocoena
  P. phocoena 42, 185
  P. sinus 120
Phrynomerus bifasciatus 135
Phrynosoma platyrhinos 80
Physalaemus nattereri 73
Physeter catodon 12, 40, 245
Physignathus cocincinus 199
pichi 115
pig, bush 169
pika *60*, *116*
pinnipeds 124–5, 183, 186, 245
Pipa pipa 72
pipesnake, red 85
Pipistrellus pipistrellus 163
Pithecia pithecia 112
plants 10, 30, 38, 40, 42, 47, 55, 56–7, 60–1
Platanista gangetica 244
Platymantis vitiensis 193
platypus 26, *28*, 65, *236*
Pleurodeles waltl 129
Podarcis pityusensis 141
Pogona vitticeps 199
polar regions 6, 40, 54–5
polecat, striped 154
Pongo pygmaeus 39, 47, 174, 186, 232
Pontoporia blainvillei 121
porcupine
  Cape *160*
  North American 48, *102*
porpoise
  harbour *42*, 185
  spectacled 121
possum 186
  brush-tailed *239*
  gliding *237*
  mountain pygmy 241
Potamochoerus porcus 169
Potos flavus 99, 218
potto *179*
  golden 179
prairie dog *52*, *53*, 101
prairies 40, 52
predators 16, 18–19, 23, 29, 30, 41, 47, 246
Presbytis femoralis 235
primates 16, 47, 59, 230
  primitive 178–9, 231
Priodontes maximus 114
Prionodon pardicolor 218
Procavia capensis 165
Procyon
  P. cancrivorus 99
  P. lotor 98
procyonids 98–9
pronghorn *52*, *109*
Proteles cristatus 150

Proteus anguinus 128
Przewalski's horse *53, 225*
Pseudis paradoxa 9, 75
Pseudophryne corroboree 193
Pseudorca crassidens 185
Pseudoryx nghetinhensis 228
Pteronura brasiliensis 6, 96, 120
Pteropus edulis 221
Ptychozoon kuhli 200
pudu, southern 109
Pudu pudu 109
puma *60*, 88
Pygathrix nemaeus 235
python
    ball or royal *147*
    carpet *186*
    green tree *208*
    reticulated *208*
Python
    P. regius 147
    P. reticulatus 208
Pyxicephalus adspersus 131

Q
quoll 239

R
rabbit 16, *17*, 21, 32, 51, 116–17,
    180
    European *180*
    pygmy 117
    swamp 117
    volcano 117
raccoon *63*
    common *98*
    crab-eating 99
racer, red-tailed *209*
Rana
    R. catesbeiana 73
    R. ridibunda 133
    R. temporaria 132
Rangifer tarandus 33, 51, *55,*
    66, 170
rat 18, *35*, 63
    Australian water *219*
    beaver 219
    black 35
    brown or ship 35
    kangaroo *56*
    water 158
rat kangaroo, musky *240*
Ratia cancrivora 194
rattlesnake 7, *32*, 51, 87
    western diamondback *86*
Ratufa indica 220
reindeer or caribou 33, 51, *55,*
    66, 170
reproduction 20–1
    amphibians 22
    mammals 26–7, 28, 29
    reptiles 24
reptiles 6, 9, 11, 17, 20, 21,
    24–5, 27, 28, 32–3, 37, 43,
    51, 55, 186, 246

    anatomy *14*, 15
Rhacodactylus
    R. auriculatus 201
    R. leachianus 201
Rhacophorus reinwardtii 194
Rheobatrachus silus 191
rhinoceros 7, *21*, 38, *53*
    black *168*
    Indian *226*
    white 168
Rhinoceros unicornis 226
Rhinoderma darwinii 72
Rhinophrynus dorsalis 75
Rhinopithecus roxellana 61, 235
Rhinopoma microphyllum 163
Rhinotyphlops schlegelii 145
Rhyacotriton olympicus 69
ring-tail *110*
ringtail 99
rinkhal 147
rivers 40, 44
rodents 18, 32, *35*, 49, 51, 57,
    63, 100–3, 158–61, 219–20
Romerolagus diazi 117
Rupicapra pyrenaica 7, 60, 172

S
sable 155, *216*
saiga *228*
Saiga tatarica 228
Saimiri boliviensis 31, *111*
saki
    black-bearded 113
    white-faced *112*
salamander 9, *11*, 19, 22, *23*, 47,
    68–71, 128–9, 188–9
    Afghan 189
    cave 69
    coastal giant 69
    fire *126, 128*
    giant *45*
    Japanese giant *188*
    long-toed 71
    marbled *23*
    Olympic torrent 69
    spectacled 129
    tiger *70*
    western Chinese mountain
    189
Salamandra salamandra 128
Salamandrina terdigitata 129
salt water 44–5
sambar *224*
sao la 228

Sarcophilus harrisii 7, *29*, 34, *239*
Sauromalus obesus 80
savannahs 40, 52
Sciurus
    S. carolinensis 100, 160
    S. vulgaris 160
sea anemones 10
sea lion 43
    Australian 245
    Californian *124*
    South American *125*
    Steller's *55*, 125
seal 16, 43, 55, 65, 124–5, 247
    Baikal *245*
    Cape fur *43*
    common *43, 185*
    grey 185
    harp *183*
    hooded *125*
    leopard 245
    Mediterranean monk *183*
    southern elephant 125
Semnopithecus entellus 235
serow 228
sheep *34*
    bighorn *107*
Shinisaurus crocodilurus 199
shrew 26, 51
    Alpine 182
    Asian musk 243
    giant mole *119*
    mole 243
    pygmy white-toothed 182
    rock elephant *182*
    Tibetan water *243*
siamang 232
Sicista subtilis 159
sidewinder *86*
sika *49*, 225
Simias concolor 235
Siphonops annulatus 71
siren
    giant 22
    greater *68*
Siren lacertina 68
sitatunga 173
skink 25
    African fire *141*
    blue-tongued *201*
    crocodile 81
    emerald tree *201*
    long-tailed 201
    pink tailed 81
skunk *48*
    spotted 95
    striped *94*
sloth 30
    three-toed *115*
    two-toed 115
slow worm 25, *139*
snails 10
snake 6, 7, *14*, 16, *17*, 19, 24,
    25, 43, 46, 47, 65, 84–7,
    143–7, 206–9

African house 147
blind 57
blue coral 209
common egg-eating *143*
common garter *87*
corn 87
golden tree 209
grass *49, 144*
hooded 145
horned sea *43*
leopard *145*
Malagasy leaf-nosed *147*
mangrove *209*
Montpellier 145
ornate flying 209
red-tailed pipe 207
smooth 145
sunbeam 207
tentacled 209
Texas thread or blind *85*
twig mimic 147
vine 47
western coral *87*
Sorex alpinus 182
Sotalia fluviatilis 121
Sousa teuszii 184
Speothos venaticus 91
Sphenodon punctatus 25, 59,
    186, *197*
spiders *10*
Spilogale putorius 95
springbok *64–5*
springhare *161*
squeaker, common 135
squamates 25
squid 9, 14
squirrel 32, *49*
    American red *50*
    beautiful 220
    eastern grey *48*
    flying 101, *220*
    giant *220*
    grey *100*, 160
    ground *11*, 53, 57
    Lord Derby's flying 161
    red *160*
    spotted giant flying 220
steppes 52
Sternotherus odoratus 77

stinkpot *77*
stoat *154*
Suncus
   S. etruscus 182
   S. murinus 243
Suricata suricatta 31, *156*
survival 18–19, 20–1
Sus scrofa 37, *49*, *126*, *169*
Syconycteris australis 222
Sylvilagus
   S. aquaticus 117
   S. floridanus 117
Syncerus caffer 173

T
Tachyglossus aculeatus 28, 59, *236*
Tachyoryctes macrocephalus 151
tadpoles *22*
tahr, Himalayan *228*
taiga 6, 40, 41, 50–1
taipan *206*
Talpa caeca 182
Tamandua mexicana 115
tamandua, northern 115
tamarin, golden lion *37*, 111
Tamias striatus 101
tapir 30, 41, *46*
   Brazilian *106*
Tapirus terrestris 106
Tarentola mauritanica 141
tarsier *59*, *231*
Tarsius bancanus 59, *231*
Tasmanian devil 7, *29*, 34, *239*
Taurotragus oryx 173
Taxidea taxus 30, *95*
Tayassu tajacu 107
tayra 97
tegu, black *81*
temperate forests 6, 40, 41, 48–9
terrapins 25, 76, 138
Tetracerus quadricornis 225
Thamnophis sirtalis 87
Theropithecus gelada 18, *177*
Thomomys talpoides 101
thorny devil *57*, *198*
Thryonomys swinderianus 161
Thyroptera discifera 105
tiger 7, 19, 50, *51*, 65, *210*, *246*
   Bengal *47*
   Siberian *50*, *51*, 65
Tiliqua scincoides 201

toad 19, 22–3, 72–5, 130–6, 190–5
   African clawed *130*
   American 75
   Asian or brown tree *195*
   black-spined 194
   cane 43, 74, *192*
   common *49*, 75, *132*
   fire-bellied 133
   giant or marine 43, *74*, 192
   midwife *134*
   natterjack 133
   Oriental fire-bellied *190*
   Surinam *72*
toadlet, stonemason 191
tortoise 25, *63*, 76–7, 136–7, 197
   desert *56*, *57*
   Galápagos giant *24*, 36, *58*, *59*, 65, *77*
   Indian starred 197
   leopard *137*
   pancake *137*
   radiated 137
tourism 39
Tragelaphus
   T. eurycerus 171
   T. spekei 173
tree shrew
   Indian *230*
   lesser *230*
Tremarctos ornatus 93
Tribolonotus gracilis 81
Trichechus manatus 123, 223
Trichobatrachus robustus 131
Trichosurus vulpecula 239
Triturus
   T. cristatus 129
   T. helveticus 129
   T. marmoratus 129
tropical forests 6, 37, *38*, 40, 41, 46–7
tuatara *25*, 59, 186, *197*
tucuxi 121
tundra 40, 51, 55
Tupaia minor 230
Tupinambis teguixin 81
turtle 14, 24, 25, *42*, 43, 65, 76–7, 136–7, 196–7
   alligator snapping *76*
   Asian leaf *197*
   Atlantic or Kemp's ridley 137
   Chinese box 197
   Chinese soft-shelled *196*
   common snake-necked *196*
   East African side-necked 137
   European pond *136*
   green 77
   leatherback *36*, *136*
   loggerhead *42*
   painted 77
   pig-nosed river 197
   wood 77
Tylototriton verrucosus 189
Typhlonectes compressicauda 71

U
uakari, bald *113*
Uperoleia lithomoda 191
Uroderma bilobatum 104
Ursus
   U. americanus 48, *93*
   U. arctos 6, *50*, 51, 59, *92*
   U. maritimus 26, *54*, *55*, *92*
   U. thibetanus 215

V
vaquita *120*
Varanus
   V. albigularis 139
   V. flavirufus 202
   V. komodoensis 58, *59*, 65, *203*
   V. prasinus 202
   V. varius 202
Varecia variegata 6, *58*, *59*, *178*
vertebrates 9, 14–15, 16, 18, 36–7, 46, 246
vervet 63, *177*
Vicugna vicugna 61, 107
vicuña 61, 107
viper 40, 57
   common 144
   desert horned *56*
   Malayan pit *207*
Vipera berus 144
viverrids 156–7, 218
vole, water *158*
Vombatus ursinus 49, 186, *238*
Vulpes
   V. cana 153
   V. chama 153
   V. macrotis 91
   V. pallida 153
   V. velox 91
   V. vulpes 41, *62*, *152*, 239
   V. zerda 56, *57*, *153*

W
wallaby *59*
   rock 241
Wallace, Alfred 12
walrus *54*, *125*
warthog *169*
water moccasin *44*
waterdog 69
weasel 18, 51, 155
   Patagonian 97
wetlands 40, 44
whale 15, *19*, 27, *33*, 38, 42, *43*, 55, 65, 120–3, 184, 247
   blue 9, 26, 42, 123
   bowhead 123
   false killer 185
   grey *123*
   humpback *122*
   killer 19, 41, *42*, *122*
   minke *42*
   sperm 12, 40, *245*
   white 121
whiskers 17

whistlepig 32, 100
wildcat
   African 149, 211
   European 149
wildebeest 18, 30, *33*, 171
wolf
   Ethiopian *151*
   grey *17*, 32, 37, 34, 41, *50*, *90*
   maned *90*
   marsupial 34
wolverine *50*, *51*, *95*
wombat, common *49*, 186, *238*
woodchuck 32, *100*
worm lizard 25, 81

X
xenarths 114–15
Xenopeltis unicolor 207
Xenopus laevis 130

Y
yak *61*, *227*
yapok 118

Z
Zaedyus pichiy 115
Zalophus californianus 124
zebra *8–9*, 18, 53
   common or Burchell's *166*
zoos 39
zorilla *154*

ACKNOWLEDGEMENTS
The publisher would like to thank the following for permission to reproduce their photographs in this book.

Key: l=left, r=right, t=top, m=middle, b=bottom

NHPA: 12bl, 20tr, 20b, 22t, 22b, 23t, 25t, 25br, 28br, 30t, 32t, 32b, 33tl, 35b, 36t, 38t, 39t, 39b, 41tl, 56t, 58t, 62b.
Tim Ellerby: 28t, 28bl, 34l, 37b, 39m, 186r.